ABANDONED

Also by Joanne Hardy

The Girl in the Butternut Dress
ISBN 9781468068412

A searing saga set near the fault line of the Civil War in Southern Illinois. Though it is Union country, the rolling grassy hills are alive with so-called Copperheads, or Southern sympathizers who give aid and comfort to Union deserters. Against this backdrop of national turmoil where neighbors become enemies comes a deep, and unlikely love story. Can their love bridge what divides a nation? To truly come to terms with her love for Cayne, Gabrielle will need to quell a deep hunger to know her own origins--to find her own identity. Gabrielle's rough-and-tumble upbringing runs counterweight to Cayne's, the son of Southern gentry. This gripping romance set during the Civil War will tug readers' heart strings making them question what they would do when faced with a choice between moral wrongdoing or love and listening to their heart.

Random Truths
ISBN 9781729170106

The year is 1938, and the little town of Amsley knows first hand the raw hopelessness of the depression. In this dismal time, a Texas oilman determines to drill a wildcat well. To discouraged merchants and landowners in the county this is a preposterous and unlikely gamble. They have been harshly taught to live with little and to expect little. But the first oil well is a gusher! A pool has been found. Many more wells follow. Royalty checks arrive in the mail representing more than a farmer would make in his lifetime of working the land. What could go wrong? How do you understand a new life with wealth beyond all you have ever seen? How do you know who you are when all the old ways don't count? How does a quiet pristine town learn to cope with mob influences that follow the oil money? What of old relationships when some are fortunate and some are not? What of older children raised in poverty and younger siblings raised in privilege? How long does it take to find the wisdom to live this new life?

ABANDONED

Joanne Hardy

Published by AquaZebra Book Publishing
Cathedral City, CA

AquaZebra™
Book Publishing
AquaZebra.com

First Edition

Hardy, Joanne
Abandoned

Website joanehardyauthor.net
Books available online in paperback and Kindle
contact: hohojo2@earthlink.net

1st edition

Library of Congress Control Number: 2023942646

ISBN 978-1-954604-00-1 (paperback)

Published by
AquaZebra™
Book Publishing
Cathedral City, California
www.aquazebra.com

Editor
Lynn Jones Green

Cover design
Kerrie Robertson

Interior Design
Kathy Bjork

Printed in the United States of America

DEDICATED

to
Judge Richard Sprigg Canby
and
Mary DeLong
and their descendants
who inspired this book

PROLOGUE

"Life is the sum of all our choices."

—Albert Camus

Baltimore, Maryland, 1845

Vachel Fletcher found the love of his life. He was fifteen. There would be others, some who touched him deeply, some tender, loving fancies, and other fleeting distractions, but only one claimed the deepest, truest place in his heart.

Vachel and his father, Ben Fletcher, boarded a stern-wheeler at the pier. The steamboat sat docked before a huge warehouse, stretching along the Ohio River front. Great, white letters spaced across the building announced:

FLETCHER AND SONS
TOBACCO BROKERS
Paducah, Kentucky

Vachel (or Fletch, as his friends and family called him) had himself helped load over a hundred hogsheads of tobacco into the hold of the ship, all rated, categorized, and ready for sale when the shipment finally reached Baltimore.

Fletch and his father, Ben, would travel with their tobacco cargo to the headwaters of the Ohio River at Pittsburg, and then ship the tobacco in wagons overland through the Cumberland Gap to the port in Baltimore. But he and his father would travel in ease by coach. After this coming year, he'd be sixteen and begin his studies at the university in Lexington, Kentucky. When he graduated, he'd be ready to learn the family business—although his instruction had long been underway. Both he and his brother, Claude Raymond, had been learning on the job since they were children. This was the first time, however, that Ben Fletcher had taken one of his sons on a business trip to meet with other brokers and then the buyers from tobacco companies. Everyone would be vying for the best price and looking for the lucrative European and British markets where tobacco was popular.

It took five days of travel—three on the Ohio River and two over land—to reach Baltimore. Now Fletch was decked out in his new suit and sat by his father at a table with twenty or more important-looking men, some with massive beards, others with ponderous mustaches and mutton chop sideburns, most with cigars. With a common interest, but competitors all, the main concern was developing a Dutch market in both cigars and pipe tobacco.

The second day's meeting broke up at noontime. "Gonna see a demonstration of this novelty everybody's talkin' about," his father explained as they sat in the hotel dining room. Fletch polished off a plate of fried chicken, grits and collard greens; two pieces of warm, thick-sliced bread, covered with butter and peach preserves; plus a piece of mincemeat pie. "Norris and Company has scheduled the demonstration especially for the tobacco brokers. Called a 'locomotive,'" Ben said. "One of the grasshopper series, they told us."

Fletch and his father alighted from a carriage, as did a couple dozen other tobacco merchants from theirs. Fletch had come to know them all. Ben Fletcher leaned close to his son. "Might as well see what this thing's all about."

The sun was still high in mid-afternoon; a soft, balmy breeze flowed through the group, whispering a coming storm. Then they caught sight of a strange-looking green contraption moving slowly toward them on a narrow track. A huge cylinder lay horizontally between two wheels, looking like wagon wheels. A wide pipe belching smoke protruded from it several feet up in the air.

There were chuckles and laughter among the men—Ben Fletcher as well. Fletch smiled too, entranced. No beast pulled it! It moved on its own! Amazing! Painted along the side, in yellow lettering read "NORRIS AND COMPANY."

When it came to a stop, a lively man, dapper and bespectacled, crawled out and stood before them. "I'm Jake Ambrose, and this, gentlemen," he announced with a wave of his arm, "was the beginning of what will soon be the transportation of the future."

A portly man—whom Fletch knew to be from Savannah— laughed outright and said, "That gimmick is never gonna replace river transportation."

"I beg to differ with you, sir." Ambrose drew himself up to the full measure of his stature. "One day all commodities will move behind locomotives like this. This engine is like a newborn babe. Just a promise. I want you to watch what happened after this little 'gimmick,' as you call it, developed over the last ten years. "

Very soon, they saw another locomotive. It was twenty times the size of the little grasshopper coming toward them, and it pulled two cars and moved at twice the speed. "Now, gentlemen, this is your gimmick grown up. This'un here was made in this country using the Stephenson design; he's a feller out of England. You folks'll be callin' on it one of these times, and it won't be only for a joy ride, but to haul your tobacco to markets like Baltimore, New Orleans, Savannah, and New York. "

"Horse whiskers!" someone called out, and laughter rippled through the crowd.

A Natchez broker, muttonchops touching his high, white collar, stepped forward and spoke in a deep bass voice. "I hear you have to use horses to pull that thing up hills, and you have to do a lot grading to lay them rails—and the rails have to come here from overseas, and they don't always hold up in the freeze and thaw. 'Pears to me it's a lot of bother. River's always there. Don't need upkeep." He patted Ambrose on the shoulder as he prepared to go back to his coach. "Son,

I appreciated the afternoon's entertainment, but my tobacco crop is going down the Mississippi River on a boat and out to the Atlantic. That thing would just be a bother."

Fletch listened as the jibes and the ridicule faded away, until the talk was just like the distant thunder in the east. Couldn't they see what this was? For the first time since creation there stood a machine that could move with no external force to pull it. It could carry crops ten times faster than a sternwheeler. Couldn't they see that? Vachel Fletcher saw it. And Vachel Fletcher was smitten.

After Ambrose finished—or more to the point, they were finished with him—Fletch ambled over to him. "So, what do you call yourself?" he asked Ambrose.

"I am an engineer, my boy."

"An engineer?" Fletch echoed.

Ambrose, apparently seeing a receptive and impressionable young man, waxed more eloquent. "There's engines more developed than this. You need to go to Philadelphia and see the great 4-2-4 loco-motive.. There's short runs here and there—some of them joining, making lines that go to the rivers and lakes to pick up the river cargo."

Fletch's eyes wandered over the great locomotive and the cars lined behind it, captivated, sensing a vast, rich life embodied here before him—a life threaded with romance and adventure. "How do you get on to be an engineer?"

"First thing I done was join a surveying party," Ambrose said. "What they did to begin with was look over the lay of the land, find-ing routes with the fewest cricks and the easiest grade to run the engines up. Then, when they got the locomotive all built, I just got to driving the big engines. Nothin' like it, son. All that power right under your hand."

The following day, when Ben Fletcher and his son came down to the wharf, the hogsheads of tobacco had arrived and sat waiting for buyers to come. The highest grade of tobacco used for cigars was placed toward the back, and the lesser quality destined for pipe tobacco or to make snuff was grouped around the edge. The morning was brilliant, the air sharp after the nighttime storm, but mixed with the smell of dead fish in the black water that slapped against the piers.

The other brokers had found places to set up for selling tobacco. Ben Fletcher turned to his son. "The buyers will begin their dickering. You pay close attention to me because this is the payoff. They name a price they say they'll pay. They know I'll not take it. I'll tell them what I'm asking. They know I'm asking high. Then we talk, we hold out, we refuse—it's a game, but it's an important one. We're remembering our customers, the growers, and, of course, we got an eye on our own profits. If it's a good crop, like this year, you simply don't back down. They know quality, and they'll keep up the dickering accordingly. First, you offer your lowest quality at a high price, then in due time you say to them you can offer better quality but can't accept a lower price. "

Fletch listened; he had been immersed in the world of tobacco all his life. But floating in the back reaches of his mind was something else—the strange little locomotive that moved quickly and effortlessly forward, free and independent as the wind.

CHAPTER 1

Amsley Illinois 1875, Twenty-Seven Years Later

Will Fletcher felt the train slowing, the swaying of the passenger car gentling, as it made the long curve, preparing to stop. He looked out the window. Large black letters on the three-story depot and hotel came squarely into view: AMSLEY. He felt the letter inside his coat pocket as the train ground to a stop. By now, he knew every word by memory. But what could it mean? As soon as he had received his mother's letter—forwarded from the War Department in Washington, D.C.—he'd skipped his last class, left the university campus immediately, and caught the noon train.

Will stepped off the passenger car onto the wooden platform and stared ahead into the gloom of early evening. Hunched deep in his great coat, bits of snow drifted in the November air and burned his face. Opposite the tracks in the distance, across the north/south tracks, loomed the gigantic roundhouse where locomotives were sent for repairs, and beyond that, the depot. Between them, light poured onto the train platform from the windows of the Dining Car Café in a row of rectangle, yellow splotches. The smell of frying onions and pork drifted on the cold air, but Will walked quickly along the creaking wooden platform, ignoring the gnawing emptiness of his stomach. Beneath a gaslight near the depot, a hack waited. Will wanted to get home or, as he thought of it since she married Judge Austin, his mother's house.

The Austins' house was a stately, rambling showplace, with a turret that stretched passed the second story and even the roof. Light spilled out onto the long porch that sheltered the wide front entrance and wrapped around the side of the house. In summer, it held several rocking chairs and side tables.

His mother was not expecting him until next week—Thanksgiving. He decided it would be better to knock.

"Will?" Violet Austin breathed, as she opened the door, her usually impassive face turning to delight. "Why are you home? Is there something . . . "

"Didn't you know I'd come when I got that letter?"

"Oh, that." She reached for his coat lapel to help him out of it. "Come in by the fire. Did you have anything to eat?"

"No," he said as he pulled the letter from inside his jacket pocket. "But I'm all right."

She went back, took her usual seat by the fireplace, and picked up her embroidery hoop. "Will, you needn't have come home for that. I'll have Sarah make you something."

Will noticed the judge was in his office, the door shut, which meant he had a case to consider. That was just as well. He preferred to see his mother alone.

He pulled a chair beside her, opened the letter and read it aloud, although he knew she knew every word just as he did.

November 2, 1875

Greetings,

We wish clarification from you regarding a claim for a pension earned by Civil War veteran Sargent Vachel Fletcher for support of his orphaned daughter, Amy Fletcher, age seven. The request for pension names Sargent Fletcher's wife as Liela Ivers Fletcher of Oak Grove Plantation, Corinth, Mississippi. Request to grant the pension for the child's support and welfare was made by Reverend Milton Hollister, in whose care the child has been placed.

Our records show Vachel Fletcher naming, at the time of his enlistment, his family as wife, Violet Fletcher, and one child, William Vachel Calvert Fletcher, living in Amsley, Illinois.

Any information you could give would be appreciated.

Secretary of War,
Alphonso Taft

She removed her thimble and anchored the needle in her embroidery work. "The War Department has got things mixed up. This is another Vachel Fletcher, Will," Violet Austin pronounced emphatically. "It was some other person named Fletcher." Her face was flushed. She pulled at her glasses and turned to face him. "There was no reason for you to drop everything and come home—for this."

Will stood, staring down at his mother. "What else is more important? You can surely understand that I want to know who he was. Why he left us. This may be the answer."

"I have told you why he left." She shook her head. "You can't . . . know how it was with the war, families separated, the confusion. Oh, Will, people were just trying to stay alive. Maybe the child didn't really know her father—maybe it's just a name she heard."

Will looked at his mother, always elegant, dressed in her signature color—violet or some shade of it—a little white hair at the temples crowding in on her reddish blonde, but still a beautiful woman.

Will was not disappointed. He knew what to expect. She would not give up that her husband was killed in the war. It allowed her to push aside the fact he had actually deserted them. And deserted them before the war. Will noticed two tight lines appearing between her eyebrows. Maybe she didn't quite believe her own lie.

"The child is seven years old, Mama. She was born after the war ended. He did not die. This proves he was alive and possibly living a life completely independent of us."

Violet shook her head. "It's not the same man, Will." She looked down at her work, replaced her glasses. "Son, I love you more than my life, and I know you want to know about your father and what became of him, but . . ." She fell silent for a while, and when she looked up, there was sadness in her eyes. "Sometimes you just have to let go." The quiet of the room was only interrupted by a soft crackle in the fireplace. "Will, I want you to write to the War Department and tell them this is a mistake. Tell them *they* are making a mistake because it is not the Vachel Fletcher we knew—it is someone else. You're almost a lawyer; you know how to write such things. Now, let's not talk about this anymore." She put on her thimble and began her intricate embroidery.

He watched her for some minutes in the dull lamplight. "I want to go to Corinth, Mississippi. Talk to this preacher, Hollister."

She didn't answer him for a long time, as she kept up the stitching. "Your father loved me, and I loved him." Violet still didn't look up. "I know that. I know he would not have left us unless there was a good reason—or he was killed. You cannot ever make me believe he didn't love us."

On the mantel, the white porcelain clock, cherubs on each side, gave a plaintive single chime—8:30. Beyond his mother's chair, the tall window was a rectangle of blackness outside, snow building in the corner of the ledge.

"I will wait until the Christmas break when I have a few days," Will said. "It is only a day's train ride—maybe there's a picture or something the child's father left."

She shook her head but continued stitching. "I am frowning on that idea, Will. You're chasing a shadow. I beg you not to go there."

"Maybe I can learn something or, at least, know for sure."

"I want you to talk to the judge before you go gallivanting around, disturbing everyone's holidays. Those poor people in the south suffered, and this little girl is still suffering. She lost her father and mother."

He knew the judge would side with his wife. The judge had encouraged Violet to have her husband declared dead, and then quickly began courting her. They were married three weeks after Vachel Fletcher had been officially declared deceased in the war.

Later, in his old bedroom, Will lay staring up at the ceiling, remembering the days when his father came home to them. He would run into his father's arms. He could still feel the furry collar of his father's coat against his cheeks, the smell of cold air about him, and his strong arms as he lifted him, laughing, high in the air.

It was the same train platform he had just walked on this evening. The place, too, he and his mother had met the train again and again, when his father did not step off. The war came and his mother told him his father was one of the lost soldiers who died in the war. She needed to believe it. Truth was that his father had left them even before the war. But now, from out of nowhere, came what might be a germ of information about his father, after the war.

Just below the surface of what filled Will's days lived a longing, a hunger to know what happened to this man he had loved so dearly, then had come to hate so intensely. Why had his father never cared to know if his son grew up or died?

The letter lay partially open on his nightstand. It made his heart pound when he looked over at it, a tantalizing promise. He glanced at it again, but didn't touch it. It seemed almost a fearful thing, cloaked in mystery. Finally, he did reach for it, but no need to read it again. He put it back.

Sleep wouldn't come, so he got up. The house was dark, his mother and the judge long since retired upstairs. He made his way to the pantry, lit a candle, and started downstairs into the basement.

He didn't think much about it at the time, but he eventually came to realize the decision he made on the stairs to the basement that night would be the reason for everything he did for years afterwards. He would find his father, learn who he was, and confront him.

He would let his mother believe whatever she needed to.

Once in the basement, he went to stacks of boxes pushed back in a partitioned section, boxes his mother had brought to her marriage with the judge, things from her other marriage, stored for Will to have when he was grown.

Leaning against the wall were the wedding portraits of his parents, wrapped thoroughly with quilts. He uncovered them and looked them over for the first time in years. They were full-size, five-by-eight feet. They had hung in the dining room of the house of his early childhood.

Now as an adult, 21-years old, he looked at his father more critically; black hair swept back over his ears, curling just over his coat collar, heavy dark eyebrows shading deep brown eyes, and a tightly defined mustache. "Silky" was the word that came to mind. In the portrait his father stood by a table. In the mirroring portrait his mother stood by the same table, wearing her wedding gown and a wedding band. He noticed for the first time; his father didn't wear a wedding band.

What would he find in Corinth, Mississippi? He moved a rickety chair that had been put down in the basement, near the great portraits. Gloomy shadows beyond the circle of yellow candlelight seemed to encroach. He leaned back in the chair. What of this little girl, Amy? Was she his half-sister? What would she look like?

Will left the two pictures uncovered as he looked through some of the boxes—objects familiar to him since childhood. A hovering presence seemed to linger with him, enlarging itself in the semi-darkness. Yet something hammered at him. The truth of it had to be buried in those boxes—or at least he wanted it to be.

He turned to look again at the portrait of Vachel Fletcher. He studied the life-size likeness of his father, the heavy brows, the liquid brown eyes, and the slight smile below a thin mustache. Will leaned forward. "Who are you really, and where are you?"

CHAPTER 2

"Train's late, Will." Cobin Rush, the ticket master, stamped his train ticket. "Might as well find a comfortable bench."

Will looked at the clock. "I counted on being back on the college campus before 10:00 p.m., otherwise I'll have to wake someone to let me in the apartment."

Rush shrugged. "All's I can say is, the train's late."

Will decided to have a cup of coffee while he waited. Outside, the wind whipped through his long hair as he hurried to the Dining Car Café.

Inside, a potbellied stove and three kerosene lamps made the long dining car warm and cozy. A couple with two small children sat at one of the tables; probably arrived on the north/south Illinois Central and were waiting for the east/west Baltimore and Ohio. At the end of the café, a half-dozen men sat at a table, men Will surmised worked at the roundhouse. A persuasive aroma, sweet as cinnamon rolls coming from the oven, filled the restaurant.

Cora Conyers ran the Dining Car Café at the depot; a place everyone in Amsley knew was a place to get a good meal. Will had gone to school with her sons and knew vaguely there were other children, too. Cora bustled in and stood before him, "Will Austin, what are you doing home?"

"Unexpected business." The letter stuffed in his inside pocket filled his thoughts, but he wasn't going to discuss that with anyone. "What's that wondrous smell coming out of your kitchen?"

"Addie Rose's apple pies."

He leaned back against his chair, looked at Cora. "Bring me a piece—maybe a *big* slice."

She came back, a blue enameled coffeepot in one hand and cup in the other. She set them down at his table, and then disappeared into the kitchen. In a couple of minutes, she returned with a piece of pie, still hot and bubbling around the edges, and placed it before him.

When Cora came by again with the big coffee pot for a refill, he said, "You can tell whoever made that pie, it's a masterful creation and I'm going to marry her."

Cora laughed, "I see you've got the makin's of a lawyer, Will. Not sure about your plans for Addie Rose, though. She's fifteen."

Will looked out at the dull gray day. No train. "Then I'll settle for another slice of her pie."

A few minutes later, a young girl, wearing an apron, her dark hair captured in a braid and wrapped in a tight bun at the nape of her neck, smiled down at him. She placed a second piece of pie before him, put another piece on the table opposite him, looked him over, pulled out a chair and sat down. "I wanted to meet the person who gave me my first marriage proposal."

Will half-stood, suddenly awkward.

Addie Rose looked at him, a faint blush coming on her face as if her first flush of bravado had deserted her, but she quickly recovered. "Mama said a customer was out here I should meet 'cause he wants to marry me—that is, for my apple pies. My mother says I should be nice to the customers."

"Well, that's right." Will fumbled for something to say. "Your mother's right, I mean . . .being nice to customers."

"Then my brother said, 'Don't go flirting. He's in college. He's studying to be a lawyer and he's too smart for you.'"

Will laughed. This girl didn't keep secrets. "I haven't seen you do any flirting," he finally got out.

Then they fell into an embarrassing silence.

His law professor had said, "Study people beyond what they say; in fact, in spite of what they say. Learn to read them." This was an easy one: a smart, happy girl who said what she thought.

"So, you're Addie Rose. How did you end up making apple pies?" Will didn't know what else to say. When she smiled, dimples appeared in her cheeks. She smelled like spices and flour.

Addie Rose looked down at her pie, as if deciding whether to go on. "How I got here and making apple pies? It was an accident—two accidents, really. Papa was an engineer on the Baltimore and Ohio Railroad."

"My father was a railroad engineer, too." Will's interest came alive.

She nodded, smiled briefly. "Papa was to go to work on the railroad out here in Amsley, at this hub. Mr. Otto Grimes—he negotiated a deal to sell the house where we lived in Baltimore and buy a farm here in Illinois. My father planned to work on the railroad, and my brothers would work the farm. But my mother didn't know about that until Mr. Grimes told her a couple of weeks later."

"A couple of weeks later? Something interrupted the plan?"

"That's what I mean about an accident."

Will leaned forward, absorbed. She stopped talking, looked out the dining car windows.

"What happened?" he asked finally.

"It was one morning—early," she began. "Raining. Someone was pounding on the front door downstairs. Papa hurried to the stairs, pulling on his clothes. I got up and watched him throw a suspender strap on his shoulder and start down the stairs to the front door. The next thing I saw was all in a haze. My father's body hurdling down the stairs, this way and that, knocking out banisters. Then he lay like in a heap below the last step.

"I ran to him, then Mother—all of us. And someone was still knocking at the door. I opened it, and Mr. Grimes was standing there. In the street, his horse and buggy stood in the downpour.

"Mary and I brought wet rags to stop the blood from my father's head wound. I saw his eyes flicker. I thought he would be all right." She looked through the windows of the café; light snow swirled in the wind. "But I was wrong."

"Did you lose him?"

"He lived eight days."

"But you had him for a while." Will leaned over his apple pie, holding her in his gaze, realizing he had something in common with this girl. "You knew him. You knew who he was."

"Well, sure. Of course I knew him. It was hard for Mama. Five children and no way to support us."

Will nodded. "It's hard to be left alone."

"I don't know how I got off on that—about my father. I don't like to think about it. Anyway, you ought to tell me your name if you're going to marry me."

He leaned back, the spell that had held him, broken, "It's William Vachel Calvert Austin."

"Lawsee, that's too many names. I never knew anybody with four names."

"I should have five—my last name is not the right one—not my father's."

"That's too many names for me. I'm afraid this marrying business is off." Her eyes sparkled with her smile. And the dimples again. "I think I hear your train."

He stood up and handed her a coin for the pie. "Can't miss my train."

Addie Rose wrote in her diary that night:

Dear Diary,

I received my first marriage proposal today. Well, sort of. It was mostly about my pie. He was kind of strange, though. Roy says I'm too young for him anyway. He has nice eyes, sometimes full of flash and sometimes, like—sad. Hell's bells, I forgot to feed Nosey. No telling where that damned old cow has got to.

Goodbye!

CHAPTER 3

Corinth, Mississippi

Will Fletcher stood before a modest, white house in Corinth. It was situated on an expansive green lawn that encompassed a white church, which looked new. He opened the gate, his heart pounding, his knees weak, resolve deserting him. What if it *was* his father and he'd learn a hard truth? What if it wasn't?

He forced himself to knock. A tall but stooped, old servant opened the door. He looked Will over but said nothing.

"I am looking for Reverend Milton Hollister. My name is Will Fletcher."

The old man's eyes met his, perked up for an instant, and then dropped again. Was he one of those slaves that stayed on after freedom? Will had heard of that.

"The Parson be with you in a minute," he said. "You wait in the parlor, here." He opened two French doors that led into a dim room with drawn drapes. Embers burned low in the fireplace. Will stood by a crimson-colored, humpback settee, not feeling he should sit until invited. He heard low indistinguishable conversation out in the hall through a half-opened door. He caught the word "Fletcher."

A tall man came through the doors, dressed in a black coat that hung loosely on his spare frame, wearing round spectacles perched on his nose. "I'm Reverend Hollister, young man." He went to one of the windows and pushed back the drapes. "Are you from the War Department?" He tossed a piece of wood into the fireplace.

"No, sir. I'm not, but that's the reason I'm here. It's about a letter sent to my mother for clarification regarding a young girl, your ward. You see, my father was named Fletcher, Vachel Fletcher, but we believe—that is, my mother has always thought—my father died in the war, and he's buried in some unmarked grave."

"Well, Mr. Fletcher . . . "

"Will, please, sir."

"Will, then. Please have a seat." The reverend sat down near the meager fire. "I remember little Amy's father quite well. Vachel Fletcher, he was. Sergeant Fletcher. Came with the Yankee occupation of Corinth. He was wounded, but during his recuperation he met Liela. You see," the parson looked away, as if reviving some memory, "the army took over their plantation when the Yankees occupied Corinth." Hollister shook his head. "But the interesting thing is, when the war was over, he came back. Helped out quite a bit, he did. They married and he rebuilt the plantation. Then something happened."

The preacher paused, pursed his lips, as if thinking about what happened or maybe how much he should say. "He took Casper with him to Natchez to sell the tobacco and cotton crop. It was the best crop they'd had since the war. Woulda put the farm back on solid ground. But . . ." Hollister's eyes met Will's, "he never came back. The story Casper always says—Casper's the one who met you at the door—is some men waylaid Fletcher, robbed him, took all the money from the crop sale, then killed him and threw him in the Mississippi."

Hollister shook his head. "The story sounds preposterous, and Casper never really saw it happen; he was just told that."

If Will's heart had calmed down after meeting the preacher, he now had a new rush of emotions. The man had stolen the crop money. That was the obvious fact.

"Liela was devastated," Hollister went on. "You can just imagine. But what made it more of a mystery was, a couple of months later, three men came to her plantation and began taking the roof off the tobacco barn, piece by piece. There'd been rebuilding all over the South and the cost of roofing was dear. Liela was out there protesting as they took it down, but they showed her a note, signed by Vachel Fletcher, her husband, saying they should have it because they won it in a card game."

Will's heart sunk. Could this possibly be the same man he remembered coming home to them, giving him toys, the light of his young life? Was it even worse, deserting him and his mother—and then deserting another "wife" and robbing her crop money, selling the roof off her building. He couldn't get his mind around it all. He thought of the man he once loved better than anyone on earth.

It couldn't be. He had hit a wall, and disappointment crowded in. He felt heartsick. But reluctantly, another part of his mind saw a pattern.

"What did he look like?" Will finally asked.

"'Bout like all of 'em that went through the war. Gaunt, inclined to take to spirits. A lot of 'em did, trying to tamp down the horrors in their head."

The reverend got up, pulled back the drapes at the other window and let in pale winter sunlight. The room was warming a bit now that flames leaped in the fireplace.

"Liela's family was in a bad way," Hollister went on. "First, the Confederates come through and picked them clean, then they moved out. Liela's family had the biggest house around, so when the Yankee army came, they made it into a hospital. Men were laid out all over the yard. Inside, it was worse. That's where the typhoid cases were. Men dying—being hauled out. Bodies piled up. They kept a fire going, burning bedclothes when one of 'em died. And Liela's father died. I'm telling you, young man, hell was right outside the doors."

"So he deserted his wife and child?" Will cut in.

"Well, now, I have to say, he didn't know about the baby coming. It was after he made that trip to Natchez that Liela learned she was in the family way."

Will's spirit rebelled at the idea that his father could take the profits of a full year's cotton crop and disappear. It couldn't be the same person. But hadn't he done almost the same to him and his mother? Much as he hated what his father had done to him, he never imagined him a thief.

But there it was. It could be him. His father left his mother and abandoned him, and then—if this same man was his father—left another woman and child, and done even more damage. Will closed his eyes, trying to shut it all out. He despised him. And yet he loved him, still. Tears came in spite of himself. He hated the comparison; he couldn't keep from thinking of the upright man the judge was, the protecting, providing father he had been to him.

"We thought him just a godsend," the reverend broke the silence. "Fletcher came back after the war and helped. A Union man! He helped rebuild two tobacco barns, the cotton shed and part of the house that was burned. Some of the slaves stayed on, like Casper. They were free, but free to starve."

Hollister looked through the long window at the bleak winter day. The only sound in the room was the ticking of a tall clock in the corner. His mother was right, Will thought. Some things are best left untouched.

"Then Liela died," the parson went on. "Left this poor child. And there's nobody to work that farm now, so I've got the care of her." Hollister went over and stirred the fire a little and added another piece of wood. He looked over at Will and shook his head. "A lot of orphans around the South." There was something of an accusatory edge when he spoke. "I'd like you to meet little Amy, if you've got the time."

Will nodded. "Yes, sure." Maybe her features would tell him something—an expression, a gesture that had been passed to her from a father.

Hollister stepped out into the hall. "Casper, will you bring Amy to the parlor to meet this young man. He's also named 'Fletcher.'"

Will's hand trembled. Would the child be the giveaway? Would she say something that would unlock the puzzle?

Casper brought a scrawny little girl, with blondish hair, wearing a gray smock-type dress into the parlor. She timidly looked up at Will.

"Hello. Are you my father?"

Will took her hand. "No, I thought I might be your brother, but . . ." He studied her features looking for something familiar. "I don't think so."

Casper held back, head down, but through slitted eyes he followed Will Fletcher's every move.

"I need that pension money to help with this child," the reverend said, "but, unfortunately, Will, I don't think we're talking about the same Fletcher. I believe this little girl is an orphan."

Will looked down at the child. He couldn't say she was pretty, and, in fact, she was pitiable. What he saw in her was the essence of an abandoned, unwanted child. Or maybe he was just seeing himself in her. He couldn't keep from feeling sorry for her. Will patted the little girl's hand, and then released it. He nodded in agreement; it was not the same Vachel Fletcher.

"Thank you, reverend, for meeting me. I sincerely hope you're right, that this man is not my father; but I hope you can get the pension money. I don't know how we can know for sure, though."

"Might I get you a buggy and take you to the train station?"

"Oh, no. I don't want to trouble you; it isn't far."

"When you go to get your train, look at that station and the rail tracks." He opened the French doors to the hall for them. "Look at it for the history it tells. It was what two armies fought over. It was what brought on all this misery."

As Will Fletcher stepped out into the hall, buttoned his coat against the chill, he noticed old Casper watching him. All the tiredness was gone from Casper's countenance. His look might have been curious, or it might have been hatred. Will nodded toward him, but Casper turned his back on him, and ambled down the hall to the back of the house.

CHAPTER 4

"Did you see the little girl you thought might be your sister?" Addie Rose asked.

Will sat in the Dining Car Café, talking to Addie Rose over pie and coffee, a pleasant little habit he'd fallen into. When he'd stepped off the train, he wasn't too anxious to go home and admit to his mother she'd been right about chasing an illusion. But was it an illusion?

"I did and . . . "

"Did she look like you or your father?"

"No, she didn't. The preacher didn't even think it was the same man."

"Well, then, maybe your father did die in the war."

Will was quiet for a moment, thinking. Was he satisfied the search was futile? "There's just this thing that makes me still wonder. "

"What is it?"

"There was an ex-slave, 'Casper' they called him, who knew Amy's father. He gave me a look I can't forget: hard, suspicious—like hatred. Why would he do that?"

"For one thing, you're a white man, and, for another, you're a Yankee. He probably saw horrors during the war from the Yankees— maybe even had brutal treatment before the war."

"I thought of that, but I can't get that look out of my mind, like hate radiating out of him." Will pushed aside his half-eaten pie. "He doesn't even know me."

"Maybe it was something else." Addie said.

A train had just pulled in, and through the frosty windows, Will watched passengers disembarking. "It was always exciting for me to meet the train and see my father stepping down onto that platform out there. It was a big thrill to see his face light up when he saw us. I'd run to him, and he'd grab me up in his arms and hold me close." He glanced at Addie and saw her dimpled smile. "I always remember that. I was the happiest then I've ever been." He shrugged. "But he didn't mean a bit of it."

"Maybe he did then." Addie looked into her coffee cup. A little Christmas tree sat on a table by the entrance, and small wreaths hung in every other window. "I think of my father every day."

"Your father didn't desert you."

Chilled air poured into the café as a couple with three small children came in and seated themselves at a table close to the stove.

Will turned back to Addie. "What always presses on me is, why didn't he care enough for me to stay with me? I think my father always wanted to be free. I remember that there would be long stretches when he wouldn't come home. He'd write to my mother that he was busy surveying down in Kentucky and wasn't sure when he could get home. Eventually, he didn't come home on the train. He didn't write to my mother. We never heard from him again." Will's fingers threaded through his hair. "You may not understand this, Addie, but it's like I don't know who I am. I'm not the judge's son."

Will was quiet for a long time. "I still don't think he's dead."

CHAPTER 5

New Year's Day, 1876

The brass band now rounding the corner by Fender's Feed and Produce Store, and moving on to Main Street, always led the New Year's Day parade.

Will had decided not to walk with the Amsley Players this year, something he had done since he was fourteen and appeared in their first production. He knew they were planning a new play, but since his trip to Corinth, Mississippi, he seemed to have little thought left for anything else. He ambled along between the storefronts and the crowd lining the street, glancing over heads at the passing parade and looking for a place sparse with people. The Grand Army of the Republic was passing now; Civil War veterans in uniforms that were stretched over girths thickened since the war.

Will caught sight of Addie Rose from the café, a few feet from him, now completely engrossed, watching a horse-drawn, flatbed wagon rolling slowly by. At one end of the wagon, a grand lady, dressed in a blue satin dress, sat on a gold plush settee, holding a teacup in her fingers and an accordion fan opened in her lap. At the other end of the wagon, a woman dropped her vote into a ballot box. A long strip of paper along the side of the wagon read, "From Ornament To Voter."

Behind the wagon, eight women marched along singing:

> Daughters of Freedom, arise in your might.
> Daughters of Freedom, the truth marches on.
> Daughters of Freedom, the ballot is yours.
> March to the watchwords, Justice and Right.
> Yield not the battle till ye have won;
> Wield it with wisdom, your hopes it secures.

Jeers echoed from both sides all along the parade route.

"Look at that," a woman behind Will said. "How can they show their faces? And they put themselves out on parade! Foolish, disgusting women."

Will watched Addie Rose, her eyes following the marching women, intently listening to their song. "So, apple-pie girl," Will leaned forward and whispered in her ear, "are you interested in those crazy women?"

She turned instantly to him. "No," Addie stammered, caught off guard. "I was . . . I mean, I was just trying to hear what they're saying."

"I think you're a suffragette in hiding," he teased.

"No. I'm not."

Another horse-drawn, wide, flatbed wagon had an organ, a quartet, and a singer dressed like Uncle Sam, holding songbooks and singing patriotic songs beside a gigantic, three-tiered, white cake decorated in red-and-blue scallops. On the bottom tier of the cake was written "1776–1876." On the next tier it said with bright red lettering "Happy Birthday, America!" and a flag was posted on the top tier. Will noticed, however, that Addie was still drawn to the "Daughters of Freedom" wagon as it continued further on down the street.

Just then, the Amsley City Players came by, walking in a group, wearing costumes from their latest performances: a clown, a juggler, a princess, a pirate, dancing girls, and soldiers.

"We're going to do a play about George Washington in February. All in costume," Will said. "I'll be in it. It's the beginning of Amsley's centennial celebration."

Addie Rose turned to him, "You are? So who are you going to be?"

"You'll never guess."

"You're right, I'll never guess."

"George." He looked at the parade for a minute and then turned to her. "George Washington."

"Sounds like fun."

"You want to try out?"

A look of absolute amazement came over the girl's face, frozen in incredulity, as she looked up at him. "Me?"

He watched her, seeing a new idea being tried out behind those sharp blue eyes. *Delightful*, he thought.

"Sure, why not?" he said. "I was younger than you when I did my first play."

She was thoughtful for a moment, then with bright eyes looked at him. "I think I will."

So she's game, Will thought.

The parade was coming to an end. A couple-dozen men from the Deer Hunters group, on horseback and wearing their signature coonskin caps, were bringing up the rear just ahead of Amsley's one red fire wagon, its bell clanging, heralding the parade's end.

"Let's go to the playhouse. You can meet everyone," Will said.

"I don't know." Addie looked about, a little unsure. "My mother needs my help. I can't be gone but a few minutes."

He took her hand and led her through the departing crowd as if she were a child in tow. They went up an enclosed staircase to a long room over the bank. The players, who had marched in the parade, were shedding their costumes. The girl who had been dressed as a princess came to them. "Will, we really missed you this year. Who is this adorable little lady you've brought us?"

Before he could speak, she spoke up, "I'm Addie Rose Conyers." She put her hand out to shake hands. "Besides being a princess, who are you?"

"This is Nola Fitzgerald," Will finally got in. "She's not so much a princess as Lord High and Chief Magistrate of Everything over the Amsley Players."

"You flatter me, Will." She linked her arm in his and smiled up at him.

"I just came by." Will raised his voice. The juggler, the clown, the soldiers and grand ladies stopped wriggling out of their costumes and looked at Will. "Tomorrow night, come to the judge's house and we'll have try-outs for the new play. My mother is planning a reception afterwards."

"Thank you, Will, for arranging this with your mother. She's always so gracious." Nola's eyes rested warmly on Will for a moment, then she quickly regained her self-ordained position as leader of the group. "We'll all be there, won't we?" There were murmurs about the room.

The morning was brilliant but fiercely cold. Will could see his breath as he hurried across the north/south tracks of the Illinois Central Railroad to the Dining Car Café. Inside, three roundhouse workers hovered close to the pot-bellied stove, warming their hands around a cup of Cora Conyer's hot coffee. Will nodded and took a seat at a table across from them by the windows, but still in the circle of warmth.

Cora came out from the kitchen. "Out so early on this cold morning?"

"I came to remind Addie Rose we'll be having tryouts tonight for the play in February."

The three men near the stove lost interest in their conversation, their attention now on this bit of news about some play.

"Ah, the play. Yes," Cora said. "She mentioned that. Part of the Centennial celebrations, she said. We'll have to have a talk about that. Let me call her."

Addie came out of the kitchen, her brother Roy directly behind her, as Cora set a cup of steaming coffee before Will.

The three roundhouse workers were now in full attention.

With what appeared to be a show of family force, Will felt uneasy.

"About this play business," Roy started. "Addie Rose has a lot to do around here. Everyone here has their jobs. We need her."

"It won't take much time, Mama," Addie sat down at the table across from Will.

"She goes to school," Roy went on, "and makes pies for the restaurant here. She's pretty busy."

"The practice'll be mostly at night," Will ventured, wondering if maybe he was a bit over his head, with Addie's family closing ranks before him.

"So if it's at night," Roy came back, "who's gonna see she gets home? She's just a kid. Oughten to be walking home late at night."

"I can see she gets home. It's just a few blocks."

"Eight blocks," Roy countered.

"Oh, hell, Roy, let the little girl be in the play," one of the railroad men blurted out. "Will, here, he ain't gonna do nothin' bad."

"Shut up, Virgil. This is none of your put in," Roy came back.

"Okay, Roy, I'll shut up, but Addie girl, if you're in a play, I'm gonna come see you."

"You done now, Virgil?" Roy shot back.

Will looked at Roy, then Virgil, and finally back to Cora, who was standing by, waiting her turn.

"Mrs. Conyers," Will turned to Addie's mother, the only opinion that counted, and said, "I'll pick Addie Rose up tomorrow night, if she can go, and bring her home. It's up to you."

"No, you won't," Roy snapped. "I'll take her, and you can bring her back after that thing's over."

The three men by the stove pounded on the table and punched each other in approval.

Will stood up, wondering how quickly he could make an exit. He reached out to shake Roy's hand. Roy took it, but looked him in the eye. "I think we got an understanding, Will Austin."

As Will stepped out of the café, cold air hit him. A welcome relief.

CHAPTER 6

Inside Judge Austin's house, Addie stood for a moment under a gaslight chandelier, a bit bewildered. A circular stairway rose to her right with a round, ornate mahogany table in its curve, on which rested a bust of Abraham Lincoln. Addie would later learn that Judge Austin, as a young lawyer, saw Lincoln try a case before the future president was even elected to the State Assembly.

A young girl, who said her name was Sarah, said, "May I take your coat?"

Addie walked through a wide doorway, draped in green velvet, tied back with gold braid, into the living room, already filled with several guests, now looking over scripts. The man who had been a juggler in the parade slouched in one of the red, plush chairs, his long legs stretched out into the room.

Addie knew a couple of them. One worked in the bank and sometimes stopped by the café to talk to her mother. The other was Mr. Webb, who ran the icehouse on Fifth Street and brought ice to the café in the summer. A woman with glasses was sitting by a table with a kerosene lamp; she, too, was studying a script. Several lamps rested on tables and wall sconces, bathing the room in a soft, yellow light. The performers, all older than Addie, made her feel seriously uncomfortable.

One of the girls came to meet her. "I'm Nola, but we met just after the parade, didn't we? Will told me you were coming." She put her arms around Addie's shoulders. "Honey, I don't know whether Will told you or not, but the only parts in this play are for adults and an adolescent boy, and you wouldn't want to be a boy, I'm sure."

Completely overwhelmed by Nola and this grand place, Addie murmured, "I suppose not."

"You're welcome to stay on and watch, anyway. Mrs. Austin has a lovely dinner prepared for us later."

Addie sat down in a green velvet chair in a corner. "Thank you," she whispered, but Nola had turned away.

Script in hand, Nola came to stand by Will near the piano. "This play is called, 'Patriot First.' The whole story takes place during a grand ball at Washington's home during the Revolutionary War, so the men will be both dance partners and soldiers. We'll need eight girls and eight men."

Nola, holding the script as if it were a silk, accordion fan, met Will's eyes over it. "We all want Will to be George Washington, don't we? " Her eyes bespoke adoration. "Several ladies want to be Martha. Every part has some lines. But we'll pick Martha first."

"When everyone has tried out, we'll vote for the best one," Will said, and they all agreed.

Mary Nell Trotter came forward and read a page from the script. Next came Jessie May Stanford, who created an extremely dramatic and emotional Martha. Finally Nola, who frequently sang at weddings and funerals and was somewhat of a local celebrity, tried out. Very confident of her talent, she read, generous with gestures and expression, and even Addie, a novice in this business, saw that she was the best. When the vote was taken, Nola won, to no one's surprise—especially Lola's.

After that, each person read for other parts and the group selected the best.

All the men wanted to be soldiers, and the girls wanted to be dance partners so they could wear grand ball gowns. No one wanted to be Washington's young nephew.

Will looked at Addie, "Why don't you do it, Addie? It's only three sentences."

Addie was not too sure about this—be a boy? Everyone turned to her, teasing her into doing it. She stood finally, read off the three lines and everyone clapped. She knew she got the part only because no one wanted it. Still, she felt she was caught up in something new for her, something exciting and part of the Centennial celebration.

"Tomorrow night we'll do a read-through at the playhouse," Nola said.

Mrs. Violet Austin had prepared a sit-down dinner for the newly designated cast members, as well as those who had not been chosen. The judge sat at the head of a long table, with Violet at the opposite end. The long table, Addie particularly noticed, had matching chairs all around. She was seated by the judge, across from Tom, Will's younger brother, who was going to play Alexander Hamilton, Washington's secretary. Nola sat by Tom with Will on her other side.

Sarah, the girl who had met Addie when she first arrived, went to the dumbwaiter beside the breakfront, extracted food sent up from the basement where it had been cooked, and began to serve the guests.

"Well, young lady," the judge picked up his mustache cup, took a sip, and turned his attention on Addie Rose. "What else do you do besides go to school?"

When the judge spoke, everyone paid attention, and now they also looked at Addie Rose. She felt small, her face hot, her waistband too tight. "Well," she looked across at Tom. "I raise chickens, and sell eggs. I make my own clothes. Pretty soon I'll have a pet lamb and I have a cow named Nosey." Once she got going, she plowed on. "And my brothers let me plant eight apple trees and two cherry trees between Mama's garden and the 30 acres my brothers farm behind our house. We live over there on Eighth Street. Oh, and I help Mama at the Depot Café, too. She needs pies so I make pies—mostly apple."

There was silence and smiles, too, but not the friendly kind.

Addie Rose looked at the judge, then down the table. Everyone was watching her. Had she said something wrong? She looked back at the judge, "Your Honor," she added.

Tom laughed. "I guess you didn't expect that from the little lady, did you, Papa?"

"You're quite the independent young woman." Violet smiled at her, but Addie didn't feel there was much joy in the smile. Around the table she saw smug, mildly amused expressions on their faces, as if indulging a child. She felt a little unsure, but what the deuce, she might as well go on. "Maybe I'll open a bakery someday, sell apple pies and other things." They were still looking at her. "Once I made a pie with chicken, but it didn't turn out too well. I used too much flour."

"Do you ever plan to marry?" Violet questioned.

"I don't think I will. Well, maybe—when I'm real, real old."

"Usually women who marry do not think about working to make money," Nola Fitzgerald said. "It's—well, unladylike."

Addie Rose slowly cut her turkey, which she suspected was left over from Christmas dinner, into smaller and smaller pieces, trying to decide what to say. She had been taught to work and not complain. No one she knew said anything about working being "unladylike."

"I think when a woman works, she deprives a man of his place." The judge pronounced.

Addie Rose's neck felt hot, spreading to her cheeks and forehead. "My mama has to make a living. If she had waited for some man to come along and help her so she could be ladylike, we'd have starved to death."

Silence again.

Addie Rose glanced at the judge. "We all help. Mama is very strict about doing well with what we've got. She used to sit on the couch like a lady, but my papa was alive then." She folded her arms and looked directly at the judge. "That wouldn't have work out too well after he died."

"Yes, dear," Violet said, and Addie thought she saw a true smile. "We admire your mother. I taught school once, too, when it was necessary."

Addie Rose went back to cutting her turkey into still smaller pieces.

Will broke in "Her apple pies are delicious, and she's going to be a big hit in the play." He had rescued her. And relief melted through her.

"I'll come home on some weekends so we can have rehearsals." Will quickly changed the subject. "Everybody study your parts and be ready."

Nola smiled sweetly at Will. "Absolutely. This year is going to be the greatest fun: parades, carnivals, fairs, band concerts, and Will and I have lots of things planned for the Amsley players, don't we, Will?"

As the Amsley Players left the house, Addie stood on the top step, ready to walk the eight snowy blocks home, but Will came to her side. "I'll see you get home. Don't want that brother of yours coming after me."

"Oh, Will." Nola looked dejected. "I was hoping we could walk together."

Will shrugged. "She's just a kid, Nola. I've got to see her home." As they walked away, Addie whispered, "You and that Nola all lovey dovey, Will?"

Will looked down at her and laughed, "Just look where you're going, Addie. Ground's slippery."

The path between mounds of snow alongside the street was frozen hard. Will took her arm when there was a patch of ice, and he listened somewhat to what she was saying, but one thought tugged at him, yet he hesitated to actually say the words. What would she think of him? Would she think him foolish or worse, a whiner? He finally stopped under one of the gaslights.

"Addie, I want to ask you something."

"What's that?"

"Maybe you won't like me asking something so personal."

"It's all right, Will."

"Addie, do you think your father loved you?"

She drew back a little. He was immediately sorry. He shouldn't have asked that..

"I never thought about it," she said, not looking at him.

That wave of aloneness Will had known so often came to him, like in the dream he sometimes had, floating alone on the ocean, water all around, and not knowing which way to go. "If you never thought about it," he finally said, "then you knew you were wanted."

"I suppose," she said softly. "Why do you ask such a thing?"

He searched her face, a face with the innocent sincerity of a child, wanting to understand.

"No reason, I guess." He shrugged, feeling awkward. Nothing to say. Yet so much pounded in his head, so much to say to someone— someone who understood.

As they came to a muddy spot, he took her hand and found it cold, so he continued to hold it.

"I like it when we talk at the café," Addie said.

He nodded, "Me, too."

They walked along in silence for a while, crossing Main Street, nearing the railroad tracks, with two more blocks to go. "I think of my father every day," Addie said.

Will didn't answer. He felt in her a natural kindness. "I think of mine every day, too, but not like you."

Squares of light poured out onto the wooden platform from the Dining Car Café. A distant train whistle sounded. "That'll be the 8:30, Illinois Central ," Addie said.

"...from Springfield on the way to Memphis," Will added. They both laughed.

CHAPTER 7

"The George and Martha play rehearsal," as everyone called it, was held in the long, graceless room over the First National Bank, a raised platform for a stage at the front, no windows, and wall sconces along each side for lamplight.

Addie Rose Conyers was enthralled to be at her first play rehearsal and overly prepared to say her three lines. Cast members stood in a circle on the stage, script in hand ready for their first read-through, with Nola Fitzgerald directing.

Nola stepped forward. "In the opening scene, there's a ball at Washington's home, so we'll have six couples dancing. If you were picked to be a dancer, step out and find a partner with the appropriate height." This brought on fits of laughter for the next few minutes as couples stood together, switched partners, switched back and forth, until they finally settled into agreeable pairs.

Nola shook her head. "We'll need to work on that. Next, we have George and Martha in a homey, loving scene." She and Will sat down in chairs brought to center stage. They each read their lines. Addie really detested the way Nola looked at Will as she recited her lines to "George."

"There will be violins playing during this scene," Nola explained to the group. "Now dancers, resume."

Addie watched, becoming completely captivated with the play.

"During the dance scene," Nola explained, "Will's brother, Tom, as Alexander Hamilton, brings a messenger in and gives a note to Washington, who tells them he must go because he is a 'patriot first.' He tells the men that he needs them, too. Then each of the dancing couples stop in place. This is where they talk about their lives. The ladies tearfully say why they don't want their sweethearts or husbands to leave and go into the battle."

Addie felt a tightening at the back of her neck, over her scalp, and creeping down her back. When the dancing couples finished saying their lines, she would be next.

And then it was her turn! As nephew "Charles," she came out of the circle and said her lines, telling the partygoers that "he" must leave the comforts of life and follow the soldiers.

"Good," Nola said, "Good job, Addie."

Who needs her compliments?

"Now, Will," Nola turned to Will, smiling. "Washington is filled with such pride in his nephew, he first shakes his hand man to man, then as his uncle, embraces 'Charles.' Will, you must read your lines telling him you are proud of him for accepting his duty."

Will dutifully read his lines. Next, he took Addie in his arms and held her in a familial hug. Addie trembled; her mind numbed. She was totally unprepared for what she felt enclosed in this sheltered place, his arms warm and strong around her, his breath feathered on her forehead.

"Now," Nola quickly interrupted, "The soldiers have one last dance with their ladies before they leave. Martha and George stand in the midst of the lamenting ladies. Addie, you need to leave the room because the nephew comes back out in uniform and departs with Washington."

Not being in a room to leave or a place to go to, Addie moved to the edge of the stage.

"Lamenting ladies, can I see you doing a little lamenting?"

The girls' attempt at crying brought on more giggles than emoting sorrow, and ridiculing laughter from the sidelines.

Nola, with closed eyes, rubbing her forehead, whispered, "Girls, you'll need to work on your boohooing."

When rehearsal ended, Addie, still warmed with the memory of Will's arms around her, decided this play business was great fun. On a wave of high spirits she hurried to the door at the back of the room. Will would walk her home. He had promised her brother.

That night Addie wrote in her diary:

Dear Diary,

Will put his arms around me—in the play, of course. It was just make-believe. Nola is disgusting the way she makes up to Will. I'll bet he is so embarrassed. Good night, for now.

At the same time Addie was writing in her diary, Will Austin hunched over the desk in his room, dipped a pen in the inkwell, and began to write the letter to the War Department.

In answer to your query, Vachel Fletcher was the husband of Violet Fletcher Austin and the father of William Fletcher. There were no other children.

Will sat back in his chair. He could write that his father had been declared dead, but something in him balked at writing that. He knew in his heart of hearts his father was not dead, no matter what the document said.

CHAPTER 8

All the town turned out to see the "George and Martha play"; the actual title, posted on a handbill on the bank door, read "A Patriot First."

Will stood offstage, feeling extremely warm in white breeches, boots, and a long wool coat with brass buttons; he turned a tricorn hat in his hand and smiled to himself as he listened to Nola out in front of the closed curtain. She was taking the opportunity of a captive audience to belt out a few songs. Across the stage, behind the curtain, he caught a glimpse of Addie Rose in the dandified outfit of a Colonial gentleman. It occurred to him, Addie might declare her resolve to be an independent woman and "probably" never marry, as she said, but he sensed she seemed to warm to him in his embrace. She would never admit it, he knew. He decided when the scene came and he was to hold her, this time, he would make the embrace especially close and last longer. He'd watch her reaction. After all, he reasoned, she was to be Washington's nephew whom Washington had always loved.

It was time for the curtain to go up, and he heard Nola promise the audience she would be back later for more songs.

That night, before Addie went to sleep, she wrote in her diary:

Dear Diary,

I have been planning to do something when we did the real play. I measured something. When Will held me close, I am just tall enough for my head to fit right under his chin.

Will's mother gave an after-the-performance dinner for the cast. She asked me to make five cherry pies. She paid me fifty cents a pie. I couldn't believe she paid me so much money! And for pies! She is nicer than I thought, but she is so proper, I never know if I am doing something wrong or not.

If people will pay for my pies, maybe I can make some money. Just making pies for the Dining Car Café is not getting me anywhere.

That Nola is the bossiest person I have ever met, and she's taken possession of Will. I don't care, though. He just talks to me because I know how he feels, not having a father. He likes my apple pies. He held me for a long time up there on the stage in front of everyone. I wonder why he did that?

When Will returned home in early April, Violet had saved a letter from Reverend Hollister. He scanned it. "I am sorry to report," it read, "that my claim for a veteran's pension was denied, so little Amy remains in my charge as something of a charity case for the church. I appreciate your concern about our situation. Amy mentions you often. She says she wishes you could be her brother. Blessings, Reverend Hollister."

Will folded the letter, and dropped his head in his hands. He thought of that sad little girl in Preacher Hollister's parlor. He understood what she wanted, knew how she felt. She wanted someone who was her own.

CHAPTER 9

Will was home for the summer and needed a job. He had one more year at the university. In the orchards, apples were ready for picking; maybe he could get work there. He went to see Al Tolliver, who owned Triangle Orchards at the edge of town. Tolliver, an old Civil War veteran, sat in his shed, a wide hat pulled over his eyes. He supervised the operation, which meant he saw that his six children did the work. And, as he saw it, his job was to be the face of the operation, greet customers, and drum up business.

"Well," Al drawled as he stood up (favoring his right leg, a war injury), "we got more'n one job out here. There's apple pickers and there's a crew that sorts, packs and crates 'em for shipping, and there's those that meet the trains and load the crates on the cars. Way yonder, in the most distant corner of that orchard across the road, there's a building where we make up the cider and jug it up."

Will got a job running the apple sorter, crating them, and making local deliveries, which included a weekly crate to the Dining Car Café. One Friday, when he made his delivery at the back kitchen door, Cora Conyers paid him and said, "We got pies right outta the oven, and I'll just bet you got time for a piece." He didn't need coaxing.

Will sat down with pie and fork at a white worktable in the kitchen, the hot stove at his back, with multiple pots of food simmering on it. "Where's that Addie girl? I haven't seen her since the play last winter."

"You just missed her." Cora wiped her hands on her apron and opened the back door of the kitchen to let in a meager summer breeze. "She was here making up these pies." Cora sat down at the table by him. "You need to come by on Saturday afternoon. It's her birthday and we're surprising her with a little party." Cora looked out the open door, wistfully. "My baby'll be sixteen."

"You wretched beast, move yourself in there," Addie herded Nosey, the cow, into the barn for milking.

Addie had found her in the dusky early morning along the hedge-row of the farm, out of the pen again and wandering loose. She drove her into the dim, cool barn.

"Can't you be good today? It's my birthday." Addie put her hand on the cow's rump. "You don't care that I have to run all over God's creation to get you out of whatever mess you nosed yourself into." But as she sat on her three-legged stool, pail below the udders, Addie laid her head on the animal's warm belly and smiled.

When she walked to the house with her bucket of milk, Addie stopped and sat on a bench her brothers had made for what she called her "special place." Four years ago, she had planted an apple tree and a cherry tree in the backyard, both now ready to bear fruit. Later, she had planted honeysuckle vines between the trees, and now, sitting on the bench by the vines, she watched hummingbirds come, attracted to her little cove, and floating on the warming summer air as the sun began to rise.

Addie dashed up the two steps of the Dining Car Café planning to make her pies before the midday heat. She opened the door and stood speechless. Her mother, sister and brothers, and—of all people! Will Austin came out of the back kitchen. They were singing a chorus of "Happy Birthday." Only one couple in the café, enjoying Cora's sausage gravy and biscuits and waiting for the next train, smiled as they watched the birthday party celebration. Her sister Mary cut the cake, and everyone crowded around her. Addie put her hand over her mouth, choking back tears, both thrilled and embarrassed at the attention. There would be no gifts, Addie didn't expect any. Cora Conyers had stopped giving them when she became a widow.

After the cake was consumed, her brothers left for their rounds through the farms to buy food for the café. Mary had finished her job baking bread, and said her goodbyes. Her mother left for a little time away from work, but Will stayed.

"Come with me to the kitchen. Birthday or no birthday," Addie called over her shoulder, "I have to make pies for the next three days. Trains come and go no matter if it's somebody's birthday or not." Will drew up a chair by the worktable, and watched Addie peel and slice the apples, mix flour, lard and water into dough.

For some reason, she felt sorry for Will. He lived a better life than she did, in the judge's house where his mother lived, but she saw sadness about him. The judge had sent him to college to be a lawyer, preparing him to join the law firm the judge had founded. But Will reminded Addie of the hobos that rode the trains and came to the café wanting a handout from her mother. They had nowhere to go. Even if they wanted to go home, they didn't know where "home" was.

The kitchen was sweltering, and the air outside felt heavy and oppressive. Distant thunder floated on the sultry air. Perspiration trickled down her back, dampening her dress.

"It's nice to see you again," he said when she came back to the table to flute the edges of the pies.

"Because I make pies you like?"

"No, no, not that. It's because we understand each other." Will looked through the open door; wind was picking up, some drifting into the hot kitchen. "We lost our fathers."

She put the pies in the oven and turned to him. "Let's sit out on the back step until the pies are done. Get some air." Thunderclaps were louder now. Lightning flared again and again on the horizon, and wind thrashed hard through tree leaves. Cooling air pouring over them.

Finally Will spoke. "I'll make myself a good lawyer, Addie; that'll be my own and I'll know I didn't need him."

"Or . . . " she said, "maybe you'll know then that it didn't matter he left."

Rolling clouds filled the sky, the day growing dark as dusk. Lightning cracked and hissed, splitting the gray heavens and thunder pounded incessantly. They sat, unspeaking, mesmerized by the awesome majesty of the storm. Addie always felt the smallness of humans in the fearful, unleashed power filling the sky. She reached for Will's hand. He looked surprised, then smiled at her and held it. The wind now carried a mist, and then raindrops began to patter on them and the metal dining car. They moved inside and closed the door as the storm hit with its full vengeance. Addie set three lamps down on the table—one for the kitchen, and two at each end of the café.

Will struck a match, lifted the globes, and ran the flame across each of the wicks. "A train's pulling in." They watched through rain drenched windows as several passengers got off the train and hurried into the depot, but none braved the downpour to come to the café.

The smell of baking pies filled the kitchen. "Do all those pies have to go to customers?" He turned back as the train began to pull out.

"You're a customer. You want a piece?"

"Pie and understanding talk," he said as she set a piece of pie before him.

He delved into it. But Addie thought, as she watched him, there's never going to be enough pie or anything else to fill that empty spot in your soul.

She stayed until nine o'clock that night and closed the café. Rain was slackening to a drizzle on the train platform as she and Will started walking to Addie's house, the night air cool and fresh. She stopped, pulled off her shoes and stockings. Will put the lantern down and pulled off his shoes. She gathered up her skirt and went barefoot out into the muddy street. They stomped in the puddles they came to, like children, until they got near her house.

"It smells like—like perfume. What is it?" Will asked.

"Honeysuckle. I planted them. You want to go out there?"

"Sure." He carried the lantern as they went behind her house and to the end of the brick walk.

"I planted the bushes between the apple and cherry trees. It makes hummingbirds come."

"Nice," he whispered. "It's nice."

Before she knew what was happening, Will kissed her lips.

"Oh." She drew back, helplessly dropping her muddy skirt. "Why did you do that?"

"Why? I wanted to be the first to kiss you . . . and on your sixteenth birthday."

She felt paralyzed, stunned. "I don't know what to say."

"I have waited all day to walk you home so I could kiss you on this birthday."

She stared at him in the semi-darkness. Finally she said, "You should know I have vowed to never marry."

"I just gave you a kiss, Addie. A marriage proposal comes a lot farther down the road."

"Oh, well," she stammered.

"Besides if I was going to propose marriage to a girl, I wouldn't do it when she has muddy feet."

"I thought you considered me a little kid."

"But you're growing up pretty."

"Pretty?"

"I think I'd better take you home."

They left the hummingbird cove, and he said goodbye at her back door.

Dear Diary,

Will... Will kissed me! Was I ever surprised? I thought he considered me like some kid who can make pies he likes. Does he think about me in a different way? I never think about him—maybe I do. Sometimes I imagine him watching me. But he kissed me—on the lips. He said I was pretty. Oh, they had a party for me today—I'm sixteen.

She didn't see Will again until the next Friday when he brought a basket of apples to the café. He was all business and only had conversation with her mother.

CHAPTER 10

The town of Amsley was caught up whole-heartedly into their most creative, patriotic spirit for the celebration of the country's one-hundredth birthday.

Men grew beards and women made dresses they imagined were in the style of Revolutionary War days, and, just to be sure, added long aprons and bonnets. On the courthouse lawn each weekend was a new event: chowder cook-offs, fish fries, tableaus, sing-alongs, patriotic quilt contests, and band concerts. The Fourth of July, from early morning to midnight, was brimmed full with celebration: first, a parade led by the marching band and followed by the Civil War veterans; an endless program on the grandstand of political speeches; a prettiest baby contest; an orneriest man contest (won by the mayor); square dancing; horse racing; all-day preaching at the churches; and finally, over the lake just outside of town, fireworks.

The culmination of the summer-long celebration—the most beloved and venerated event of Amsley—was the Old Settlers Picnic, a tradition started long before the Civil War, that happened for the early settlers between planting and harvest season, on the last weekend of August. Families sat on the wide lawn of the picnic grounds with blankets spread about, eating lunches from wicker baskets; listening to fiddlers, singers, and sometimes speakers, up on the grandstand. At the edge of the grounds, for this special year, the city had brought in a carnival.

Addie Rose walked with Sarah, the girl she'd met at the judge's house, the length of the row of carnival booths, each a two-story apparatus, with painted canvas on the top structure and, as a back-drop on the ground level, picture-painted canvases. The fire-eater captured their attention for a while. At the next booth, a man, dressed in a blue brocade suit and powdered wig, threw knives at a woman standing against a wall, with a curled, piled-high, white wig. They watched as he took aim and threw the knife that cut through the top of her hair. She screamed. The crowd went wild, so he threw another knife, cutting in the puffed sleeve of her elaborate yellow satin dress. Addie winced as the woman screamed. Everyone stood horrified as again and again he narrowly missed her. Then one knife came within a fraction of an inch of her throat. Sarah clutched Addie's arm, "I don't want to watch this."

"It's just a show," Addie said.

"I know, but I don't like it."

As they turned to move through the crowd to the next act, Addie caught sight of Will Austin walking arm in arm with Nola Fitzgerald. In spite of herself, she caught her breath. Why was he with her! A sour resentment began to twist inside her. She had thought often of that feather-light kiss on her lips.

"Men are despicable creatures. That's why I like animals," Addie pronounced.

"I thought you didn't like him anyway."

"I don't know who you're talking about." Addie tugged at her.

"Of course you do," Sarah said. "I saw you looking at Will Austin and Nola."

"I was not . . ." She couldn't finish. There was a big lump in her throat.

"Maybe we should go."

"No, Mrs. Judge gave me the day off and I want to stay. Why should Will Austin ruin your day or mine?"

"He has nothing to do with it," Addie snapped back. Sarah mea-sured her friend with a questioning look. "Let's go over by the grandstand. There's a crowd over there."

"If you want to, " Addie sighed, but the carnival had lost its edge.

They found seats on benches in front of the grandstand, watched a woman walk up to the center of the grandstand and stand on the top step where speakers always stood.

"I'm Ina Pilcher, and I am here with a petition for women to have a say in the government—that is, to vote. I want you to come up here and sign this. We have to live under laws, same as men do, but we have no say in them . . ."

"Go home, moms!" a young boy called out. Addie looked across at him. Buster Jensen! He had sat across the aisle from her in their one-room schoolhouse. Buster was backed up with boos. "Nobody wants to hear you," he continued. "Why don't you act like a woman s'pose to, moms."

"Our country was founded because we had no say," Ina persisted. "That is, men had no say ."

More booing.

". . . and women are still in the same fix."

A group of men moved closer to the podium. One wore his Centennial-style beard, along with red, white and blue suspenders, and began mocking her by immediately echoing her words. Everyone began laughing, men and women.

"This here is better'n than that freak show over there." Buster picked up a peach and threw it at her, hitting her arm and partly splattering on her face. Everyone laughed, but still she kept talking, even though no one could hear her now for the man echoing her words, the crowd clapping for him and Buster's taunts.

Sarah tugged at Addie's arm. "Let's go. I don't like those women."

"No," Addie pulled free, her eyes blazing, her heart pounding. She began to make her way to the podium. She held her arms up over her head. "You want to throw food like you're little kids? Throw it at me! Let that woman talk."

"Sit down, Addie Rose Conyers," Buster yelled.

"Before I die, I'm gonna vote," Addie shot back at Buster. "I work. My mama works. My sister works and none of us can vote! I may be a kid, but I know what's right, and I know what's wrong!"

A man dressed in a full-black suit, who looked like he was headed for a funeral, came up to the steps. But Addie knew all the preachers in town, and he wasn't one of them. "See what happens? Women like this teach the young ones. Then the young ones learn to unsex theyselves." He was speaking with a kind of moral authority, and the audience grew quiet and listened; a rustle of agreement poured through the crowd. Ina Pilcher stood by, quiet for a moment until the man bowed to her and left the platform.

"'Sides, Addie Rose," Buster took up his taunting again, "you're too pretty to think about things like that,"

"Buster Jensen, you are a dirty, stinking polecat. I got more smarts behind my pretty face than you got behind your ugly one."

The crowd calmed down a bit, enjoying the attacks between Addie and Buster.

"You want a date, Addie?"

"Don't insult me."

"I like it when you get your dander up."

"Shut your stupid flapper." Addie leaned forward. "This woman's got something to say that might help you from being so stupid, but I doubt we've got that much time."

At that moment an apple came flying across the open space toward Addie, but she caught it and hurled it back at a red-bearded man with a plaid shirt. It hit him in the shin and broke apart. The crowd began to laugh again.

Then there was a ripple in the standing crowd. Will Austin appeared, parting his way through. "Addie Rose, what are you thinking?" He took her arm, but she pulled away and looked past him at the two hecklers. "I meant it when I said you were stupid," she yelled at Buster.

"Addie, your mama would be mortified at this. Come down here, now." Will tugged at her elbow.

"You're not telling me what to say, Will Austin."

"Addie, get a grip on yourself," Will said.

She finally walked down the three steps and faced him. "I suppose Nola wouldn't be doing such a thing."

"No, she wouldn't." He shook his head. "And no other self-respecting woman would, either. Think about your mother, Addie. She would be absolutely humiliated."

"My mother is exactly who I was thinking about."

Late the next day, Will was at the café in time to walk Addie home.

"I'll be leaving for my last year in law school. I wanted to see you before I go."

As they neared her house, Addie said, "Let's go 'round back to my hummingbird cove."

They had hardly sat down on the bench when Will turned to her. "I want to know why you would go up there and defend that woman, Addie?"

"Because she's right. She wants women to have voting rights and be recognized." She stood up and turned to him. "I'll never let anyone do to me what my papa did to my mama. She works all the time— every day— and she had no part in the choice that put her here." She watched for a moment a hummingbird fluttering before the honey-suckle blossoms. "I am never going to be a dependent person—never, never will I let anybody put me in the place my mama has to be."

"I understand all that, but just how are you going to be so independent?" he asked.

"I will sell pies. Raise chickens." She looked again at the hummingbird. "I can plant trees like these, and sell fruit. I can make my own way. You just watch and see if I don't."

"You say you had a good father, but he made a mistake. Now you're going to make over your whole life because of it?"

"Well, now that's interesting, Will. I could say the same for you," Addie shot back.

"It's not the same."

"It never is the same when it's in your own life."

Abruptly Will turned to her. "Addie, do you like me?"

"You're all right." She was flippant, but then she studied him for a minute. "Course I like you."

"I mean, do you *really* like me?"

"Well." She had just said she would never soften to a man, but now the memory of his kiss was with her. "I guess I do."

"Now promise me while I'm gone you will not get up at one of those rallies and embarrass yourself—and your family—defending some militant woman."

"I will not promise you that, Will Austin. They are speaking the truth, and I agree with them."

"Honest to God, Addie Rose, you're like a fart in a hot skillet."

"I'm what?" Her face flushed hot, sharp words ready to spill off her tongue. "I'm a—fart?" She stared at him for an instant, then began to laugh until she could hardly get the words out. "I have never ever been called a 'fart.' Not even my brothers . . . ever." She bent over laughing.

"Addie." He reached for her, pulled her up to standing, and kissed her long, insistent. "Your kisses are sweet," he whispered near her ear.

She moved closer into the nest of his arms.

Will stood with the judge and his mother, ready to board the train.

"You've done well," Judge Austin grasped Will's hand and patted him on the back. "One more year to go. I know you'll be a fine addition to the firm next year."

Violet took her son in her arms and embraced him. "Yes, son, I'm proud of you. We'll miss you, but Christmas break will be here before you know it and you'll be back with us."

Just then, Will saw Nola Fitzgerald breathlessly hurrying down the platform. "I was so afraid I'd miss you, Will. I wanted to see you off." She took the opportunity to reach up and put a kiss on his cheek. "I'll miss you," she whispered.

A bit surprised she would kiss him in front his parents, he put his hands on her shoulders and said, "And I'll miss you, too, Nola." Then he swung up onto the steps of the train car.

"Well, goodbye. Don't forget to write!" Will yelled over the train whistle.

He moved down the aisle of the passenger car, and found a window seat just as the train jerked forward and slowly moved out of the station. Outside, the three of them were waving at him. He waved back but then his eyes turned toward the Dining Car Café. He felt an unaccountable kind of emptiness as the train began to gather speed.

That night, Addie wrote:

Dear Diary,

Will went away to school, and I watched from inside the café as Nola Fitzgerald came running up to tell him goodbye. I will start back to school next week, too. Not much doing around here now. I made ten pies yesterday and went with my brothers in their wagon out around the farms to pick up vegetables and meat. I sold all my pies.

I think I'll make me some new dresses—for Christmas when everybody's back. Maybe Sarah can get me an invitation to one of Mrs. Judge's Christmas parties. Will must be up there in his college room by now. I wonder what his room looks like.

Good night.

CHAPTER 11

A t the university in Springfield, Will buried himself in work. It was not only the usual pressure from his professors and their extensive and overwhelming reading requirements. It was coming from within himself, and the sobering realization that, what had been up to this time theory, would soon be a fearsome reality, and what he did would affect the lives of people; sometimes it could mean their life or death.

Will punctually received letters from his mother written on Sunday afternoons, as well as frequent letters from Nola, telling about the latest play and wishing he had time this year to join the Amsley players. But one person did not send letters, Addie Rose Conyers. He was surprised at the passion she'd shown for the woman talking about women's voting rights. The Supreme Court had just last year ruled against it after several bitter lawsuits filed because women had attempted to vote and were turned away.

He considered it. Could women vote? He had not thought about it until he saw how strongly Addie had spoken for it. Were women reliable enough to cast votes that might direct the country? His mother was certainly more reliable than his father.

Another idea then toyed with him. If Addie Rose was capable of such strong feelings, could he court her into having that kind of passion for him?

At times, after a day of practice in mock trials or spending hours on a legal brief, he would lean back in a chair and remember that day in Corinth, Mississippi, and the little girl, Amy, abandoned and unwanted. He thought of the choices, as a man, he could make in his life, choices that would be denied her.

Somewhere he had read, "Study cleanses the soul." He had found it to be the perfect comfort for the desperate, depressing isolation that sometimes came upon him. He would spend his life helping people in trouble, and that would carry him away from that isolation, too. Amy would not have that opportunity, he realized. And that, in turn, made him think of Addie.

When he lapsed into that memory, the one in Corinth, the face of Casper, seething with something unspoken, seemed to Will to overshadow it all.

CHAPTER 12

Chicago, Illinois 1854, Twenty-three years earlier

"Gentlemen, we are going to build a railroad—a 163-mile railroad from Chicago to Galena—and we are going to build it first."

Vachel Fletcher looked at the lanky raw-boned man, graying hair and close-clipped mustache who had draped his rangy frame over the corner of a wooden desk. He had introduced himself as Oscar Weidner to the dozen or so men standing about or lounging on one of the two open window ledges in the log cabin office. Behind him, seated at the desk, was a man named Amos Brown, according to Weidner's introduction.

"We're going to do more than build a railroad. We're going to create history," Weidner flung his long arms about, eager words pouring out. "Those 163 miles are more than a stretch of track. Consider this: goods coming out of the ports of Philadelphia, New York, and Boston can go through the Erie canal, into the Great Lakes, to a pier in Chicago, over our railroad to Galena, to the Mississippi River, then potentially down to St. Louis, to the confluence of the Missouri River, and on to the most distant reaches of the West on the Missouri River." He leaned forward and opened his arms wide. "Do you see why we are making history, gentlemen?"

"We are, those of us in this room," again he waved his arm as if to take in an embrace, the crowd before him, "and shareholders in the Eastern cities, the impetus for this endeavor and—make no mistake—it will make us all wealthy."

Fletch was caught up in Weidner's fevered exhilaration. There was something fresh and wild and thrilling about this—creating not a new business, but a new way of life.

"Once the placing of the track bed is determined," Weidner continued, "the ties and rails laid, you will learn how to run the locomotives, how to repair them, and do any job in the railroad business. This is the future, men. It's your chance to show us your mettle and have a job for life."

Amos Brown stood up from behind the desk and took charge. A short, solid man, with a balding head and round, thick-lensed glasses that made him look wide-eyed and somewhat surprised. "Men, this is what you will do." He was serious, business-like and efficient as a banker. "We'll send you out in pairs, scouring the land for a likely path for the track bed, fanning out about five miles apart. You'll have a wagon and team to haul the chains. Each pair will measure about five miles a day, stopping every mile to sink a ground test of the soil. You'll map your location and record the soil quality as you go. You'll leave stakes where you test, so we can locate your testing results. The Illinois prairie is open range, so you will not be infringing on anyone's property."

The door and two windows were open, and flies poured in. Fletched noticed a mud dauber building a nest in one of the topmost corners of the log cabin roof.

"We'll be covering the lay of the land in a swath 30-miles wide, terminating in Galena," Brown was saying. "We estimate it will take about six weeks to do it. We're looking for ground that is most resistant—that has hard-packed, dense soil to create and support the roadbed. You'll be cognitive and record any copes of timber that might be appropriate for ties. You will observe rises in the land—hills and valleys. You'll recognize what will require more grading when we lay track, and more trouble for an engineer when the trains are running. Record on your maps streams and rivulets, because that will require building trestles, which adds expense and makes the rails more apt to become slick in icy weather."

The dauber flew out the window, but Fletch knew it would come back, again and again.

"In the evening, Cook will fire a gun so all of you can find the wagon for grub, both evening and morning," Amos Brown explained.

The man put up a large slate on which he had sketched a chalk diagram. "Now, about assessing the soil and how layers would look when a ground test rod is opened. The top layer," he pointed to his sketch, "is, of course, surface growth and decay, weeds, grass, etc. Below that is harder soil that the organic material doesn't penetrate; then the clay, sand and possibly loam, which is the least desirable. We are searching for ground most resistant to weathering. The composition of the rail bed is of paramount importance for supporting the track structure, locomotives, and—ultimately—cars loaded with cargo. Men, your findings are absolutely crucial in deciding where to place the track for optimum stability. Any questions?"

There was a bit of foot shuffling, but no one spoke up.

"Well, then," Brown said, "if you're interested, report here tomorrow, and if you want to pair up beforehand, that'll save time."

Fletch walked out of the little room, onto the boardwalk along sparkling Lake Michigan. It was a balmy, summer day, with a breeze from the lake bathing over his face, ruffling his hair, his spirit soaring, feeling the adventure that lay ahead. One day he would hold the engineer's stick in his hand, maneuvering a great locomotive under him, a line of cars trailing behind.

He ambled into a weathered, wooden frame building, an ugly expanse inside with grimy windows that fronted on the street. The swinging sign out front said, "Pinaire's Tavern." He ordered stew and beer. Seated at the next table was a well-dressed gentleman, graying hair, who took pains to fill the bowl of his pipe and tamp down the tobacco, before leaning back for a soothing smoke. It reminded him of his father.

Fletch looked away. The bitter scene with his father—still raw— began to play in his memory. But he had known he couldn't stay there and go into the tobacco business. If he hadn't made the break, it would have enveloped him, sucked him in, as surely as a man drowning in quicksand.

Words still seared his conscience. "Why do you think I sent you to school?" his father had stormed, "to chase some fool dream? It was to educate you to run a business your grandfather built, and I continued to build. It was my plan to pass it on to you and Claude Raymond. But you walk away—go your own way. Selfish to the core."

"I can't stay."

"*Won't* stay, is what it is."

"I hate the business."

"You're spoiled, willful . . ." and the argument went on, both men resolute, shouting words that would be remembered forever, words that could not be unsaid. Fletch had walked out of the room, down the hall and slammed the front door. But it was more than just that. He had closed the door on his family, his childhood, and all they expected of him.

When he watched the man at the next table light up his pipe, Fletch felt an overwhelming aloneness; the emptiness of the choice he had brought about. But in truth, he'd had no other choice. He wanted a future—*his* future—not a life mapped out for him. He wanted to be a railroad man. Fletch finished his stew, and as he was ordering another beer, someone walked up to his table, one of the men who had been in the meeting with Weidner and Brown this afternoon. He remembered him sitting on the window ledge, the lake gleaming under sunshine through the window behind him.

"Name's Will Stone." He extended his hand. "Mind if I sit?"

"Go ahead." Fletch nodded.

"You up for joining the surveying crew tomorrow?"

"Why not? I need the money." Fletch reached for his beer mug. "Where you from, Mr. Stone?"

"Indiana. Crossed the river from Louisville. Be obliged if you was to call me 'Stoner' and leave off with the 'Mister.'"

"Thought I heard shades of a southern twang in there—Stoner."

A smile lit up his face. "Reckon you did."

They looked up as Weidner and Amos Brown walked in.

Fletch glanced at Stoner. "Looks like the bosses are here."

"Reckon so."

Through the front windows, a dusky evening turned to darkness as they laughed, talked and drank together. Stoner was a comfortable sort, easy to talk to. Fletch vaguely felt, as they walked out into the night, Stoner had unknowingly pushed the raw wound of broken family ties to a distant corner of his mind.

The next morning—after preliminary instruction and being assigned a wagon and team—Fletch, with his new partner, Stoner, began his first day's work toward building a railroad. The easy life of a successful tobacco merchant's privileged son and college student had never asked for a day's work like this. When he stretched out under the stars that night, every muscle in his body screamed. The men had had little to say; the work had been grueling, and they were ready to eat and go to sleep. Still, there was something invigorating about using his body, sleeping under the stars, and being a part of a grand adventure.

Progress was painfully slow. They stretched out 66 feet of chains, again and again making up a mile, then pounding a soil test into the ground, recording it, and leaving a two-foot stake planted in the ground. The men gradually got used to the demanding labor, and when they came together at night—after Cook had called them in and they ate—they had much discussion, along with some arguments, about the route, although the decision itself was not in their hands.

It was becoming clear that the six weeks estimated to go from Chicago to Galena was a hopeless miscalculation. After four months— during which they stood in summer downpours, worked in scorching heat, steadied horses when lightning came so close you could hear the sizzle and the immediate air-shattering thunder—they became hardened as soldiers. They sloughed through mud or sand and waded rivulets, slept under the wagon, and worked under glaring sun until every inch on them was wet with sweat.

It was early September, four and half months later, when the crew finally folded up their chains for the last time on the outskirts of Galena. Amos Brown and Oscar Weidner met them at the edge of town and eagerly gathered up their recorded logs. "We've put you all up for a week at the DeSoto House Hotel. You'll find more than the comforts of home there, and tomorrow you'll collect pay for your work."

In the early dusk, walking along the main street of Galena, clean, shaven and trimmed, they ambled down to the riverfront. Several ships were anchored at the pier. Galena was the busiest Mississippi port between St. Paul and St. Louis. They waited as a large stern-wheeler maneuvered in near the dock, moving slowly to position itself. Music poured from its lower deck; the gangway placed, Fletch and Stoner watched a hoard of passengers disembark and walk up the incline to the town. It was a mix of single men and families, then in the milieu, someone caught Fletch's eye. She wore a bonnet, but reddish blonde curls peeked out. He moved slightly to get a better view through the crowd, and, in spite of himself, he moved still closer to the crowd to get a better perspective. She was apparently with her parents, walking up the dusty path to the town, probably the hotel. She was wearing a lavender-colored dress. He followed her, with Stoner by his side, until he watched her walk up the three steps to the DeSoto House.

Fletch finally looked back at Stoner and saw someone as entranced as he was. They decided the very place to have dinner that night was in the hotel dining room, but later, inside and properly seated, the lovely passenger was nowhere about. Stoner talked of his farm in Indiana and how he'd seen a train once and how that looked like a lot better work than following a plow for the rest of his life. Fletch didn't feel like talking about his family life.

CHAPTER 13

They finished the meal and moved into drinks. The girl descended the stairs with a man Fletch assumed was her father. She was not wearing her bonnet now; her long hair fell over her shoulders. He watched her, not seeing a person with pretty features, but something of a vision wrapped in a glorious aura. She was the most beautiful girl he had ever seen. Then he admonished himself for staring.

There was a problem. He was a stranger in the town, and she apparently was, too, or else she wouldn't be staying at a hotel. How could he get an introduction? He could go up to the father, but he was pretty sure that wouldn't do. Maybe it was because he had just come off of months of hard labor, or that he now was a railroad man and felt a grain of importance, or maybe it was those last two whiskeys, but he got up and walked to the nearby table where she was seated.

"Sir, I am a stranger in town, been working to build a new railroad into Galena. We are to have a meeting in town with one of the financiers tomorrow. I was wondering if you were the man."

The man looked up, a bit puzzled. "No, son, I'm sorry to say I'm not a big financier. I'm just a professor in a small college in Pennsylvania, but I watch with interest the different rail lines popping up all over the East, even moving into the West. What's this one called?"

"It'll be the Chicago-Southern Illinois Railroad when it's complete—gonna connect the Great Lakes with the Mississippi River. It's history in the making." He could hardly keep his eyes averted from the gorgeous creature so near him.

"Here, why don't you sit down? This is my daughter, Violet. I'm Robert Ikamire."

"Thank you. I'm Vachel Fletcher. Pleased to meet—both of you." Fletch kept a studied focus on Professor Ikamire.

"One day, they'll take us wherever we want to go," the professor said, and Fletch nodded in agreement.

"Tomorrow, we have a big meeting where the exact route will be mapped out and then the work will begin in earnest." Fletch didn't want the conversation to die and he'd have to excuse himself before he got to talk to the girl. "I plan to be an engineer on the new Chicago-Southern Illinois Railroad, and who knows what will unfold."

"Where are you from, Mr. Fletcher?" The lovely girl finally spoke and Fletch's heart thundered in his chest, his hands trembling.

There was a dry lump lodged in his throat as he turned his attention to the girl. "I was raised in Kentucky. Just graduated from the university there."

She nodded, "I just finished my education, too. My parents are here with me, in Galena, to help me get settled in a boarding house or something. I will be a teacher in the school through this winter. I wanted to see life out West," she said.

Fletch looked into her saucer-blue eyes. "No teacher of mine ever looked like you." He tried to sound casual, but every fiber in him quickened as he looked at her.

"Thank you. That doesn't make much difference to the little ones I'll be teaching," she said.

"Well, I best be getting back to my friend. We have an early morning. Pleased to meet you both."

When Fletch sat down again at his own table, Stoner gave him a cold eye. "'Financier'? Where'd you come up with that?"

"Who can ever tell? There's financiers backing the railroad and they're bound to want to see what's going on out here—with their money. One might show his face sometime, maybe it'll be tomorrow."

Stoner looked across the fancy eating room of the DeSoto House and shook his head.

CHAPTER 14

Amsley, Illinois, 1877

"It's a wonderland," Addie breathed, awestruck.

Will was beside her, just inside the front entrance of Judge Austin's house. By the curved stair banisters, draped with holly and velvet ribbons, was a lavishly decorated Christmas tree stretching to the ceiling. In the long parlor, another tree sparkled in candlelight, and every windowsill, every mantel, held evergreens tied with huge, red ribbons.

The house was already filled with guests, and someone was at the pianoforte playing carols. Will had insisted she come, and now he took Addie's arm and escorted her through the crowd, talking to this one and that. Nearly every guest had at one time eaten in the Dining Car Café, townspeople she already knew. There was never time to do much Christmas decorating at her house, and certainly not enough money for parties.

Everyone was dressed in grand holiday finery, but Addie felt herself well turned out, too. She had taken the money made from pies her brothers sold on their weekly routes, and bought material to make her first party dress.

It was last fall when she had gone to Blair's Department and Dry Goods Store, stood at the counter where bolts of material were stacked, imagining being invited to this, the best of all parties in town. Finally, she decided to imitate Violet Austin's penchant for wearing the color violet. She would wear rose. Why not? She studied the patterns in Goday Lady's Book, found just the right one, bought yards of rose brocade, and then made a creation that, according to Goday, the gospel of fashion, was the latest style. But she would *not* wear a bustle for anybody's party!

Nola Fitzgerald stood by the piano, singing Christmas carols. Happy to be the center of attention, she sang at least a dozen songs before she stopped and said there would be some recitations next, but—not to fear—she would be back with more songs.

Addie didn't know why it irritated her to have Nola there; Will had come to her house and taken her to the party as his date.

When Nola did come back to the piano, she asked the guests to join her. For Addie, the party began to pick up and she was just getting into the spirit of things, when she noticed people beginning to take their leave. She hardly realized how late it was; she'd had such a glorious time with Will. He even asked her to stand with him in the hall as he, his mother, the judge and brother Tom thanked guests for coming and wished them a Merry Christmas.

Finally the house was empty; the candles on the tree extinguished; the judge and Violet had said their goodnights and gone upstairs. Will and Addie were left alone with only the light from the fireplace. Will looked at her for a long moment as she sat on the green velvet humpback sofa. He noticed she was beginning to feel uncomfortable. "You . . . you look so grown up. I was really proud of you," he said. He stopped for a minute. This was not going well. How could he propose marriage to someone who said they didn't ever want to be a married person?

"Thank you," she said.

"You look just . . . beautiful."

"Thank you. Your mother wears violet so I thought I could wear rose." She smoothed her hand over her wide skirt. "What do you think? Good idea?"

"Yes." He mumbled, not really hearing what she said. "While I was away, Addie, I thought about you—sometimes." He wasn't sure, stumbling in fact. "Not—sometimes." He turned to her and took both her hands. "All the time. That is, it was like you were with me whatever I was doing—in my mind, I mean. I'm not doing this very well; I've not been sure how to tell you what I've found out."

"What have you found out?"

"That I love you."

She looked up at him, surprise in her eyes. He saw her swallow.

"I'll be out of law school this June," he went on, "and you'll be seventeen the next month. I know that's young, but you grew up fast," he held her in his gaze, "faster than most girls. Would you—I know what you've said, but . . ." And the words seemed to rush out. "would you consider marrying me?"

She stared at him, stunned. "Marry you! You like my apple pies that much?"

"Addie," He shook his head. "This is not a joke."

"But, Will, I don't want to feel I'm owned by anybody. I've told you."

"I know all that. I know how you feel." He stood up, went back near the fire and rested an elbow on the mantle, his back to her. How could he make her understand the desperation he felt to be on his own, and to have her with him? "What I want," he finally said, "is a home, my own—and not live in the judge's house. He has been good to me, Addie, like a father, but I'm not his son. I want a life that is . . . my own and . . ." He turned, went back and sat by her, watching shadows of the firelight playing her face, and touched by how deeply serious she was. "And I want a wife. I can't even imagine anyone else. I want you."

She looked down at her lap, "I don't know what to say. I'll think about it—but," she shook her head, "I don't expect I will."

"We could have some big adventures together," he coaxed.

She still didn't look up, but she smiled. "Yes, we could do that."

He moved closer, and put his arm around her. She didn't resist. There was something calm and sweet in this haven, a soft warm feeling flowing through him, and when she relaxed against him, he knew she felt it, too. "We have reason to understand each other. We can build things just the way we want." Will whispered, "Make our own life."

"Yes," she nodded, "but I have to think about it."

He cupped her face in his hands and kissed her, long and slow. "It's enough now—that you think about it."

Dear Diary,

Get married? Be an old married woman? An old, corset-ed-up, married woman sitting prim and stiff. Puke! Popping up all the time to wait on old gentleman when he wants something? I don't think so, Will Austin—or whatever your name is.

Addie slammed the papers closed, slid the book into a drawer, and crawled into the bed by her sleeping sister. She bunched up the pillow, and lay staring into the darkness, remembering his arms about her and how sheltered she felt; a feeling she had lost somewhere back a ways. What would it be like to sleep in the arms of a husband every night instead of sharing a bed with a sister? She turned restlessly; moonlight streaming across the end of their bed.

The next morning she pulled out her diary.

Dear Diary,

The Christmas party last night was the most beautiful thing I have ever been to. I think I like Mrs. Judge. Will said his father used to call her the Iron Violet. She's still awful fancy. I don't know about this marrying thing.

The next afternoon Will came to Addie's house. She had finished her work at the café and left her mother and sister busy with their tasks.

"I wanted to see you again before I leave for school tomorrow," he said, stiffly, as if he had rehearsed it, "and I brought you a present." He put a long package in bright red wrappings in her arms.

"A present?" She looked at it unsure how she felt about taking a gift from him. "I got a present once," she said, still standing in the doorway, "when I was five years old. My father gave me a little doll with a chubby face and a stuffed body. I liked it all right, but I never liked to play dolls like my sister did. Mama doesn't give presents now."

"Are you going to unwrap it? Maybe invite me in?"

"Oh. Sure. But it's a beautiful day; let's go outside."

She led him through the house, down the long brick walkway in back to the bench by the honeysuckle bushes. She sat down on the bench, tore open the paper, and uncovered a carved wooden box. It had an oval picture in the center of the carving, of a girl standing by a cottage with a thatched roof.

"It's to keep your diary in," Will said.

She ran her fingers over the deep carving. "It's so pretty," she said softly.

"The truth is it was a present my father gave my mother," he said,

Addie smoothed her hand over the lid and then almost reverently opened it. It was very pleasant to be given something. "It's a nice thing for you to do."

He stared across the wide lawn to a row of winter-dead hollyhocks stocks that encircled Cora Conyer's garden,"But it was a lie, like everything about him," Will said. "He didn't care for her."

"What about you, Will?" she turned to him, and lifted the wooden box from her lap. "Is this a lie?"

"You know it's not. I . . . you know how I feel, Addie. You know I want you to have it and . . ."

"And what?"

"If we can make something for ourselves . . . We can. I know it." He stopped, took her hand in his, and said slowly, softly, "And I will so cherish you and our life together. I will never, never leave you."

He was so profoundly serious; she didn't know what to say. She touched his cheek gently and then kissed his lips.

After a quiet moment, he said, "I won't be back until I graduate, and then I'll go to work in the law firm that was the judge's."

She felt what he was leading up to and, even now, she wasn't sure which way she would go: being a married woman, loved and cared for, or living independent and free.

"I want you to begin that life with me," Will said.

Addie sat quietly. She had to admit she thought of him all the time. Sometimes she even felt like she needed to take care of him. *And we do understand each other—mostly.* "There is one thing," she finally said.

"What's that?"

"I want both of us to be who we naturally are, grow in our own way, like those honeysuckle vines, and not interfere with the way each of us needs to grow."

"Of course."

"No, I mean it, Will. I can't be the usual wife. But I think I'll give it a try."

"Addie." He whispered and held her so intensely close against him she thought she couldn't breathe, and then he buried his head in the crook of her neck.

"I have found my home," he whispered.

CHAPTER 15

Amsley, Illinois

On August 10, 1877, standing in the hummingbird cove, they were married.

When Will and Addie turned to face people seated in rows of chairs on Cora Conyers' lawn, who had come to see this splendid young couple become man and wife, the preacher did as Will had instructed.

"Ladies and gentlemen, I am proud to introduce to you Mr. and Mrs. William *Fletcher*."

The judge did not smile, and Violet caught her breath in a sob. Addie noticed her mother dabbing her eyes.

The judge and Will's mother had lobbied to have the wedding at the base of the circular stairway in the judge's magnificent home, with the bust of Abraham Lincoln watching over them. Addie's mother wished for the ceremony to be in her Presbyterian church on Second Street. But Will and Addie knew where it should be.

After the ceremony, the bride and groom rode in a decorated carriage to the Amsley Hotel, where a feast had been prepared in the dining room. As toasts were finishing, Will stood with Addie and said, "This toast is to my new wife, my apple pie bride." He raised his glass of champagne, "To Addie Rose Fletcher, to whom I proposed three years ago."

Cora Conyers had broken her rule of "no presents" and given them an elaborate wedding cake that now stood before them. But before her mother and sister Mary had helped her dress in her mother's wedding gown, Addie had dropped off a pie at the hotel, and now, looking out before the sea of guests at the round tables, she said, "Before we cut the cake, I want to feed my new husband a piece of apple pie." Everyone laughed and clapped.

The party continued until the newly married Will and Addie Rose Fletcher boarded a train for St. Louis.

The night William left with his bride for a honeymoon, Violet made her way downstairs to the basement, carrying a lamp above her head, to the room where the remnants of her marriage to Fletch were stored, waiting for Will to take them to his home. She unwrapped the long portrait of herself in her wedding dress then the companion portrait of her then new husband, Vachel Fletcher. She stood looking into his eyes, which seemed so real, they appeared to look back at her. Tears sprang to her eyes and she whispered, "Why, Fletch? Why?"

CHAPTER 16

Galena, Illinois, 1853

The morning after Fletch had met Violet, in a bright room on the ground floor of the DeSoto House Hotel, Amos Brown, Weidner, Stoner, Fletch and the men who had made up the surveying party hovered around a table. "We have spent the last twenty-four hours studying the findings of your work," Oscar Weidner explained, "plus your reports, and have mapped out the most dense land, with the fewest creeks and hills, and with an eye to accessible timber. We have determined where to put the railroad," he explained.

On the table was a map, five-by-six feet, with a prominent ink line traced over it. "We will be heading back to Chicago in a couple of days to hire a crew to build it. While the roadbed, ties, and rail construction are in progress, the parts of two locomotives will be shipped to Chicago, the northern terminus, and will be assembled there.

"You will decide whether to join the crew building the railroad, or help assemble the locomotives and learn to run it."

Fletch looked at Stoner. There was but one choice for them.

At the end of the meeting, the men filed passed Weidner, as he took bundles of bills from a long wooden box and paid them for their five months' work.

As Fletch, with Stoner, leaving the DeSoto House Hotel, stood for a moment on the front steps, absorbing the soft fall breeze off the river, money bulging in his pockets, he felt a swell of pride. He was definitely a railroad man, deep into the business.

They sauntered down the street for a couple of blocks when Fletch decided to step inside a dry goods store.

"What do you need?" Stoner asked.

"Nothing much. Just a look-see." He turned to the man behind the counter. "You people have a school here in Galena, not the college kind, more for little beginners?"

"Sure, over on Twelfth Street, twelve blocks back from the river. Easy to find."

"Thanks," he said and turned to Stoner. "Let's you and I take a walk."

When they found Twelfth Street, they had to walk another four blocks before they found a two-room, log structure with a bell above the roof.

She would be in Galena all this winter, Fletch realized. He hadn't for a minute forgotten those big blue eyes looking up at him. Now he could see her again—and again.

CHAPTER 17

Chicago, Illinois, 1851

B ack in Chicago, Fletch and Stoner put in long dull days, waiting for enough track to be laid in order to begin building the great engine on a track. Parts of the locomotive sat under tarpaulins in a cavernous barn. In addition to waiting for a few feet of track to be laid, they waited on a crew to come from Philadelphia and direct them in assembling the two engines.

Fletch could hardly contain himself. He and Stoner occupied themselves each day in a nearby inn emptying bottles of whiskey. No matter what entertaining adventures they found in the city, his thoughts were not far from the beautiful schoolteacher in Galena. He wondered what she was doing. Was she lonely? Her parents had no doubt returned to Pennsylvania. But what if she met someone? A girl like that wouldn't go unnoticed for long. Was she safe alone in that river town?

An idea was beginning to take shape. He reached for the glass and downed another whiskey. While they waited for the locomotive parts, he should ride back to Galena. Surprise her. That's just what he would do.

But what if she didn't remember him?

The log schoolhouse was covered with wainscoting and plaster inside. A potbellied stove near the teacher's desk stood before rows of desks, and tonight that desk and a table beside it were covered with baskets or highly decorated boxes. Two long tables in the lunchroom were also covered with sacks, baskets and boxes of delectables.

Box suppers were popular when Fletch was in school. Women, especially young single girls, brought a box with a pie or cake, besides a full meal to go with it. It brought in money for the teacher to use during the school year, but no one thought much about that. The main attraction was always the romantic drama of watching young men outbid each other for the opportunity to share delicious surprises in a basket with the girl of his choice.

Besides parents and children, most of the town poured into the room. Bound, dried corn stocks stood about the room with pumpkins in the windowsills. On the school grounds, pumpkins carved with smiling or frowning faces promised a romantic, semi-dark place to spread a tablecloth on the ground and eat the prized dinner.

Fletch walked in, buoyed with expectancy to see the pretty young woman that filled his thoughts. It was some moments before he discovered her at another door, welcoming parents and students.

"Before we begin auctioning off this scrumptious-looking trove of food." A tall man, with a mustache, and a booming voice—stepped up behind the teacher's desk and announced, "we're gonna have a contest. The one we're all looking forward to—the prettiest girl contest. Come on up here, girls."

Shy giggling girls were jostled to a line in front. One by one the girls received merited applause. But there was a tie, and this caused some discussion. Only one prize had been prepared.

Fletch spoke up. "I can break the tie." People stared at him, smug in their dislike of his audacity; besides, he was a total stranger. "There's one here that's the prettiest of all." There was a hush for a moment. "The schoolteacher."

Then the applause came. If the parents who packed the room did not agree with the stranger, and most probably did agree, it was not a wise thing to alienate their child's teacher for the next year. So the applause roared on and the school bell rang out again.

Violet shook her head. "I do not accept. This contest doesn't include me."

"Let's let them decide if the contest is yours," Fletch said and turned to the crowd.

The hand clapping and desk pounding continued, accompanied by the bell ringing.

Violet shrugged and looked out at parents crammed into student desks. "With apologies to these two lovely girls, I'll accept."

When the noise died down, Violet glared across the heads of the crowd at Fletch. Everyone in the schoolroom was focused on this couple and a show they never expected.

"Who are you?" Violet whispered, but everyone heard because everyone was watching, silent.

Fletch stared at her in disbelief. She didn't remember him! And he had thought of her every day. How could she not remember him? He had hoped, even imagined, she had thought of him as much as he had her, but now she didn't even remember meeting him. "Your father introduced us. On the day you arrived in Galena."

She looked puzzled. Then a spark came into her eyes. "You're the one who tried to suggest my father was a financial backer of a railroad. I do remember you."

Was she unimpressed? Disdainful? Dismissive? Fletch wasn't sure what she thought.

Violet turned to the auctioneer. "We have to get on with the box supper."

One by one the bids came in as he opened baskets and held up something special from it. Bids and outbids continued. Young men came forward, picked up the basket, and led a smiling girl to a quiet corner inside or out onto the school yard by a flickering pumpkin face.

Finally, the schoolteacher's basket came up. "We have here a beautiful chocolate cake, fried chicken, biscuits, honey, and a pumpkin pie. What am I bid?"

Fletch stepped up with fifty cents, fifty-five came another, then fifty-six. Seventy-five cents," Fletch spoke up, determined to have the basket. He only had three dollars in his pocket. Someone said," A dollar." Fletch took a breath and said. "A dollar-fifty."

The room became quiet. No bids ever went that high.

"Too rich for me," his competitor said to Fletch, who came forward, his spirit pounding in him, took Violet's arm and led her to the schoolyard by a garish-faced pumpkin.

When they were comfortably settled, away from the ongoing auction, Fletch said, "I rode for three days."

"For a box social?" Violet said.

"For you."

"But you don't even know me."

Not know her! She had been in his thoughts every waking moment. He had so embroidered this meeting with her, he couldn't believe she thought he didn't know her.

"I know enough to know what I like."

She didn't answer.

Finally he said, "There is so much food in this basket. I'll need to finish it later. Could I see you tomorrow and finish this?"

"I may have overdone it a little bit, just trying to help the school."

"That's not what I asked."

She smiled and nodded.

Fletch looked out at the downpour beyond the porch of Mrs. Ackor's Boarding House, where he and Violet sat finishing the basket of food Fletch had saved from last night's box social.

Violet picked up the pot of coffee, filled their two cups. "I'm a little flattered, not only that you remembered me, but that you came back here."

"I rode for three days." A light breeze carried a mist over them and Fletch got an idea. He turned to face her and took her hand. "The first morning it began to rain, and for two hours it pelted me, but I rode on, even though I was soaked to the skin." In truth, not a drop of rain fell on him, but he thought it a good thing to say; that it would further his case with her.

"That's terrible you had to ride for two days with wet clothes. "

"Well, being rained on was nothing compared to the hardships we encountered as a surveying party, carrying those heavy chains, sleeping under the sky no matter the weather, crossing raging streams, and then the horses would go crazy when there was an electrical storm. So a little rain wasn't much." He leaned back in his chair, coffee cup in hand, and watched her eyes shade slightly in skepticism. Maybe she didn't believe him. But how could she know the weather in Chicago?

"I know it was very hard work to do that surveying." Violet sounded sincere.

"It was the hardest thing I'll ever be called on to do." Fletch watched her, hoping for more sympathy.

The rain slackened but water dripped from the eaves.

Maybe he shouldn't tell her that her beautiful face, her very presence, loomed behind everything he did. "It was good to get away," he said, assuming a more business-like manner. "When I return, the parts will be there, ready to be assembled into the great locomotive. There will actually be two, and they'll be built on the track where the railhead will begin." He reached across the table and took both her hands. "I will drive it, be an engineer . . ."

". . . on the new railroad," she finished, and he was ecstatic to see the pride she had in her eyes for him.

Just then, Mrs. Ackors came out onto the porch. "Young man," she looked down on him. "Mr. Fletcher, I think it is, just so you understand how things are, Miss Ikamire can entertain you or any young man in the parlor—or of course, here on the front porch—but I promised her dear father I'd look after her, and she has become like a daughter to us."

Fletch sobered his face, striving for sincerity. He let Violet's hands go, and took the sweet lady's two hands in his. "I wouldn't have it any other way." He looked earnestly into her eyes. "It's an assurance to me that she's safe under your roof and your sheltering concern."

"Oh, well," the lady stammered, "you are most welcome whenever Violet—Miss Ikamire—wants to see you." Mrs. Ackors retrieved her hands.

"Thank you," Fletch said humbly as she took her leave and went back inside.

He turned back to Violet. "When will your parents be here?" Fletch promptly asked.

"For the holidays, I expect. Why?"

"I want to talk to your father.

"Oh? Why is that?"

"I want to ask your father if I can pay court to you."

Violet smiled into Fletch's eyes. "I think it may too late for that."

"Why, is there someone else?" He was afraid of this.

"No, not that. Fletch, you've already pretty much gone ahead with the courting, *without* that permission. I'd say you're well into it."

"I don't have the luxury of time," he whispered, lost in those beautiful eyes.

"I'd like to kiss you goodbye," Fletch stood beside his horse ready to mount. "It'll be a long time till I see you again. Putting the engine together will take a lot of my time. I want something to remember."

"I still hardly know you."

"I feel I know you. I couldn't get you out of mind. That's why I rode for three days to see you."

"And in the pelting rain?" she prompted, with an odd little smile.

"Yes, the pelting rain."

"I suppose because of the hardship you suffered on the trip—not to mention the tremendous workload you carried when you were surveying the railroad—I could allow a little one."

Fletch took her very gently in his arms and softly kissed her lips. "I'm going to miss you, every minute of every day," he whispered. Then again, he kissed her much stronger. He noticed she didn't resist.

CHAPTER 18

Chicago, Illinois, 1852

A snowstorm raged outside as Fletch sat huddled near a stove, periodically feeding it sticks of wood. He had a writing paper on his knee, writing his almost-daily letter to Violet. He poured out his thoughts and heart to her on paper. He had done most of the writing at first, and then slowly the return letters began to come, occasionally and then frequently.

He took that as a good sign. She was lonely, just like him. She, too, was away from the comfort and familiarity of family. But his loneliness was different; he had severed ties deliberately. He felt an aching tug anytime he let himself think of it.

As he sat closer to the heat, his mind wandered, imagining her standing before her students, walking home along the Galena Streets, sitting with Mrs. Ackors and the other boarders at dinner, brushing her hair. In his letters he couldn't help but praise her beauty and talked of his longing to see her, to hold her, to kiss her lips again.

He told in each letter how he and Stoner, with Amos Brown and Oscar Weidner of The Chicago and Southern Illinois Railroad, were building the mammoth locomotives on two tracks that ran out of the great roundhouse on the outskirts of Chicago, the route he had helped survey.

It would be fall before the 163 miles of rails were laid and the locomotives and cars could travel between Chicago and Galena. "Once that is done," he wrote, "I can come to see you often, maybe every week—but I can't wait that long to see you again. We still work every day, and I cannot get away long enough to ride to you."

Fletch leaned forward, looked about. He and Stoner shared the two-room house—hovel, Fletch thought—with two other men who worked for the railroad. All four slept on cots in one room, and they ate and did all the rest of their living in the other room. One small window with twenty, tiny square panes faced south and let in feeble sunlight when the sun shown.

The door opened with a blast of cold wind and snow. Stoner stepped inside, and pushed the door closed.

Fletch folded the letter, put it in his pocket to post when he got the chance, shared a drink with Stoner, then crawled onto his cot, warmed by memories of Violet in his arms.

It was late April before the locomotive stood proudly on the tracks inside the round house, awaiting its maiden run as soon as all the tracks were laid. Fletch had counted the days until the weather moderated, and the first whispers of spring brought warmer days. Fletch told Amos Brown he needed to be away for a week. He got a horse and began the long ride to Galena.

When he got there, he went immediately to Mrs. Ackors' boarding house and learned Violet would not be home from school for at least three more hours. He had thought of her so constantly, writing his heart out to her, he wondered how it would be to stand before her and see her, touch her. He realized he had only been with her a total of three days in his life. His life—she was his life—and yet, he hardly knew her.

When Fletch saw her walking toward the Boarding House, he hurried to meet her. He wanted to take her in his arms and hold her, but he resisted—here on Main Street. Maybe she didn't feel the same as he did.

He studied her for a moment. "I've missed you." He held off saying how much he longed for her.

"It's so good to see you," she answered. Could she really feel so formal? "Have dinner with us tonight, then," she smiled, and he felt better.

"Maybe I'll put a bug in Mrs. Ackors' ear, and she'll let us open the parlor—put a log in the fireplace and have some time to—get reacquainted."

That evening, sitting in the parlor, the fire crackling, he smiled at her, but he felt awkward. She was so prim, reserved. He wasn't sure what to say, and yet he had so much he wanted to say. "I should have brought flowers," Fletch blurted out. "No, I should have brought violets. That's what I should have done. For a beautiful lady. That's what you should have."

"No, Fletch," she spoke softly but the spirit in her eyes belied her calm words. "It's enough you're here. That's good enough."

"Do you mean that? You really think that?"

"Yes, of course. I recognize it's not easy for you to come here."

"But nothing could stop me. I wanted to come before. I wanted to see you more than anything."

She didn't answer for a moment, and then she said, "I'm not sure about that. I think you may love that great locomotive you've been writing about more than anything."

"Maybe I get a little carried away, but it's so engrossing and exciting to be part of this big adventure."

"I could tell. I . . . I got to looking forward to your letters coming," she paused, "to see how the engine was coming. When none came, I went to my room and read your old ones."

Fletch studied her, "You did that?" He looked away at the organ sitting in the corner, a crocheted doily over the top, and a kerosene lamp pouring warm yellow light over them. He was not just hoping, but realizing, that this beautiful creature who simply awed him, thought about him, too. The wonder of it!

"I've kept all your letters, Violet. I feel like I know you so well." He leaned forward and touched her cheek. She didn't pull away, so he leaned closer and kissed her lips. "I haven't forgotten that kiss."

Then she did an unexpected thing. She moved into his arms and laid her head on his shoulder. He held her as if she would break.

That night, Fletch lay in his room at the DeSoto House Hotel, arms over his head and thought of her head on his shoulder. He wanted her—wanted to marry her—but was it too soon to ask? Would she pull away if he asked her to be engaged? Still, he couldn't see her very often, and surely other men must have noticed the pretty teacher.

The next day, while she was at school with her class, he went down to the riverfront and sat watching the steamers come in, anchor, and unload their cargo, but only one thing filled his mind: Should he ask her to marry him? Would she back away, thinking he was rushing her? But if he didn't have her promise; he could lose her to someone else. He wished he could talk it over with Stoner, but it wasn't something for him to decide, either.

Fletch ate dinner across the table from Violet at the boarding house. Three other women and two men had rooms upstairs. Fletch had not been allowed above the first floor. Mrs. Ackors had made it clear his approved space was in the seldom-used parlor, usually closed behind French doors.

He and Violet talked of the things they had written about, his work on the railroad, and the steam engine he had spent months assembling but was not ready to make its run. They talked of her days in the classroom, her students, the puzzling ones and the endearing ones.

"Tomorrow night there is to be a shivaree," Violet said. "The other teacher was married last week, and we are going to surprise them at home. It really won't be much of a surprise. They'll be expecting some terrible prank, and then they'll treat us and we'll have a party. You must come with me," Violet said.

"Of course. Sounds like fun. I've heard of them in Kentucky when I was growing up."

"Fletch, you never mention your family. Do you have any brothers or sisters?"

"I have one brother, but I really don't see any of them anymore. I was . . . it's a story I'll tell you sometime. Tomorrow is Saturday," he abruptly changed the subject. "Would you like to go for a boat ride along the banks of the mighty Mississippi?"

"I'd love that! I'll make a picnic basket for us."

Fletch smiled, his certainty growing. He would finally have her alone and maybe, if the moment was right, he'd ask her to become engaged. He'd lead up to it slowly, but he was sure she was encouraging him. But did she love him?

"How long has your teacher friend been married?" he asked.

"Only a couple of weeks. She won't be able to teach next year. School teaching is not for married women."

Fletch hadn't thought of that. He'd be asking her to give up working with children, which he knew from her letters, she dearly loved.

"Were they engaged for a long time?"

"Yes, I think so. She's been planning her wedding ever since I have known her."

Fletch decided to drop the subject and give it some more thought. As he told her good night just inside the French doors, he leaned in to kiss her, and as he held her, he felt her heart beating, and he knew she kissed him back. At that moment he decided: tomorrow he would ask her.

The next day, in a rowboat, they drifted slowly just at the river's edge. It was a bright spring day, with the smell of fresh foliage. The sun played peekaboo behind fluffy clouds.

As the boat rounded a corner, they saw a wooded area, pulled the boat up on the bank, carried the picnic basket to a sheltered spot, and spread out a ragged quilt Mrs. Ackors had loaned them. Wildflowers were growing out from under a nearby fallen log. She opened the basket to fried chicken, deviled eggs, biscuits and honey, with slices of chocolate cake.

"Your friend, the one who just got married, is she regretting that she can't teach next year?"

"I don't think so. She's—well, she's in love with Johnny and she had to make the choice—and she wasn't going to lose Johnny."

"What about you? Are you going to keep teaching when young men try to tempt you away from it?"

"I love teaching. Love the children. But I suppose, sometime, I'll follow the destiny of most girls."

"Be somebody's wife?" He ventured.

"Of course, but why do you ask, Fletch?"

"Just testing the water?"

"And . . .?" she whispered.

"And . . ." Fletch was for once in his life without words. He looked down, pulled up a blade of grass.

"Yes, but I'm afraid you'll think we don't know each other well enough, afraid you'll think I am moving too fast, afraid I'm assuming too much."

"I already know you're 'fast,' as you say. I already know you care enough to ride for three days to see me."

"All right, then there is another question." He held his breath, almost knowing she would say "yes." Almost. "Would you be my wife?"

She leaned forward, touched his lips, and whispered, "Yes."

They walked into the woods. He helped her as they stepped over new spring growth and picked little blue-and-white wildflowers. Then they sat down on the fallen log, just holding hands, not talking, simply feeling at one with each other and with nature.

Finally, they went back to where they left the picnic basket, sat down, and then lay down, looking up at the sky, watching the clouds scudding across the sun, talking only occasionally of the new world before them, of their new life.

They did not make it to the shivaree.

CHAPTER 19

On November 8, 1853, The Chicago and Southern Illinois train rolled across the prairies on its maiden trip to Galena. It carried the financiers of the railroad and their many important guests.

When the day had begun, Fletch rode in the locomotive alongside the engineer from Chicago to Galena. On the next run it would be him taking the throttle—beginning the new scheduled run.

The first time he sat in the engineer's seat and laid his hand on the throttle, it was the most exhilarating feeling he had ever known. The power under him as it picked up steam, the power under his hand controlling it—it was intoxicating. He learned the feeling of being almost at one with the great engine.

Slowly the train pulled into the station, a little wooden depot. A crowd had gathered; everyone came out to see the link between Chicago and Galena, connecting the Great Lakes to the Mississippi River. When the train came to a stop, Fletch, along with a dozen dignitaries, stepped down onto the platform to roaring cheers and a 13-gun salute. Fletch smiled, looking at the mammoth machine he had helped build. He felt—he just knew—Violet was somewhere in the crowd watching him. Soon he and the others formed into a procession—as if they were celebrities—making their way to the DeSoto House Hotel.

While he was walking along, Violet caught up with him and joined the procession. He took her hand, smiled down at her; he couldn't imagine a better day than this one. When they entered the ballroom, a grand banquet was prepared and waiting for them. He took her with him where he, with the others from the railroad venture, were given places of honor at a table stretching across the front of the room.

"Building this railroad has been a backbreaking feat," Amos Brown told the packed room. Cheers and applause. "Hundreds of men have worked on the track, bringing shovels, picks, wheelbarrows, crowbars and sledgehammers. Some brought saws and stump pullers. Oxen and horse-drawn wagons were used for transportation of materials and provisions. And the men who kept doggedly at it, made it happen." More cheers. "Working through mud, bad weather, and sometimes what seemed impossible terrain challenges, they succeeded." More handclapping. "And now, it is done!"

Several more men took to the podium and told of the daily, backbreaking work it had taken to create this new railroad.

It was an intoxicating experience for Fletch to be singled out when his name was called and lauded with the others for bringing the railroad to the booming river town.

Three weeks later, Vachel Fletcher married Violet Ikamire in a small banquet hall in the hotel where they had first met. Fletch had searched out a florist in Chicago and ordered three-dozen pots of violets, which banked the wall before which they said their vows. Present were her parents, those who lived at Mrs. Smith's boarding house, and her newly married teacher friend and her husband. Fletch had written to his parents about his impending wedding; they had not responded.

Violet was given special permission to complete her year as a teacher, even though she was married. Fletch could now come home every four days as he made the runs from Chicago to Galena.

When he came for Christmas, he handed Violet an envelope, "Benjamin Waverly has been commissioned to come to Galena and paint each of us for a wedding portrait. So you must plan to wear your wedding dress many days for him so he can do your likeness." Fletch did not mention that his parents had life-size portraits of each of them hanging above a huge fireplace in their Paducah home, where he grew up.

CHAPTER 20

St Louis, Missouri, 1861

Fletch had finished his run as engineer on the Baltimore and Ohio Railroad from Vincennes, Indiana, to Alton, Illinois, then took a ferry across the Mississippi to the hotel where he stayed before making the return trip. Every other week, Stoner's schedule coincided with his. Stoner would finish his run tomorrow, and they would meet at The Planter's Hotel in St. Louis. Both had been devastated when the little railroad they helped found, the Chicago and Southern Illinois, had gone bankrupt—like many others.

It was a bright spring day, so Fletch walked up Olive Street, planning to stop in Shultz's beer garden for a drink as he always did. He noticed a crowd further down the street. There weren't any of the usual pedestrians on the boardwalk along the storefronts. Then, emerging from the crowd, Fletch saw double rows of blue-uniformed soldiers marching on either side of manacled prisoners stumbling along in the center. The crowd was moving along with the entourage, jeering and taunting the soldiers, chanting Jeff Davis's name.

Fletch stepped into another tavern but found nobody, so he followed at a distance, wondering what was going to happen. Across the road a crowd had gathered on a little rise filled with trees he had heard called "Lindall Grove."

Something happened. Screams poured out over the din. He couldn't see through the crowd. Some soldiers broke rank and moved in on the shrieking crowd. Stray bullets began to tear into storefronts and tree trunks. Fletch glimpsed a flash of sunlight on a bayonet. Then more gunfire. The crowd raced up the grove, leaving the prisoners to one side. There was return fire from the trees on the hill. Two were down, just off the road. One was screaming for help, the other silent.

A bullet whizzed three feet from his head, and Fletch decided to take cover. He dropped down behind a wooden loafer's bench outside a store and lay still as the mayhem continued. So the war had come to Missouri, Fletch thought, instantly and acutely aware he was in something of a battle without a weapon.

The soldiers kept firing into the thickest part of the crowd, and he saw a woman and a couple of children drop as others rushed around them up the hill, soldiers in pursuit. Fletch extricated himself from his hiding place and crawled inside the store. As he stood up, he faced a shotgun aimed at his head. "You a Jeff Davis man or a Lincoln man?"

"I'm not either."

"You're one or the other." The gun didn't waver.

"I've not thought it all out. I'm not a soldier. I'm not a prisoner. I'm a railroad man. Baltimore and Ohio."

"Don't matter. Railroader or chicken farmer, you got to go one side or the other."

"I'm looking for a drink before I go to my hotel," Fletch tried to motion toward the hotel. "It's couple of streets over."

"This ain't no tavern or hotel. You just stay . . ." Just then a bullet crashed through the front window and into the kerosene lamp on the table by Fletch. Both men dove to the floor.

"What in the hell is going on out there?" Fletch yelled to the man behind the back counter.

"It's that devil in the White House. Lincoln demandin' troops from Missouri to fight the secession people what done no more'n what they had to do. General Jackson told ole Abe he wasn't gonna do it. Wasn't gonna call up troops for him when ever'body in the state is again' it. We're not gonna fight them that pulled out of the union."

Fletch stretched out and leaned back against the counter, the shotgun now lying on the floor by the owner.

"So Jackson calls up the militia," the shopkeeper related, flat on the floor, talking out of the side of his mouth, "to gather troops, and he plans to fight them that's tellin' Missouri what they ought to be thinkin'. It was them that made that tented camp out there—Camp Jackson."

A rock came flying through the open window. The two fell silent. The front entrance was wide open.

"Then in comes this Captain Lyons," the shopkeeper finally went on. "He's a Lincoln man. Cleaned out the arsenal and shipped the guns clean outa the state. Across the river to Illinois."

"Looks like the crowd out there don't like that," Fletch answered.

"I reckon not. And he took down Camp Jackson and the militiamen in it. That's what you see: them Union bullies marchin' Jackson men back to the arsenal."

"Taking them to the arsenal?"

The owner grunted. "They're using it for a jail. Where you from? You got a way of speakin' like a southerner."

"Kentucky, raised in Kentucky."

"I knowed it. You're one of us. We're all throwed off on that Lincoln. He's evil, he is. He wants to be a dictator. They're gonna see that 'fore long. No more'n got to Washington, than he calls up this big army."

"You think so?" Fletch's life had been the railroad. The country was divided, he knew that, but he hadn't thought which way he'd go if it was brought to him to make a choice.

"I *know* so."

A light breeze flowed through the shattered window. There was a space of quiet, so both men slowly stood and moved cautiously to the front entrance. They took care peering out. Rifle fire was in the distance, but down the road, several injured were lying on the rise with people tending to them.

Fletch hurried back to the Planters Hotel and tried to go to sleep. Stoner would be in tomorrow from his run. Fletch had left the Illinois Central Railroad three years ago to work for the Baltimore and Ohio, and Stoner had gone to work for them a year later, both engineers.

The lumbering racket of an ambulance wagon on a cobblestone

pavement below his room woke Fletch the next morning. When he got out on the street, the sun was just coming over the rooftops of the stores. An eerie quiet had settled in, along with a sense that an unseen presence hovered about, maybe a rifle at a window. He went back inside for breakfast, sidled in on the bench of a long table and listened to the talk. "This engineer on the river was walking along Olive," one man leaned forward, talking softly as if somebody sinister might hear, "and a bullet hit his head. Scattered his brains on the door where he was passing." Another cut in, "This man was stooping over picking up somethin' in his yard and they fired three shots into him. Weren't doin' nothin'. I heard there was near to thirty murders."

Later in the day when Stoner had completed his run, they pored over a hurriedly published newspaper sheet, detailing what had happened. Crowds had now come out and milled about, morbidly fascinated and drawn to the spots where bodies had lain in the grass and mini-balls had shattered doors, shutters and crumbled bricks.

But now there was another presence. St. Louis was under martial law.

"I got to go, Fletch," Stoner said, as they walked down Seventh Street. "We're at war and I got no reason not to go."

"I'm going with the Union. You are, too, aren't you?" Fletch said.

"You don't have to go, Fletch. You got a wife and boy. I got nothing to keep me back."

Fletch turned quickly away, staring but not seeing, not really registering with his mind, the mob wandering about where bloody violence had played out yesterday. Stoner didn't know. It had been nearly two years since he had gone to see Violet and little Will. He never mentioned it to Stoner and had diverted conversation when Stoner had asked about them. Fletch couldn't say why he had not gone home.

At first, he'd squared it with himself that his work had kept him busy, and indeed he had been become busier as more and more responsibility was given to him on the B and O Railroad. It had been necessary to leave Galena and relocate Violet and baby Will in Amsley, a little town on the Baltimore and Ohio line. It seemed the best place then for his family. It was at a junction where the north-south Illinois Central crossed the east-west B and O and a great round house was located there.

Fletch had come to find the deepest satisfaction he'd known as he rode along; feeling the engine with him, at his fingertips; understanding every part of it; knowing how they worked together. And at the depots, seeing how people flocked to board the train, he filled with pride. He felt it was somehow *his* train.

In the beginning, he had come home to Violet and their little boy after each run. Then his assignment changed, and the run ended at the terminus on the east side of the Mississippi. He could have taken the train back; he had a few times. But as time passed, he didn't go back. Finally, he would consider what he could say to her when he did go home. Nothing seemed plausible. So he didn't go, and the time had stretched out and stretched out until he hardly ever thought of them. Sometimes it crossed his mind that he should send them money or see about them, but all he could say for himself was, it just hadn't happened.

"Don't think that's going to matter, Stoner," Fletch finally said. "In time, they'll get us all."

It came to Fletch that this would be the answer to his unfixable situation with Violet. Go off to war. If he lived, he'd go home, and she would be glad he lived through it. And if he didn't . . .

With this unfixable situation before him, maybe the best thing to do, was just go to the war. So he said, "If you're going, Stoner, so am I."

CHAPTER 21

St. Louis, Missouri, 1877

The first morning of their new life as Mr. and Mrs. William Fletcher, Will took Addie for a carriage ride through the streets of St. Louis. The city was awakening to a bright summer day, with a soft breeze that carried the whisper of a hot midday.

She said little, looking about at this strange city. She whispered to Will, "I've never seen so many people."

In the afternoon, Will and Addie arrived at the dock. He asked about a trip in the new hot air balloon. When they stepped up to the platform to board the basket, the great, red-and-yellow balloon above, he leaned near Addie. "Are you scared to go up so high?"

"Of course." She took his hand. "But this is one of those adventures we planned."

Gradually, they lifted off the platform, a fire blowing above them. "Are you sure this is safe?" Addie held Will's arm.

"They've been using them in France for more than a decade, and they used them in the South during the war."

Slowly the balloon soared upward, the basket swinging slightly in the air, floating over buildings and streets, the wide world below growing more and more minuscule. Then they were gliding over the great river with barges and paddle wheelers plowing down the great

Mississippi. The balloon followed the river for a while before drifting back over the city and then the countryside, punctuated with ponds, trees, and squares of green below like a patchwork quilt.

He felt unbounded freedom, floating so high, unburdened and unshackled from the limitations of life below. What couldn't you do, with this unencumbered openness? He grasped the roll top of the wicker basket and looked down over the countryside. "Nobody gets to look at so many people below, all at once, like this," he said not really talking to anyone. "I could soon feel like a great king looking down on everyone," Will put his arm around his wife and smiled into her eyes. "And I could move everything around as I please."

He saw a skeptical look on Addie's face "It was just a thought that came to me," he said.

The balloon ride was the greatest, most exhilarating thing they had ever known and even back on the ground, they talked about the airy, floating freedom they felt. Walking along a street near the wharf, they heard a drumbeat, and turned to see what seemed to be a small parade—strangely, all women. They were marching toward the waterfront near the old cathedral.

"Let's go," Will said. "It's those crazy women."

Addie held back, looking at the signs they carried. "No, I want to see."

Four women in the center of the vanguard wore cuffs and chains.

Along the waterfront, newspapermen were stationed with ponderous cameras on tripods, catching them as they trooped by, singing:

Sound the good ole bugle, boys, and let the truth be shown,
That woman has as many rights as any man has known.
Let us help her win the fight. She may not win the fight.
She may not win alone, while we go marching together.

They marched on the river road, singing, coming close to Will and Addie Rose, and passing on by.

Will and Addie sat down on a bench and picked from a sack of warm peanuts Will had bought from a vendor. "The next thing you know, they'll be wanting to go to war," he said.

Addie cracked open a peanut shell as a paddle wheeler glided slowly by, moving toward the pier. "No one believes women can think. Men and a lot of women feel a woman is somewhere between a grown man and a child."

Will looked after the little band that had marched on, ignoring the cheering and jeering bystanders, but he said nothing. He stood up, took Addie Rose's hand, and led her down to the pier. "Let's see about going on an excursion." A steamboat race was in progress, so they watched the race until the sun began to drop below the city skyline. Later, they boarded the paddle wheeler, the *Robert E. Lee*, for the evening.

At dinner on the boat, they were seated at a long table with ten other passengers among a couple dozen other long tables, and served by a Black man named Ulysses. A small band played on the platform at the end of the dining tables. When dessert came—ice cream and peaches—the band launched into "Dixie." Some passengers began to sing and clap their hands. When that ended, the band took up "Marching through Georgia." In a merry party mood, they began to sing along with that, too.

Two men at the opposite end of their table stood up. One shouted, "Stop that song. Stop it, I said. Stop it right now." The band droned to silence. "Hell's fire can't be no worse'n what Sherman done. Satan's work was let loose." The man's eyes seethed with hatred. "And you want to sing about it?"

Just then the Captain came in. "They played 'Dixie' and now they're gonna play 'Marching Through Georgia.' We're recognizin' both sides."

A chair came flying through the air, across tables, then another and another; tables were upended; plates, glasses and food crashing; people yelling and scrambling to get away from the gutter fight.

"We've gotta get out of here, Addie." Will hurried her out of the room, onto the deck, down to the stern where the giant paddle lifted and dropped water, propelling the ship and leaving a cascading wake behind them. In the background, the din of a fight roared on. Members of the band poured out the doors and fled below.

Will's arms rested on the rail looking at the moon reflected on the river. "I wonder if one of those men with Sherman was my father."

Addie leaned her head on his shoulder, looking at the white foaming wake behind the paddle wheel. He slipped his arm around her and pulled her close. "When you feel the hatred," she said, "in there, and the violence still, I think there's every possibility your father died in the war."

He'd like to believe that, but he didn't. "A possibility, maybe," he muttered.

The next morning, Addie woke to find Will missing from their bed. She slipped on her robe and went to the window. Their second-story window reminded her of looking out on the sunrise from her room in the Baltimore house when she was a little girl. Now, rippling clouds masking the rising sun painted the eastern sky purplish-red and golden in places, giving the buildings a pinkish hue. Below, the city was waking with milk wagons, buggies, and fancy carriages rattling along on the street below. She turned to see Will entering the room with a man in a white jacket, wheeling in a small table with a brilliant white tablecloth, gleaming silver and a single yellow rose.

"You are being served breakfast, Madam Fletcher." Will lifted silver lids off chafing dishes.

She giggled. "This is a bit different from me rushing to the café to help Mama get potato hash ready for the roundhouse workers."

"I've only begun to spoil you, my dear one." He brought a chair around for her and pulled one up for himself.

"There was a telegram waiting for me at the desk," Will said. "The judge has arranged for us to meet Robert and Virginia Campbell and be guests at a dinner party tonight. Campbell is a wealthy merchant in St. Louis. This is quite an opportunity for us."

Addie said nothing. She suspected this would be like one of Violet's formal dinner parties—only worse.

The house was a straight-up, white building, stretching three stories against the St. Louis graying twilight. Mr. and Mrs. Campbell greeted them with a most gracious welcome in the long entrance hall and ushered them into a wide, double parlor. Soft music came from the pianoforte in a distant corner. Half a dozen or so guests had already arrived, and Addie heard more being welcomed out in the hallway.

It was a dazzling room. Heavy gold cornices topped both windows, and long mirrors hung between them. She and Will sat down on a long, red, tufted couch with three, arched-back humps. A sparkling vase of roses sat on a tiny table before them. The house seemed velvety soft and ornamented. Addie tried to sit with ankles crossed like Violet, but she gave that up in about five minutes, deciding it was the most uncomfortable pose imaginable.

"So you are the newlyweds?" A lady, with white hair, in bright green silk and wearing a long string of pearls, came forward, smiling. She took a seat by them. "I'm Hallie Taylor."

"We were married just four days ago." Will answered.

Since Mrs. Taylor was so friendly, Addie decided she would try to talk like she thought ladies did. "We've been having the most wonderful time in St. Louis."

"Oh, well, when you are young and in love, everything seems to shine through a beautiful prism. My husband and I went to New York, and I was in awe the whole time. I have been there several times since, but it was never like that first time—on my honeymoon."

"We went on a balloon ride over the city and the river," Addie answered properly. "And it was sure enough awesome—sometimes, breathtaking."

"Oh, I can't imagine doing that."

"It was interesting looking down on all the people from such a vantage. I liked it." Will added.

They were seated at the dining table near Robert Campbell. Across from Will was a man who looked familiar to Addie, but she couldn't remember where she had seen him. He had tight, sculpted features, with reddish hair and strikingly intense eyes. Hallie Taylor was seated by him, and her husband, a man with a thick girth and white mutton chop sideburns, was seated on the other side.

Addie looked down the table to twelve diners seated before elaborate white china with scalloped red and gold borders. She studied the complicated silver service by her plate, and three wine glasses before her, but just as she was deciding she would carefully glance about and follow what the others did, Robert Campbell stood and offered a toast to the new bride and groom, "Will and Addie Rose Fletcher." There were smiles and cheers from everyone, and Addie began to feel more at ease than at Violet's dinner parties. Everyone was beaming at them and holding their glasses high.

"You carry the same name I do, Will Fletcher." The man with the reddish hair said later as three girls came around with soup tureens and, with remarkable efficiency, served the first course.

"Do you mean Fletcher?" Will asked.

"No, no, the first. William."

"And Will," Mrs. Taylor turned her attention to the man with red hair, "where is your lovely wife?"

"She's visiting her parents."

Addie decided this must be a close network of friends who seemed quite at home with the Campbells' dinner party.

"Those women are at it again," Mr. Taylor, of the thick muttonchops, boomed across the softer conversations. "Saw them marching along the river road, carrying signs."

"What do they want?" The man with round spectacles seated down the table by Mrs. Taylor said. "I don't understand them."

Addie thought, *You never will. You've not been a woman.* But she knew she must not say it aloud.

"I do believe those women have abnormal tendencies," Taylor pronounced.

"Any man I've known loved women from his old grannie to his granddaughter, and revered his wife and mother." It was the man who said he shared Will's name. "And would do anything to protect them."

They don't all, Addie thought. *What of women in dangerous homes?* She wanted to throw that one at them. *Here in your world, you don't see that.* It drummed in her head, but she couldn't bring herself to say it.

"I have always thought that a woman was one of God's miracles," Mr. Taylor cut in. "A woman's body can create a human body and bring a living being into this life."

Addie looked down the table to Virginia Campbell who had brought ten living beings into this life and wondered what she was feeling about her part of God's miracle work.

"Unwomanly," Muttonchops said, "of a low deviant persuasion. We know that and thank God not the type who graces our table."

Gracious ornaments, Addie thought. Sharp comebacks pounded in her, but she dared not say them. They were the newlyweds at the table, the romantic pair who made the others smile at them, no doubt remembering those idyllic days after their own nuptials.

And it would embarrass Will. She glanced at him. She loved him, cared for him and meant every word of her wedding vows. He was smart and, best of all, he talked to her like she was his closest friend. Sometimes, when he was in a dark mood, the hurt little boy that lived in him showed through and she wanted to hold him, give him comfort, and say she knew how he felt. No, she could not answer back to these people who were providing them with their fine hospitality, but she felt something thick and heavy and dark hanging over her—over all of them—woven from centuries of accepted oppression, startled and resistant when they heard straightforward honesty from her sex.

She twisted at the hem of the cream-colored damask napkin in her lap. She hated the need to subvert what she thought, to play out a role imposed on her. And yet, as she looked about the table, smoothing again the napkin across her lap, she knew every man there would do anything necessary to keep any woman from harm's way.

"If you could look into lives of those women," Muttonchops was saying, "you would see there is something else going on. You would find they're mistreated—maybe abandoned, maybe children have broken their hearts—something that has made them unhappy."

"It's a distraction for them," Campbell nodded in agreement.

". . . and a reprieve from responsibility," the be-speckled man said.

"Well," Taylor added, "it's something in vogue now. Go out and march. But it's a passing thing. We'll all be laughing about this in a couple of years."

Addie sneaked a glance at Robert Campbell, again twisting at her napkin. They had talked themselves into a comfortable conclusion over this uncomfortable ripple in their ordinarily comfortable, regulated life.

Besides Virginia Campbell and herself, three other women were seated, interspersed around the table, but no woman offered a comment. Only the men deemed it was unhappy, unnatural women who were suffragettes.

Riding back to the hotel, Will said, "I want to build a house like that."

"The Campbell House? In Amsley? What will people think?"

"They'll think that Will Fletcher has the handsomest house they have ever seen. They'll say it is the finest in three counties—and it will be."

CHAPTER 22

When Will and Addie returned to Amsley from what Will termed "the best honeymoon anyone anywhere ever had," they moved into the house that still belonged to his mother and where she and Will had lived until she married the judge. After all the things that had once belonged to Violet and Fletch had been moved to the little house, Will hung the two portraits of his parents on each side of the fireplace, as he remembered them from when he was a child, but he didn't remember how totally they dominated the little living room. He found a box of toys Fletch had brought home to him and took them to the attic room. As he was coming down the stairs, he said, "One day, when we have a big house with lots of rooms and lots of children, too, I'll have these toys to give them."

Addie smiled at him. "We've not been married two weeks and you have built us a great house and given us lots of children."

"You want that, too, don't you?"

"I do, but I want just *us* now, and I love this little house. I can plant apple and cherry trees in the backyard, and honeysuckle bushes, and there's room to raise baby chicks. I can sell my pies and make money even if we have babies to care for."

"You won't have to do that. You don't have to work at all. Lawyers do very well. I'll do well. Look at the judge."

"Yes, I know. I want you to do well, but . . . a place like that Campbell house. I don't know."

"We'll have a bigger house than the judge's. We'll have the biggest house in town, and you will have the best clothes and you won't have to make them. You'll get a seamstress."

"But I'm as good as any seamstress."

"I know that but . . ."

She came to him, snuggled against him, but over his shoulder, she glimpsed the picture of Fletch looking down on them. Would he always hover over them? A malignant presence?

She turned and looked into her husband's eyes. "We have 'us.' That's enough," she whispered.

CHAPTER 23

It was more than a year later, in the late fall when the trees wore a riot of bright rust and reds, when Violet came one afternoon to visit. Twelve pies sat on the counter of Addie's small kitchen.

"These are for the Jennings family, and these are for those two old maids, the Middleton sisters, Ida and—I forget the other one's name. And these . . ." Addie explained.

"Do you really need to do this," Violet interrupted. Always the picture of fashion, she wore a fitted, plum-colored dress, with a fringed, sweptback skirt revealing a cascade of layers beneath. She sat only a few feet from her own portrait above. Addie had been stunned when she had first seen her as a beautiful young bride. Even now, she was intimidated in Violet's presence. Why would any man leave such a woman?

"I know Will is—making, well, more than a living," Violet said. "The judge tells me about his clients. He is often representing them in the judge's courtroom.

"He is, and I knew he would. He has such grand plans. I can't hardly even imagine things the way he wants them, He . . ." She felt herself babbling on.

"In due time, Addie, you'll need to change—all this." She motioned to the pies on the kitchen table. "It's just that it's not expected of a successful man's wife."

"I don't see that Will's life has got a thing to do with my . . . what I do."

"It's something you may want to think about." Violet reached for her purse. "I really came over because a telegram was delivered to our house for Will."

She opened her little beaded purse and pulled it out. "It's from Corinth, Mississippi."

"Oh, dear. Corinth, Mississippi!" Addie caught her breath and sat down.

"Yes," Violet dropped her head in her hands.

Addie looked at the woman, her face covered, this woman with granite-bound dignity, giving way to—something.

What does she know?

That evening when Will came home, Addie said, "There's a telegram for you. It's from Reverend Hollister."

Will grabbed it and read it aloud, "Casper's sick, near death. Wants to talk to you. Won't tell me. Hollister."

He looked at Addie; his hands were trembling. "That Casper knows something. I know he does. We've got to go."

CHAPTER 24

Corinth, Mississippi

"He's in the back bedroom," Hollister said when he met them at the door. He shook hands with Will, then he turned to Addie, "And this lovely lady is . . ."

"My wife, Addie Rose," Will explained.

The reverend nodded his recognition with a smile. "Newlyweds, then?"

Will took Addie's hand as they walked with Hollister down the narrow hallway in the center of the house. "Says he wants to talk to you before—before he meets his Maker."

They found Casper, gaunt and weary, lying on a cot in a room at the back of the house, bright with afternoon sunlight, a white porcelain pitcher and basin on a bedside table. He was thinner than Will remembered two years before. "Sorry to see you so poorly." Will pulled a straight-back chair up near the bed, took his hand and said, "Did something more come to you?"

"Never come to me." His voice was low. He adjusted his pillow, trying to sit up, but soon leaned back. "I saw it right off."

Hollister placed a chair for Addie by her husband and found one for himself in the corner near a square table with a lamp on it.

"Ain't got much breath in me now, but I got somethin' needs tellin', layin' hard on me, holdin' me in this world 'cause the Lord knows it's a secret that needs rightin'." He closed his eyes and rested a bit. "I knowed when I saw you a-leavin', Master Will. I saw it when you was a-standin' there in that door when you's here, with the house dim and the light bright on the outside. I saw the shape of you and the way you stood and the way you walked and I knowed. I knowed, you was the child of that Lucifer that come here and ruined the lives of all of us, but most particlar, Miss Liela."

Will swallowed. It fell heavy on him, and his heart pounded with both excitement and dread. Tears wanted to come. *But he had to know.*

Addie's hand found his. Warm. And he was glad for her being there.

"I had to make a promise." Casper's voice was reedy. "A vow to that devil that I'd never tell what happened, but it layin' on me like stones, knowin' the right way it happened."

"Yes." Will leaned close to him, Casper's voice thin.

"He come here with them Yankees after the Rebs left. He got wounded . . . some little. The Yankees took over the house and the great lawn of Master Rob's—Miss Liela's pa. Typhoid took the old master; took a lot of 'em. Yankees that was laid up after the battle, they got the fever and there was a-plenty that died." Casper's voice drifted off. "Piled them up like logs by the wagonloads. After Miss Liela's pa got the fever and died, old Miss—her mamma died, too. Poor Miss Liela never knowed which way to turn. Farm all tore up from the fightin' that went on. Confederates took everything that was loose and some that weren't, and then in come the Yankees and they did the same. The tobacco barn burned down . . . some of the house, too." Casper tried to sit up, but then, too weak, fell back on the pillow. He lay quiet for a long time before going on.

"Men was scattered ever which way over the grounds, ravin', sick and dyin'. The awful fightin' moved on and so did that devil Fletcher. The war been done for a spell when he come back. Acted like *he* was the old Master. Liela was so glad for help, she just did what he said. He got hisself a boat and went up and down the river, selling stuff out of his floating store."

"The Tennessee River?"

Casper nodded. "Folks be a needin' things. They got no horse to hitch up, no more. So's he made up this floating store. I went with him up that old river, and we brung back money. I seen 'im pour out a sack on the table. He says he's gonna rebuild the 'baccy barn and the house that was burned away and then a church.

"He say we was to start plantin' cotton and tobacco. We say we free and we wasn't workin' less we was paid."

"How many slaves stayed on, Casper?" Will asked.

Casper closed his eyes, thinking, and then, with one hand touching the fingers of the other hand, he counted. "There was me, Froggy, and that Jasmine; Orliff and his woman, Lennie; they girl doll; and old Virgil. Fletcher say he pay us, and on Friday, after we work all day, we line up outside that 'baccy barn. He give us money from his week on the boat store."

"So he was helping to rebuild the plantation?" Will was, in spite of himself, wanting to find a positive implication.

"He say so. We believes him. He holds preachin' on Sundays out under the tree and we come. They come from all over. He preach and preach—lawz, he preach good—and he be full of the spirit. Then we sing and sing. Ever'body happy. He say we gonna have our own church right here, soon as he get done making the 'baccy barn. He say he gonna put a good roof on it. Then he pass his tall hat and take back a bunch of the money he paid us Friday. I done it, too. I believed 'im. Then he brung in two men, and they put a double roof on the new 'baccy barn. It was some sight, and people come over just to look at that barn roof. They fix up the summer kitchen that got partly burned away. We went through that summer, workin' in the fields and him runnin' the store on the river and preachin' on Sundays. Things goin' good. He full o' ideas, that one, and plans and gittin' things worked out and done. After three years, we was doin' better'n anybody around that got hurt in the Corinth fight."

Casper stopped, turned his head to the wall.

"Thank you, Casper," Will said, thinking he was finished.

Casper began to shake his head, reaching toward the pitcher. Addie poured out a glass of water from the porcelain pitcher and gave it to him. Will looked over the lanky body that lay before him, startlingly thin, a life nearly spent, used always for the demands and wishes of someone else.

Casper drank and handed the glass back to Addie. "I got to tell you the rest. We had the best year since the war; sugar cane and cotton and 'baccy fields all done good. One day we go on the train, me and that Fletcher, and that big crop in the train cars. 'We goin' to Natchez,' he say. Then he say he's goin' to talk 'em into the best pay he could get. Said he was raised up as a boy on the Ohio, his family always buyin' and sellin' 'baccy." Casper smiled to himself then looked at Will. "I felt real proud, ridin' into that big city on a train and seein' the great Mississippi with the steamboats, whistling down on each other as they go on the old river. Natchez—war never went there. It still purty like things used to be.

"You see, we was aimin' to carry away sackfuls of money to make that old plantation big again and he's gonna make money and we's gonna get us our own church . . ." Casper was taken with a coughing spasm.

Addie looked back at the preacher in the corner. "My mama used to put two pillows to our backs when we were coughing a lot."

Hollister brought back pillows, and Addie propped Casper up, pumped up the pillows behind him, and handed him a glass of water.

"Thank you, Miss Addie."

"No 'Miss,' Casper. Just Addie."

He looked her over, studying her. "Never knew none of the Yankees' women." He was thoughtful. "Don't reckon I ever seen one."

"They're very fine, Casper," Will said.

"I 'spose."

Will leaned forward, taking the glass of water from him. "What happened in Natchez, Casper?"

"Well, Fletcher," Casper leaned back on his pillows, quiet for a while. "He liked his hooch, that one. So after he sold all his crop to them big people at the warehouse on the waterfront, he went into this here tavern. He never could get his fill of it. Kept it up all night.

"I was sittin' over in the corner, nobody take no notice of me. I goes over and says, we's gonna miss the train, Mr. Fletcher. And we did. Then he got in this card game with some of them river men and he lose money—little by little, he use it up and then he got no more.

I says to 'im, we needs to go home, and he say he got to get it back. He say to them other men he be playin with—he say he got one more thing he can put on the table—the roof on a new 'baccy barn.

"They laugh at him hard when he say that. He say to 'em, folks is buildin' up all over the south and they could sell the roof easy. They made him sign a piece o' paper sayin' he owned it. He never owned that roof, no more'n me—but he signed the paper."

"But," Hollister explained to Casper. "as Liela's husband, he did own it."

Casper shook his head and lay quiet. He ran an index finger over his lips, seeming to reach back into his own thoughts and then he went on.

"Fletcher went back to the game. It last all that day. He never won nothin'. That riled him up bad and he got hisself roarin' drunk. He like somebody I don't know when he was drinkin'.

"He tell me the next day, I have to play the hobo to get back home 'cause he ain't goin'. I never jumped no train in my life, and I never took no big trip without a white man. I was scared to go off by myself. Mighty lot a white folks still mad about Black people bein' set loose. He says, I was to tell Miss Liela that he got robbed and stabbed and throwed in the Mississippi. He made me swear never to tell Miss Liela no different—and I never did."

Casper raised his head off the pillows; the tired eyes he turned on Will held sympathy. "I never knowed where he went from there."

"Casper," Will said quietly, the reverend doesn't think that man was my father and I hope to God he wasn't."

"He your father. It coulda been that very devil standing there in the doorway 'stead of you. I saw it and I knowed sure."

He paused for a long time before he went on. "Miss Liela, I seen her sittin' by herself out there in her yard, sobbin' hard, real broke up, thinkin' that rascal dead, and me knowin' he ain't.

"She come down to the table one morning and Lennie make her up breakfast, but she no want to eat. We think she grievin' herself sick, but 'fore long she tell Lennie she in the family way. It was bad times for her—all of us. All of us see that we ain't gonna get paid and we ain't gonna get the church like we thought.

"I swore I never tell what happened 'cause it would break poor Miss Liela's heart to know he caused the whole thing."

"You did the right thing, Casper," the reverend said. "You got the burden off your soul now."

"I ain't got no burden lifted off me 'cause the real secret I ain't told yet. The reason I told the reverend I want to see you."

"Well, what else, Casper," Hollister stood up, impatient. He raised the west window, where the yellow, fall sunlight poured in with cool, fresh air.

Casper took a breath and continued. "When that Yankee devil first come back after the war was over, he stayed right there with Miss Liela. Her pa and her mama—they done gone home to be with the Lord, and she worried outta her mind. Folks saw that Yankee man and Miss Liela together sparkin' sometimes, then." Casper looked up first at Will and then at the preacher. "This here preacher, he come around and he say folks is talkin', sayin' Miss Liela might be sinnin', and she say to the preacher that one of them church men that goes with army married them. That thar were a lie.

"I never told a soul she was a-livin' in sin. I was right there in the hall that day Miss Liela was born. She held onto my hand when she's learnin' t'walk. Folks be talkin' bad about her. She have the little girl after the Yankee man gone off. Then I says to myself, you can't never tell that little one she just another woods colt left behind by the army men."

The preacher stood at the end of the bed, "I think, Casper, it might be better if you had kept your peace. You have now told me Amy is an illegitimate child, a bastard."

Casper closed his eyes. "I am headed to meet my Maker. I never done nothin' myself to hang my head for, so's I think to myself, Casper, them white folks make lies come off your lips. You don't have to carry white folks' lies to your new life. This boy here," he laid a cold hand on Will's, "he know what's true. He was your pa sure, and he was a livin' Satan in our lives."

He felt Addie touch his arm and when he glanced at her, saw caring in her eyes.

"You have answered a lot of questions, Casper," Will said. "Thank you."

"I feel better. I blew away all them lies that was on my soul." He closed his eyes and the reverend motioned to Will.

"You should see Amy now; let him rest. She's a pretty little thirteen-year-old."

"I guess so. She might be my sister."

"Might," Addie whispered to Will as they left Casper's room and walked to the parlor.

Amy came in wearing a long grey dress, her little girl figure just beginning to show its promise. "Reverend says you are my brother." She looked up at Will, her eyes sparkling. "I'm pleased to know that. I don't have a family."

"You may be," Will said, still resisting in his heart the man who deserted families with ease and left lives in shambles. "Did your mother ever tell you anything about your father?"

"Not very much." Amy was shy and soft-spoken, and set prim and straight on the settee, as if she shouldn't take up too much space in this world. "She said he came back after the war to help because he felt bad for her, and how the Yankee Army had ruined her farm. That's where I lived when I was little before Mama died."

"I'm sorry you lost your mother, Amy," Addie Rose said.

Amy was looking at Will with adoring eyes. "Could I write letters to you? I never had a brother or sister."

"I have two of 'em." Addie Rose, only five years older than Amy, had been subdued long enough. She leaned forward, "Let me tell you, it's not always that great!"

"I'm going to find him." Will stared out the train window as the changing countryside slid by, his jaw set hard. "I wonder what else he's done?" He turned to Addie. "You're unusually quiet."

"Casper didn't say you looked like him. He said when you stood silhouetted in the doorway you reminded him of this Fletcher. That's hardly proof."

"Do you doubt what he said?"

"I think he told what he knows of a man who came to their farm and did try to help them before he left."

"Deathbed stories are notoriously truthful."

"Will, if you were questioning a seventy-eight-year-old person on the witness stand, who said the room was dim, and that he didn't look like the person in question but was sure it was him just because of the way he stood, you would tear that testimony apart. You know very well that could have been any one of a thousand Union Army men on their way home. Someone who remembered being hospitalized in that house and came back."

Will watched out the window, unseeing, mesmerized as the train rattled passed devastated houses and tired, depressed villages. He was confused, both pleased and disappointed. He might have found out something about his father, but he wasn't sure. He had, in truth, no solid proof one way or the other. And yet, he felt some relief that, as Addie said, it would be a chance in a thousand that it was the same man. "Whoever he was, he saw a vulnerable woman with a plantation to take over."

"Yes, I can agree with that." Addie took his hand. "But who was he?"

CHAPTER 25

B efore Will had time to consider what he had learned from Casper and whether he accepted it or not, he was informed when he went to his office that a new lawyer wanted to interview for a position with the firm. The judge, who still held a keen interest in the firm he'd founded, wanted Will, along with the two other senior partners, to meet and interview the prospective member.

Will met the new prospect in the waiting room, ushered him into the office of Oscar Jameson, where Clemet Sampson sat in a wooden chair beside Jameson's desk. Will found himself and the young lawyer a couple of chairs.

Before them sat a young man, impeccably dressed and sporting a thick mustache, which Will thought was an affectation to make him look older.

"And what's your name, young man?" Sampson had a pad of paper before him, ink well at his elbow and a sharp pen, held at ready to write if there was need.

"I am Otis Tolbert. Just out of law school—not long ago." Will saw his nervousness and realized, gratefully, he had not had to go through this himself.

Sampson went first. "So why do you want to work for this firm? Your home is in Chicago."

"I'd like to get out of the city. Maybe work my way to Springfield. Lincoln began downstate and it worked pretty well for him." Tolbert laughed at his little joke.

Will chuckled, but neither Jameson nor Clemet Sampson changed their somber countenance.

"We're a small-town firm. Don't have the volume you would encounter in Chicago," Jameson said.

"People are about the same as people everywhere. They have problems, need a lawyer," came his quick answer.

"We try to serve them—and serve justice just the same as lawyers in the city," Jameson said.

"That's what I thought." Tolbert shifted in his chair and seemed to not know what to do with his hands.

"I would say," Will felt he should get in the interview, "that we know just about everybody, and everybody knows us, so when somebody is in trouble, we will have a pretty good idea what went wrong and who would be the troublemaker and who never would. This is an asset that would not be typical in your hometown, Chicago."

"That's true, of course," he nodded toward Will. "But I'm sure I can adapt."

In the end, they accepted the new lawyer and set him up in a small office next to Will's. Across the hall were the offices of Jameson and Sampson, who each enjoyed rooms with tall windows that looked down over Main Street.

It was no more than a week before Will heard Otis Tolbert's first critical comment. It was about the waiting room, something about which Will secretly agreed. The firm Austin, Jameson, Sampson and Fletcher was on the second floor of a three-story, red-brick building in the new style with a turret at its corner, which faced the town's central intersection, Main and North Avenue. Inside, the turret created a curved alcove in the waiting room, and Will's mother had decided that space called for a fancy settee.

The judge, still a lawyer at the time, found it difficult to say "no" to his new wife. After standing with her for some time, studying the fancy turret, and rubbing his hand across his mouth, he said to Violet, "I supposed if a man thinks he's headed for a hanging, it might be nice to just once sit on a velvet couch."

So now the room held a curved, maroon-velvet settee in its corner, with rows of utilitarian straight-back wooden chairs around the room. There were pictures of Judge Austin (a young man then), the other partners, and framed copies of the Constitution and the Declaration of Independence.

CHAPTER 26

Since second grade when Arlie Daniels started walking by him-self to the country school by Dismal Creek, he had met Emmett Eckert at the end of his lane by the mailbox and the two had walked together. As they got older, a morning ritual developed—a challenge, actually. As the Baltimore and Ohio engine 52 left Amsley train sta-tion, gradually picking up speed before switching to the curve going south, the boys raced alongside the train. Finally the engineer would wave to them, and the train would steam on ahead. They'd fall back, laughing and then try again the next morning.

It was Arlie who first thought of it, bringing in coins and nails, putting them on the track and then smiling after the train passed and they found them smashed flat. One day, Emmett brought in a half-dollar he'd stolen from his father's overall pockets.

"Here, Arlie, put this on the track. The old fool won't spend that on a bottle." It was the biggest coin they'd ever tried. After the train went by, they found it—flat and curved like a half-moon. The next day they chased the train, and Arlie said he'd bring a five-inch screw. They bet the engine could crawl over that—for sure.

It was Friday morning when they wired the long screw down on the track and hid in the bushes, not far from it, watching. After the train had passed, they found the screw broken in two.

"Old 52 can take anything! My pa says it's the most powerful locomotive the B and O's got," Arlie said.

That got Emmett thinking, and by Monday morning, he had hatched an idea and had something to show for it. "This rusty old flatiron was in the smoke house. My ma don't use it no more. Let's try that."

"I don't know. It's kinda thick." Arlie took it in his hand, just like the ones his own mother used for ironing: a piece of iron, two-inches thick, about four inches long, narrowing down to a point.

"It can do it. Old 52 can do it. You seen what it mashes out."

So the two boys positioned the flatiron, wedged in where the track switched to go south. They poked wire under the track and wrapped it tightly around the flatiron. They heard the train whistle leaving the station and ducked behind the bushes.

The train was chugging along the track coming even with the boys. Then, as the locomotive turned south, it hit the iron, jerked and screeched. It began to list to the right toward the creek, hanging for—what to the terrified boys seemed—long minutes. It loosened from the track, teetered like a tall man losing his balance, toppling over, sliding to its side, and with it, twisting and pulling car after car, as one by one they jumped loose from the track, wavered, and crashed down the slope toward the creek. Thunderous, shrieking tumult rang throughout the woods along the creek.

The cars, once loosed from the rails, slid down the slanted grade on which the rails had been laid. Doors slid open, and wooden cars split, releasing cargos of crops destined for market: corn, beans, and wheat, as well as freeing livestock. Wild-eyed cows found their footing, and hogs grunted in terror, and all ran senselessly in all directions. Down the line, terrified, trapped passengers screamed from passenger and dining cars, where they had such a short time ago boarded the train and settled in for a comfortable ride. Somebody down the line was knocking out the windows of a passenger car, screaming for help. As hysterical screams poured out through the sharp morning air, Emmett said, "Run, Arlie. Get outta here."

Emmett Eckert and Arlie Daniels ran like they had never before run, and they arrived at school (for the first time ever) before any other students. Only the teacher was there, now stoking the stove to take the chill off the room.

Surprised at the boys' unusual punctuality, the teacher, Miss Sedonia Treadwell, stared at them through her thick, round glasses. "You're early today. Anxious for school?"

Neither boy was calm enough to recognize the remark as slightly snide.

"Since you're early, why don't you go out and ring the school bell."

"We can do that." Arlie felt the need to be obedient.

As the other students began to arrive, they breathlessly told of the terrible train wreck they had seen or heard about, of people crying along the tracks, and wagons out on the road, on the way to help terrified and wounded passengers.

The teacher listened, and concluded it was going to be pointless to have a serious instructional day, so she asked each child to tell what it saw.

"There was two girls—little girls—standing by a tree, crying, and a man who got there said for them to hold each other's hands 'til somebody come for 'em."

"A woman was layin' on the ground. Somebody come along and covered her up, even her face. Folks were crying. Some had bloody faces."

"It was scary. Wagons coming up to put people in."

Miss Treadwell looked back at Emmett, "You haven't said anything, Emmett. You walk right along there, don't you?"

"Yes, ma'am, but me and Arlie always race the old engine. I reckon we just kept runnin'. That's why we was early today." He pushed an unruly lock of brown hair off his forehead. "Wasn't that right, Arlie?"

Arlie solemnly nodded.

CHAPTER 27

The town of Amsley was stunned as word of the train wreck spread. Injured passengers were brought into the hospital. Most were in shock. Two people died.

The sheriff said it was nothing short of a miracle they were able to get most of the passengers out and more didn't lose their lives. Farmers thought there was nothing miraculous about it. The farmers around Amsley and for seventy-five miles along the rail line poured into town to see what had happened to their crop shipments on the way to the Mississippi River barges. Angry farmers and wounded, shocked passengers cursed the railroad for their losses or injuries.

The next day the law offices of Austin, Sampson and Jameson got their first client. He wanted to see Judge Austin's son. Clovis O'Dell sat in the chair opposite Will's desk. Clovis was not happy. "I worked all year gettin' crops out and then bringin' them in. Hired me the neighbor boy to help out. I's out that expense, and then the damn railroad runs amuck and destroys it. A year's work, gone." His eyes glinted above a wide bushy ginger-colored beard. "They're gonna pay. You'll know what to do. I want you to file—whatever it is you do. Make 'em pay me back. This is gonna ruin me."

Will knew Clovis O'Dell; knew he had two large farms with a

barn and silo on each, and a tall two-story white clapboard house on a spacious lawn. He doubted this would ruin him, but this was Clovis, and he did deserve reimbursement.

"Okay, Clovis," Will said, "I'll go to work on it. I agree, you need satisfaction."

"Not satisfaction—compensation."

"I'll get right on it, Clovis. I'll try to take care of you."

Clovis stood up, turned his sweat-stained, felt hat in his hands. "You'd better—if my children are to eat this winter. Otherwise, this is gonna ruin me."

The next morning three more farmers found their way to the firm. Then on the third day, it seemed the floodgates opened. Every chair was filled in the waiting room, with one man forced to sit on the velvet settee.

Before they began seeing clients that day, Clemet Sampson called a meeting in his office. Will and the new lawyer, Otis Tolbert, sat in chairs before Sampson's desk, with Oscar Jameson, the other powerhouse of the firm, seated near Sampson. Behind them, the brilliant September sunshine poured through a wide window, obscured partially by gold lettering that still had the original name: Law Offices of Austin, Sampson, and Jameson.

"Because of that train derailment, we're going to have more cases than we've had collectively in the last five years." Sampson said. He was a small nervous man with round, black-rimmed glasses that tended to slide down his nose and kept him busy pushing them back. He looked at the two young associates. "Forget vacations. We'll be working full tilt for months—maybe years. The railroad will fight it, but I don't see how they can win."

"One of the death claims is being filed in Indiana," Oscar Jameson said, "but the other one will probably be here."

"Oscar and I'll take on the cases, especially the death and injuries; you associates will be asked to sit second chair." Sampson shoved his glasses up to the bridge of his nose.

Jameson said, "The load is going to be heavy, and we'll do all we can. I know the both of you are just getting your sea legs in this business, but there's a likely possibility you'll have to take on some of the property loss cases, crops or livestock shipments." Jameson had a square face with high cheekbones, and a determined chin.

Sampson, his wife, Ann, and Jameson and his wife, Hazel, had been guests of the judge and his mother many times during Will's growing up years. The judge admired both of them for their talents but didn't mind disclosing his opinion of them in private. Sampson, the judge said, was proud as a bandy rooster, and enjoyed personal admiration almost as much as winning a case. Jameson, according to the judge, was a ferocious fighter in the courtroom, a man not to be trifled with.

"Farmers'll want to sue the hell out of the railroad." Jameson pursed his lips.

Will said nothing. He was ready to practice law, had studied for it, and now here was the reality of the thing. The starch melted out of him for a time and his knees felt rubbery.

"Clovis O'Dell came to my office yesterday, mad as hops," Will mentioned somewhat sheepishly, feeling he might have overstepped his boundary in the hierarchy.

Sampson interrupted. "He asked for you. Said he'd gone to the judge when he was here practicing, and he wanted you." Sampson looked over the top of his glasses, eyes leveled on Will. "So, son, you got him."

Tolbert, who had been silent throughout the meeting, spoke up. "How does a judge, any judge, have influence in here?" His voice was crisp.

Sampson leaned back in his chair. "He doesn't. Austin and I were the original partners of this firm, but he went on to be a judge. He did work for O'Dell years ago. Will, here, is his son. That's why O'Dell wanted him."

Tolbert turned full to face Will. "So this means I am to work with two established partners and the founder's fair-haired son. Have I got that about right?"

"It's not quite like that. I've only had one case," Will said. "It was defining the property line between a man's lawn and the church's parking lot."

"So far, I haven't even had that. Maybe Chicago wasn't that bad."

Oscar and Clemet exchanged glances.

Clemet put palms down on his desk as he stood up, meaning the meeting was over. "You'll both get your share and be well into it before this is over. So far, you're both second chair. We'll see how it goes."

"Tolbert," Sampson said, "you'll hear claims with Jameson, and Fletcher, you'll join me." He reached for the doorknob. "Gentlemen, the battle awaits."

"That's another thing," Otis Tolbert turned as he started to follow Jameson, "If he's Judge Austin's son, why is his name 'Fletcher'?" Will thought he saw hostility in his eyes.

"That's a story we can share over a drink sometime, Otis."

More than three-dozen lawsuits were filed against the Baltimore and Ohio Railroad. The two senior partners, at first, invited the two new lawyers, Will Fletcher and Otis Tolbert, to sit in, but as the caseload mounted, they passed some of the crop and livestock cases to their associates, kept the personal injuries, and the new lawyers sat second chair when those cases were heard.

Throughout the fall, and until the frigid weather clamped down and forced the people of Amsley to become housebound, the main topic of conversation was the train wreck. Everyone seemed to have or contrived to have a connection to those who had received damages.

However, two small boys, Emmett and Arlie, did not talk about it, not even to themselves, as if not saying the words might make the whole thing fade away from their memories and lives. But it didn't. Arlie woke up sometimes in the night and sat up in the dark, breathless, hearing again the screeching wheels and the screams of passengers, and his face would get wet from sweat even in his cold bedroom. What if Emmett said something. They would take them off to prison!

The next day as Emmett and Arlie walked home, Arlie said, "We need to take an oath, a blood oath that we will never speak of—of— you know."

Emmett, who had been through similar nightmares, agreed. Just after they walked across Dismal Creek, now frozen solid, Arlie took out his pocketknife and made small slices on their index fingers. As the blood oozed out, they put their fingers together. "Now we repeat together, 'I promise to never speak of . . .'" Arlie couldn't finish.

"What happened," Emmett finished.

"Yeah, that."

"No," Emmett said. "It's 'I solemnly swear . . .' That's the law. I saw that when my pa was in court that time."

So together they repeated, "I solemnly swear never to speak . . . about what happened."

No one found the flatiron. The boys knew what to look for. Emmett found it and pitched off to the side as they walked home from school. He slipped it into his pocket, and that night he threw it in the well behind his ma's kitchen.

Arlie felt somewhat better after the blood oath, but not much. Emmett too had nightmares, but nightmares were not new for him.

Emmett lay in his bed—his little brother, Joey, hunkering close to him, and the girls in a bed across the room—sobbing softly, so no one would hear. Emmett's ma and pa were fighting, yelling at each other, and Emmett prayed his pa wouldn't hit her this time. He heard the crack of something. Maybe it was a fist, or a broken chair. He waited, listening for his mother's cry. But it didn't come. He knew why she was yelling at him; she knew where he was going. She knew all about it. Emmett knew, too, because one night he had followed him.

He knew, also, that when his father slammed out the kitchen door, his mother would sit at the table or throw herself across the empty bed and fill the room with heaving sobs. When he was little, before Joey and the girls came, he used to go to his mother after they had argued or his pa had hit her and left her alone, crying. Emmett would pat her arm, wanting her to stop crying, wanting her to be happy. He didn't do that anymore. There wasn't any way to fix it, not 'til he got big. Then he'd take care of it.

CHAPTER 28

A week before the Thanksgiving Day parade, Mrs. Walter Powell posted a notice in the newspaper: "All those who believe in a woman's right to vote, come to the Community Room over the bank and help make placards with the purpose of carrying them in the parade. Men are welcome, too."

Addie had not discussed joining this group with Will. He'd had very little free time at home since the train wreck and the avalanche of claims that followed. His days and, often, his nights were filled with research, interviews and court appearances. She had noticed he seemed to at last be happy in the swirl of a massive amount of work. Deeply conscientious, he wanted settlements for his clients. Immersed in work, he had a new confidence, a brightness in his eyes, a quickness in his actions, as if he'd found an island within himself that was his comfort and wellspring.

With some misgivings, Addie climbed the wooden stairs alongside the bank building to the Community Room. She should have told Will about this, she knew, but once in the big room, that thought faded. A couple-dozen women were already there and seated in a large circle, with Mrs. Ina Pilcher standing in front of a long table.

It was a dark November day, and the room had no windows. A kerosene lamp set on a table in the center of the circle cast shadowy yellow light on the earnest faces of the women.

"First thing," Ina nodded a welcome as Addie found her seat. "I want to know from each of you why you want to be here to make placards and to walk in this parade."

The women were silent at first. "My husband will be angry with me if I walk with you ladies," Lorraine Spicer, a short plump woman with white hair, spoke softly. "But I know we have to have our say."

Hattie Powell still wore her coat and played with gloves clutched in her right hand. "The men will not budge on this. Why should they? To give women the vote would ask them to voluntarily give up power and control in legal affairs."

One by one they spoke, most feeling strongly that a woman should be able to vote but with words uttered as almost a whisper and a guilty demeanor. Addie felt it too in this darkened room, as if they were in a secret conspiracy.

It was Alice Farrell's turn. "My husband will not tolerate this. He can get really mad . . . and then sometimes . . ." She didn't finish, and everyone knew why.

Hattie Powell interrupted; grasping her gloves in her right hand, she raised them in a fist. "All over our country the women—women just like us are meeting and marching to make our opinions known. It's an uphill battle, but it has to start sometime. Why not now?"

Mrs. Ethel Burgess stood up, mother of eight, middle-aged. "No one is going to hand this to us. We can't get it done without breaking the rules we were raised with—to sit back and let others tell us what to think. That won't work with this." Ethel was an ardent follower of Elizabeth Cady Stanton, read everything Stanton had written and devoured newspaper copy of her speeches. "Mrs. Stanton says the best protection a woman can have is—*courage.*"

"Agreed," Ina Pilcher said. "So how many are ready to carry signs?"

"I will," Addie's hand went up immediately and then others joined.

"My heart is with you, but I can't do this," Mrs. Scofield shook her head. "You know my husband is a pastor. I can't undermine what he says in the pulpit. I can't undermine his authority to the parishioners."

"We understand, Sylvie," Mrs. Powell said, but then quickly turned her attention to the meeting now breaking up. "It is the time to think of our daughters," she said.

They spent the next hour painting large twenty-four by twenty-four inch signs.

As Addie was finishing her second sign, Ethel Burgess came to her. "You seem like a bright girl. Have you read Stanton's 'Declaration of Sentiments'?" When Addie said she hadn't, Mrs. Burgess put her hand on Addie's. "I'll loan you mine. You need to read it, my dear."

On the morning of Thanksgiving, Addie Rose met Mrs. Powell and a dozen or so others who dared to step out and march, picked up signs that read, "THE TIME HAS COME. WOMEN MUST VOTE." She followed the little band down the bank stairs, to the Village Green on Second Street, and took her place in the line-up for the parade. She liked the feeling she had—like a warrior cutting into the fray.

The law offices of Austin, Sampson and Jameson were closed for the day, but Will had told Addie he would miss the parade because he needed to do a little work in the morning. When he heard the band passing by, he took time to go into Clemet Sampson's office and look down on Main Street, the parade route. He smiled as he saw the Amsley Players walking along, and behind them . . . "My God!" he gasped. A small group of women walked together carrying signs, and on the front row was his wife.

Will was waiting for her at the kitchen table.

"I had no idea you were going to do such a thing. Why didn't you discuss it with me?" He was dressed for the day at his mother's Thanksgiving dinner, but clearly they had some things to hammer out before going. "I think I know the answer to that. You knew I'd disapprove."

"Yes, probably. But I don't think I need you to approve—or disapprove of what I do."

He shrugged. "You may be right about this thing. I haven't decided, but I am just now trying to build us a life. I need your help. Not for you to be traipsing off involved in what everyone thinks is foolishness." He looked weary, elbow on the table, his head resting in the palm of his hand.

Addie suddenly felt pangs of regret. He was working so hard, and he didn't need anything more to worry about.

"Now we'll have to go to the judge's house for Thanksgiving dinner and sit through it looking like fools," he said.

"You don't have to look like a fool. I'm the only one who carried a sign," she answered matter-of-factly.

He looked out the back kitchen window at the dark, winter-barren tree limbs and shook his head. "We should be together on things."

Addie sat down in a chair across from him. "You know what I think about this. I did it for myself and for my daughter . . ."

"Not good enough." His fist came down on the table.

She leaned back in the chair. This, she decided, was not the time to tell him her precious secret.

They sat under a frosted gas chandelier at the judge's Thanksgiving table.

Silence hung over them like a black cloud before a storm, low and heavy. Platters of ham, turkey, and fried fish were passed. Butternut squash, potatoes, corn, cabbage, carrots, rolls and butter went by with only the sound of the silverware clicking on plates.

Since the judge was scowling, everyone else was quiet; even Violet was subdued. Finally he turned to Addie Rose for the moment she knew was coming.

"I ask this in all the kindness and the affection I have for you—and concern. Why, young lady, why do you associate with those women? They are agitators, troublemakers. They are an embarrassment to themselves and their families. You are a successful lawyer's wife. You must see that what you did is—unseemly."

The judge, cloaked always with the dignity of his robe, spoke with authority and was seldom challenged.

"What I see," she knew the judge liked her, and she liked him, too, but she would not be muffled. She turned to face him. "And I say this with both affection and respect for *you*, a wrong that needs to be righted. I believe that. Will may be embarrassed, but he knows how I feel, and I know it's right."

The judge seemed to take her measure, hesitating. "It's not exactly what Will *thinks*. It's the way it looks."

She looked across the table at Will's teenage brother, Tom, whose eyes were beaming. Someone else was riveted to the judge's hot seat. "I can't be anything but my own person, sir." She started to take a bite and realized she was not hungry.

The judge leaned back in his chair as Sarah served his coffee.

"I was going to take you with me to St. Louis," Violet said, "to this new designer I've found, and fit you out with a new wardrobe. It would be your Christmas present."

Addie turned to her, ready with a quick answer on her tongue, but stopped. She recognized what she was doing, but she was Will's mother; then she remembered Mrs. Burgess quoting Elizabeth Stanton about "courage," so carefully, with measured words she went on. "I suppose you mean that if I play 'the lady,' I can wear your new set of clothes. But if I continue working with these women—as you call them, the 'suffragettes,' there will be no new clothes. Do you not see that what they want is more important than fancy clothes?"

Violet looked out the window at the fall day, apparently realizing Addie was getting the better of the situation. Still, she took up the challenge. "What I would say is, the two kinds of woman you describe have different purposes in life."

Addie decided this was the time. She had intended to tell Will alone, but that hadn't worked out. She unexpectedly stood, and looked around the table and then down at Will. "Why did I march in that parade? I'll tell you. I did it for our daughter, which we just might have in a few months."

A different kind of silence filled the room. Stunned silence. Brought on by a whiplash change of topic and emotion. Violet stopped, fork in hand, ready to take a bite, and stared at Addie, the implication sinking in.

Will looked up. "A baby?"

"Yes, a baby."

Will caught her up, held her close, kissed her forehead.

Violet dropped her fork, her hand flew to her cheek, "Oh, my," she whispered, tears filling her eyes.

Addie caught sight of her over Will's shoulder. Sometimes the real woman showed through.

"Addie Rose," the judge shook his head. "What's next with you?"

As Will and Addie rode home in the buggy, it crossed her mind that having a baby made all animosity melt away. Being a breeder was approved, she concluded, but having a mind of her own was dangerous and not to be tolerated.

The next afternoon when the house was quiet, Violet opened a drawer in her dresser. She felt toward the back, into a corner, and found a little velvet sack with a drawstring. She opened it, and shook out a small, plain, gold ring. She slipped off the ring the judge had put on her finger and replaced it with the plain gold one. Tears began to come.

"Fletch, we are to be grandparents. This new little creature will carry the blood of both of us, as it was with Will," she whispered. Tears fell on the dresser, and she made no attempt to stop them. Finally, she slowly slipped the ring off and put it back in its pouch, pushed it far back into the drawer, and replaced the ring on her finger that said she was Judge Austin's wife.

CHAPTER 29

I t was a cold, dark December morning. Will stood before a long, oval mirror in their bedroom, dressed to meticulous perfection. Today he would argue his first case before a jury. He turned to Addie—still propped up on pillows, fighting morning sickness—and asked, "How do I look?"

"Like you're getting married."

"I've already taken care of that," he said with a smile; but what he didn't say—as he looked back, taking a measure of himself—was, *I hope they take me seriously.* Doubt pounded through him, with myriad fears chipping at the edge of his confidence. But he couldn't upset Addie.

Will met Clovis O'Dell, the plaintiff, in the courthouse corridor, just outside the courtroom, and he made a great effort of casualness to keep O'Dell from noticing his nervousness.

After Will left, Addie got up, dressed, hitched up a horse, and drove the other buggy into the courthouse square. She slipped into the back row and kept herself concealed behind a row of spectators. She watched as Will interviewed Clovis O'Dell, clearly making the case that the Baltimore and Ohio Railroad took a year's worth of

O'Dell's work and dumped it, plain and simple. Now he was without money to start a new crop in the coming spring.

The lawyers for the railroad argued that, beyond a doubt, railroad transportation was the safest to be found, and this train derailment could only have been the result of some type of human error in maintaining the tracks.

Will argued that, at this point, no such human error had been found, and Clovis O'Dell would not have lost his crop if he had not relied on the Baltimore and Ohio railroad.

In the end, the jury, which included seven farmers, returned a verdict in just two hours in O'Dell's favor, and Will had won the first case.

That evening as she sat on the sofa before a roaring fire, a winter wind at the windows, Will's arms wrapped around her, he told her all that had been said at the trial that day; how everyone had looked, and how much he enjoyed being in the center of it all. She started to tell him she had watched and then thought better of it.

"I am proud of you," she whispered, and then motioned to the portrait of his father on the right side of the fireplace. "He would be proud of you, too."

Will gave her a gentle hug and brushed her cheek with his lips. "Possibly."

CHAPTER 30

The road was frozen, snow nearly gone except for banks piled up along each side.

"Addie, I want you to take a ride with me," Will had said over breakfast, and now they were making the three-mile drive up Cameron Hill, a small rise north of town that everyone knew of (although no one knew anyone named Cameron or how the name came about).

Will helped her down from the buggy and they stood on the edge of a cedar grove, some boughs still weighed with snow, looking over a wide vista which sloped imperceptibly down to where the buildings of Amsley began. Will turned to her. "What do you think?"

"Nice. Are we going to have a picnic here?"

"We could, but not today. I was actually thinking of something else. How about putting a house here, at this highest spot on this hill."

"A house? Our house?"

"I asked Clovis O'Dell if he would sell me five acres of land up here. I knew he would say no, just because he's Clovis, but he owes me. I got him a nice settlement from the railroad, so he said he might consider selling two acres, but not a foot more.' Addie, we don't need more than that for a big, beautiful house."

"A big, beautiful . . ."

"We're going to be a family and this little one might not be the only one and . . ."

"I like our little house—where we came home to from our honeymoon. And you lived when . . ."

"I do not want to live there my whole life."

She looked up at him, teasing, "And you can stand at the window of your biggest, beautifulest house and look down on everyone."

"It's not that, it's . . ."

What she did not say was, *You need to do the most, be the best, and have the biggest of whatever so you can tell yourself that your father deserted a remarkable person.*

"The reason I brought you here is, I want to know, would you like to live in a house on this hill and raise our family? "

She looked at him, adoring him. "That's a very good reason, Will," she said, "but you already had your reason. I think it's a lovely spot."

At the law offices of Austin, Sampson and Jameson, all efforts were bent toward the case of Mrs. Eugenia Patrick, who died in the train wreck. Her husband, Dale, was one of the seriously injured and still bedridden. Jameson, with Otis Tolbert as second chair, was representing her interests in her husband's suit.

Sampson and Will would be handling her husband's injury case at a later date. Will had so far prosecuted four property damage cases and succeeded with a settlement for each. The lawyers were gearing up for a furious fight because this was a death but with an unusual twist: She had actually died of a heart attack during the train wreck.

During the trial, the lawyers for the Baltimore and Ohio Railroad argued that she was in fragile health, and in fact, her husband was taking her to St. Louis to see a doctor for her serious condition. They brought in expert witnesses who testified that she could have had a heart attack at any time, even on the train had there not been a derailment.

Jameson, his jaw set like a bulldog, his big eyes wide, honing in for an attack, argued that anyone in a frail state of health would have, in the terror and hysteria of the wreck, succumbed. If the derailment had not happened, she would no doubt have traveled on to St. Louis received the needed medical assistance and be alive today. "Any *reasonable* person," he roared, "would see that the train wreck brought on her heart failure and caused the end of her life. It is clearly the responsibility of the railroad," he pronounced, "to award her husband $25,000 compensation, which is a great deal of money indeed, but a very paltry compensation for the loss of his beloved wife."

Perhaps it was because the jury was overawed with the many out-of-town experts who spoke for the railroad, or they couldn't get their reasoning around such a large sum of money, or because many of them used the railroad themselves for travel and transportation. But whatever their reason might have been, Jameson and Tolbert lost the case.

The next day, the mood at the law office was as gloomy as the February day. Winning that case would have brought the firm its heftiest fee. In the late afternoon, the four lawyers met to review the case. Jameson pointed out to Tolbert, who had taken the floor to do some of the questioning, that there were a couple of things he might have brought out to strengthen his case.

Tolbert stood up and turned on Will. "Maybe if the fair-haired boy here had been up there, we'd have won and be sitting on a pot of money. That's what you're saying." He walked out of the meeting, went to his office and closed the door. Jameson, notoriously unflappable, raised his eyebrows briefly, and went on planning, with Sampson and Will, the strategy for prosecuting the claim of Dale Patrick, the deceased's husband.

Three days later Will laid out on the kitchen table the blueprint of a house he wanted to build. Addie Rose looked at it. She sat down slowly in one of the chairs, her body beginning to become cumbersome.

"Will, I'll almost feel embarrassed to tell people I live in a big house high on a hill."

"It'll set in the middle of the two acres," Will went right on. "With a winding drive—lined with Italian cypress. It will be the show place of the county. Nobody else's place can come near to it."

"I won't have time to run my pie business and take care of chickens and babies with a house like that to maintain."

Will stared at her. "You won't be doing all of it. We'll get a house-keeper, and we don't need to raise chickens and sell pies to make a living."

Addie frowned. "I've been working for my mother and myself since I was twelve, making my own money, and you want me to be a dependent person. I won't understand it."

"Addie Rose, you are never going to be a dependent person, sweet-heart; it's not in your bones."

"Why do you have to have the biggest house, the best suits, finest carriage, and the fastest horse you can find, Will?" Finally, she had said it. It was out there in the air for him to know what she thought.

He stared at her. "Don't you want the house?'

"Yes—yes." She looked away wistfully, her hand unconsciously moving over her big belly as the child inside kicked. "But I would like to keep my chickens."

CHAPTER 31

"Addie, we should have a little party to celebrate," said Will. "Mr. Patrick was awarded $18,000 and the firm will get a healthy slice from the railroad."

Addie was well trained in turning out delicious, bountiful meals, so that was the easy part. By late afternoon on the day of the dinner party, her big, black, cook stove was covered with dishes warming and ready to serve. The problem was, they only had the kitchen table, five feet by five feet, and the kitchen didn't seem the place to entertain.

Besides the kitchen, the little house had only a bedroom and parlor. Will moved the table into the parlor in front of the fireplace, under the ponderous wedding portraits of his mother and father—but, still, there weren't enough chairs to go around.

At six o'clock, they began to arrive. After a round of toasts to Will and Clemet Sampson for bringing in the prized case, nine adults gathered and tried to be seated in unmatched chairs, jostled tightly together. With every passing minute, Will felt the need for his imagined big house where he wouldn't have these problems.

Both firelight and candlelight flickered on the guests. Ann Jameson, tall and plump, was not only a contrast to Hazel Sampson, who was tiny and birdlike, but Addie thought they would have been better-suited if they switched husbands. Violet (who had not approved of Addie entertaining when she was "showing") was seated by the judge and dressed in a purple-velvet dress, a long rope of pearls hung from her neck, regal as a queen.

Conversation turned immediately to the next cases on the calendar. Will noticed Otis Tolbert withdrawing more and more from the table talk. "You feeling cramped here, Otis?" Will asked.

"As a matter of fact, I think I will move over and sit on the sofa with my plate, if you'll excuse me. More room for everyone else."

Will felt acutely embarrassed over the cramped situation, but helped Otis resettle, then went back to the table conversation dominated mostly by Jameson, with Sampson and Judge Austin jumping in now and then.

While Addie served coffee and her long-awaited apple pie, the lawyers brought up the case they had avoided during dinner, the only one they had lost—Eugenia Patrick's.

"You might as well say it," Otis's voice boomed from the corner seat, "You lost because of me. Don't beat about the bush."

Sampson turned back to face him, "No one said that, Tolbert. The railroad brought out their top guns. They were willing to go to any lengths because that was going to be big settlement."

"And there was a hitch in it," the judge said. "She died of a heart attack, not injuries that were easily apparent, like the others."

Otis leaned back, apparently not convinced. Addie hoped serving dessert would lighten the mood. She handed Otis Tolbert a big slice of pie and sat down with him on the sofa.

"Thank you, Mrs. . . ."

"Addie Rose," she cut in. "Call me Addie." Otis smiled, then said loud enough for all to hear, "How is it Fletcher has all the luck, a pretty wife who's a good cook and soon to make him a father?"

Addie knew that for him to give words to her condition would shock the ladies, especially Violet. Whatever they thought, they didn't say, and conversation about their work, obviously engrossing, lasted until nearly midnight.

The judge and Violet left first, then Sampson and his wife. Jameson with his Hazel, stood in the door, making their good-bye and getting ready to brave the ride home on a chilled February night. After they left, Will turned back to see Otis still sitting before the fire.

"I see two great paintings. Wedding portraits, I take it. One is your lovely mother," Otis said. "Who is the groom?"

"I promised you that answer over a drink sometime. It's a cold night out there. Stay a while and have another drink."

Addie, with a weary smile, served them both whiskeys. "I think I'll leave the two of you with it, if you'll excuse me, Mr. Tolbert."

They nodded as Will sat down with his drink. "That's my father, Otis. Vachel Fletcher, he was. He left us when I was about five years old. The judge later married my mother and raised me."

"Still more luck, I'd say." Otis finished his drink and put the glass down on a nearby table as if it were a gavel.

"I wish I could see it that way."

"Where is he now?"

"No one knows. Dead, some think."

"Give your wife my compliments on a wonderful meal, but I must be going." Otis stood as Will retrieved his coat. "I'll see you in the office tomorrow—Fletcher, is it? Or is it Austin? I'm never sure."

CHAPTER 32

In early April, Addie left the house with the excuse she wanted to talk to her mother. But instead, awkward in her last weeks of pregnancy, she crept up the stairs to the room above the bank.

The number of women had grown from a couple of dozen to about thirty, but not all were openly active. They were seated before a podium.

"I will moderate the meeting," Addie said as she took the place behind the podium. Without her coat, it was obvious she was soon due to give birth. "The deer hunters will be gathering at the picnic grounds this coming Friday afternoon. After that, they will go out on their hunt for—I think this time, it's for squirrels. We should march in on their camp, carrying signs. Surprise them."

"That will surprise them all right," Addie's sister, Mary Conyers, said.

"How many are with me on this?" Addie went on.

Sylvia Schofield finally spoke up, "I will make signs, but I cannot force myself to go among those men and listen to their remarks."

The women began to murmur among themselves.

"All right, ladies back to business.," Addie said. "Let's meet at my house and we'll make up the signs. Then on Friday, about two-thirty, when their gathering is in full swing, we'll swarm down on them, singing and waving our signs. Then we'll go up to the grandstand on the picnic grounds and each one will speak our piece about being respected enough to vote in this country we live our lives in."

Mary stood. "Think not only of yourself, but all the women who can't go out and make their voices heard. And think of your daughter's daughter."

"Yes." Addie's hand unconsciously rested on her belly.

They met on Wednesday afternoon, with cardboard signs, and painted them with red paint which read: "Votes for Women. It's time!!"

"I have asked to borrow the Dining Car Café wagon my brothers use to go out to the farms for meat and vegetables. We can ride out there together with the signs at our feet, then pop them out when we start walking in on them," Addie Rose said.

On Friday, seven women drove a wagon up before a group of men who were involved in target practice, their dogs yapping loudly as the wagon rolled in. When the women begin to scramble down from the wagon, a couple of men rushed to help the ladies. But once they were on the ground, they picked up their signs, waved them, and began to chant, "Votes for Women," the two chivalrous hunters faded quickly back into the group.

Jeering began toward the women, with each of the two sides striving for the loudest protest. The two men who had courteously helped the women were soon the object of scorn and shoved aside.

The women kept up the chant as they wove a path around the campfire, the wagons, and the tethered, noisy dogs, until the grounds and the woods beyond rang with chants, catcalls and barking dogs. Then Addie took her sign and bashed it over the loudest dog.

Rifles came out.

"We was out here gathered for target practice, and you all come out here, cause trouble and then assaulted this animal." It was Buster Jensen. He held the dog in his arms as if it were a baby. "I'm holding you, Addie Austin, and all the rest of you la—women 'til we get the sheriff in here. You ought'n to be out here showing yourself, with a young'un on the way, much less disturbing the peace."

In a few minutes the sheriff arrived and went immediately to Addie. "Mrs. Austin, what are you doing here?"

"My name is not Austin," Addie slammed back at him.

"You're Judge Austin's daughter-in-law." The sheriff pulled out a tattered notebook from his pocket.

"My name is Fletcher." Still defiant, Addie said sourly. "Be sure you write that down right—Fletcher."

"You don't need to get sassy with me. I know who you are, and you're making a perfect spectacle of yourself. Think what Judge Austin's gonna say to you."

"I've already heard all they have to say to me. All these women are right. This is a fight we have to make. This is for the little girl I may bring into this world." She rubbed her big belly and the men, now having stepped back to let the sheriff handle it, began to howl with laughter.

"Our mama taught all of us to make our own way, just like she has." Sister Mary stepped up to stand by Addie. "She runs her own business and still she's not considered smart enough to vote."

"So take me to jail," Addie said.

"That's just what I'm gonna do." The sheriff began to pull Addie's arm and push her toward the wagon, but then, confused, he helped her and each of the others up into the wagon before he crawled up and took the reins.

The sheriff was at odds as to how he would get them all back into town and into the jail. "Gonna need a couple o' you men to ride alongside the wagon to see to—the prisoners."

Addie would not shut up. "We're all willing to go to jail and stay there. I'm not going to escape, and I'm not embarrassed." Then they began clapping and singing.

Two armed men crawled into the wagon to watch the prisoners, and two on horseback rode alongside as the wagon jolted out of the picnic grounds.

The chanting and sign waving continued as they rode through town and on to the jail. The sheriff locked the seven women in two of the four cells. "Now," he said to the new prisoners, "I've got to ride

around and tell your menfolk why you're not home making supper."
He then slammed the door to the vast room housing two noisy cells.

"What in the hell were you *thinking*, Addie Rose!" Will stood in the
opened door of the cell.

On the way home after he got her out, he was tightlipped but boiling.

"It has to be done," she volunteered by way of explanation. "You
should read what they had to do in England."

"Are you in England?

"No, but it's the same . . ."

"I don't want to hear a *word* about this! If you start, I'll explode.
I don't want to have an argument while you're in your condition, but
you don't seem to care much about that. You're pregnant! Most women
prefer to not even go out. But not you; you take the fight to the streets."

"It's an honorable thing to be pregnant—perfectly natural. Bringing
a human being into the world is a noble thing. I am not going to hide
away like it's some disgrace. And what I'm doing is honorable, too,
Will Fletcher."

Once he had her in the house and comfortably seated, he went outside.

Addie saw him sitting on the back step, calming himself, she
supposed. Finally he came back in.

"Addie," she could tell he was trying to tamp down his anger.. "I do
wish you wouldn't let those women talk you into doing those things."

"It was my idea."

He stared out the window and shook his head. "Will you just
promise me you will not do any of these things while you are pregnant.
It is so—so unladylike.

"I will not promise you that. It is right and it is necessary to win
this fight. Maybe our daughters can be ladylike if they want to, but
then they'll have rights."

The weekly newspaper headlines blared, "Judge Austin's Daughter-in-
Law Jailed." Two long columns followed, highlighting Addie and the
six other women who—in extremely unwomanly fashion—entered
the camp of hunters where they were meeting before going on a
hunt." It concluded with a damning line: "Mrs. Austin filled the air

with profanity, struck an animal with her infamous sign, and seemed indifferent to the fact she was well-advanced in pregnancy."

"My mother is a bright woman—educated," Will said that morning as they read the paper. "She taught school after my father left us, and your mother is practically heroic, coming out here from the city with her brood of children, running a business alone and raising all of you to be capable adults. I can see that women should have a say in their life situation. I do see your purpose. But will you please curtail your assaults on male fortresses until you give birth to this child?"

She stood up. "I have to feed the chickens."

CHAPTER 33

It wasn't the daughter that she had imagined. On May 5, 1879, Addie Rose gave birth to a son.

Late that afternoon, Will—looking proud and a bit baffled—presented his son to his mother, the judge, Addie's mother, sister Mary, and brothers Roy and Alex, all of whom had assembled in the living room, nervously awaiting this new arrival.

Propped on pillows, Addie held their tiny newborn. Looking down on him, it didn't really matter whether it was a son or a daughter. Something of a miracle had happened to them. His name was William Austin Fletcher. In the next week, a steady stream of visitors came by: Violet's friends, Will's clients, Addie Rose's apple pie customers, and her suffragette warrior comrades.

Lost in the joy of watching their little son grow, they also watched their house rise, brick by brick on Cameron hill. At least once a week, they made the trip up to the building site, a picnic basket in the buggy. Sometimes they lay on a blanket, little Willie between them, in the dense cedar grove that would be behind their house, staring up through the trees at the blue sky. It came to Addie that Will didn't seem as lonely and lost now as he had when they first met; he was engrossed in his work and found it so satisfying, he never mentioned his father.

But that was about to change.

CHAPTER 34

"Casper died about two weeks ago." Reverend Hollister sat in Will's parlor with the young girl, Amy Fletcher. "Before he died," Hollister explained to Will, "he said there were things at Liela's plantation house that belonged to him. Said it was stuffed in a feed sack. Amy and I went there—to where he told us. We found it on the back porch, in a cabinet behind the cream separator, just as he'd said—in a feed sack."

Amy held a cardboard box in her lap on which had been pasted dozens of pictures. "When I saw pretty pictures, I cut them out and pasted them on this box my mamma left me." She opened the box almost reverently. There was an old pocket watch that didn't work, buttons, and a stub of a railroad ticket to Natchez.

"What's this?" Will's attention zeroed in on a little green card, about three inches long, with five letters at the top: CSIRR. Will caught his breath; everything in him tensed. He took the card and read the name out loud. "Vachel Fletcher."

"It's something about a railroad my father worked for before the war," Amy said.

"I don't think Casper knew what it was," Hollister said. "He never learned to read, but it says right there, 'Vachel Fletcher, Engineer of the Chicago and Southern Illinois Railroad.'"

"It's a badge for an engineer," Will said. "Those letters stand for Chicago and Southern Illinois Railroad. It was the rail line that started up before the war, but it failed. My father was the surveyor and engineer for it until the creditors came in and it went bankrupt. Then he worked on the beginnings of the Chicago and Illinois Central Railroad."

There was no doubt now. This man was his father and Amy's. He was the man who deserted them, started another family and deserted them too.

Amy watched, her eyes wide and questioning. "Do you think this was my father's—and yours?"

Will hardly heard what she said. Tears burned in his eyes. His hand shook holding the card between his finger and thumb. He studied it for a long time, and then finally looked up, realizing her question. "It was, Amy," he whispered. "It was. My mother has a card just like this one."

It was as if he had struck gold. But , also, it made him heartsick.

Here it was, in his hand. Irrefutable proof that his father had lived and made a life with a new family.

"My papa is your papa, too, then?" Amy kept asking.

Will looked at her, not really seeing. What this meant was overwhelming.

She had moved closer to him on the sofa. "I so wanted you to be my brother, but you didn't act like you wanted that."

"It's just that—I didn't believe it to be true." Maybe he should embrace her; he didn't know. She was hungry for some affection. He could see that. She was his sister, but she was a stranger.

He fondled the card, periodically glancing at it. "This railroad," he looked down at Amy, "was one of many that didn't last. When he worked for the Illinois Central later . . . " Will swallowed, then went on. "That's who he worked for when . . ." Will stopped and looked out the window. "When he used to come home to . . . my mother and me." He stopped. It would do Amy no good to explain that her father had deserted another family before he deserted hers.

"So he knew he had a wife and son when he met my mother, didn't he?" Amy was no longer a child.

"Yes." It was all he could say. "He loved railroads. They were the most important thing in his life. He told me he saw them when they were first on tracks, and it was amazing to see something move down a rail with no animal pulling it. It was a great fascination to him."

"I wish I could have talked to him like you did."

"If he's still alive, Amy, I'll find him. I will. I promise you that."

"But Mama told me he's dead, drowned in the great river."

Will decided to say no more. That was just another lie. Instead, he pointed to the life-size portrait that hung on the wall and dominated the whole room.

"That's him in the painting," Will watched her standing at the foot of the great picture, absorbing every detail, saying nothing, a forlorn image he wouldn't forget.

"You see neither of us look like him," he said.

"No."

"We must go, Amy," Hollister said. "We'll catch the train back in the morning. I have services this Sunday."

"I am sorry we can't put you up . . . " Will motioned to the small house.

"Oh, no. We're at the hotel."

"I appreciate you bringing me this card, the proof."

"It was for Amy. She hoped to find something of a family, and she has. And I've never traveled in Yankee country."

Once they left, he turned to Addie, who was rocking the baby to sleep. "I will find that man."

"And if you find him, what will you do?"

"I'll tell him the trouble he caused and that I hate him from the bottom of my soul."

She put the baby down in his crib by their bed, came back to sit by Will, and laid her head on his shoulder. "You rob yourself by hating him so much."

He took her hand. "You're the straightest-thinking person I know."

"I'm glad you said 'person,'" Addie finally said, "and not 'woman.'"

After a quiet minute, Will asked, "Where do you think he might be, Addie?"

"Wouldn't he finally go to his parents? His old home. Where did they live?"

"Kentucky. But my mother said he had nothing to do with them. They had educated him to take over the family business—tobacco brokers—and he wanted nothing to do with that. He wanted to be a railroader. His father thought he was chasing a dream."

"He was wounded," Addie said. "There's a Civil War veteran's home in Quincy. How old would he be now? How injured was he?"

Will got up and closed a window against the cool evening air. "I don't know. Obviously, the War Department doesn't know much about him. They say he drank."

"Maybe because he was wounded."

"I wish I could be as generous as you are. When you are well enough," Will said, "we'll go for that long a ride. We'll go to Quincy to the Old Veteran's Home and see what they know."

"I am well enough!" Addie looked up at him. "We'll tuck Willie in with us and take him on his first train ride."

CHAPTER 35

A few days later, at the Veteran's Home in Quincy, Illinois, Will walked through rows of beds where men were resting or sitting by their beds, reading.

He asked each if they had been in the battles of Corinth, Mississippi, during the war, or if they had heard of a man named Vachel Fletcher. Many were eager for some conversation, but some were withdrawn and only shook their heads.

Finally, outside, they came to an old soldier who'd had his leg amputated and sat in a chair in the early summer shade of a tree. "No, I never was in Corinth." He looked thoughtful for a moment." There was once an old boy here who'd been in those battles. Don't recall his name though. Seems like he called hisself Stone or something like that."

"Stoner? Did he go by Stoner? My father's best friend was Will Stone." A wave of elation poured through Will. Maybe, just maybe, he was onto something, the way he felt when Amy showed him the old railroad card, like a thread to success. "That's who he named me for. Called him 'Stoner.'"

"Well, that feller left here more'n a year ago" the old soldier explained. "They probably got information over there in the office 'bout where he called home. Men come in and they go out. I ain't got no home. This here's my home."

"Thank you; you've been very helpful." Will shook his hand.

"That man—Stoner, you called him," he called them back, obviously not wanting the chat to end. "He had the pains in the belly; said he got the typhoid in the war. I reckon he musta got better and went home."

"Thank you. I'll see what they have in their records."

"It's nice to see a pretty young woman with a baby." He seemed as if he was trying to hold them for more conversation. "You give me a little bit of joy—just to look at you—a woman with a baby. I seen action in Chattanooga and Kennesaw Mountain. I's with Sherman. Lost my leg at Kennesaw Mountain."

"Would you like to hold the baby for a minute?" Addie asked.

He took the child into his arms, and smiled down at him. "He's a mighty fine boy." He worked his finger into Willie's tiny fist, the baby's fingers curled over his. "A fine boy, he is." When he handed the baby back, a bright glint showed in his eyes. "Thank you for that."

In the office they asked about a veteran named Will Stone. Another vet took down a huge grey notebook. "Yes, I remember the old boy. Quiet kind, he was. Seen a lot of action." He looked up from the notebook. "Says here, he was suffering from the effects of having typhoid."

"Does it say where he lives?"

"Says Indiana. Corydon, Indiana. You know 'im?"

"Sort of. He knew my father. Looking for something about my father."

"Ah, well, a lot of folks are lookin' for somebody they lost. I wish you luck. Sometimes, young feller, you just kinda have to let go. There's many a questions hangin' out there with no answers. Lots of mysteries that just stay that way."

"I have to find out," Will replied. "I'll go see if this Mr. Stone knows anything." Will leaned across the counter, hoping for more information. "He worked with my father surveying a railroad. Sometimes a man with the name 'Will Stone' came home with my father. That's who I was named for—'Will Stone.'"

The veteran looked up, nodded, his eyes glazed over. He'd heard it all a thousand times.

Before Will could plan his trip to Corydon, Indiana, Oscar Jamison requested his help in preparing for a murder case. It claimed most of his time, and he lamented to Addie that he was not able to see the development of their new house on Cameron Hill or get ready for the move they planned in the fall.

CHAPTER 36

Violet sat in her buggy, looking over the crowd at the Old Settlers' Picnic. She knew those women were to speak, the ones clamoring for the vote. She prayed Addie Rose would not be one of them. She was a mother now. Maybe she had mellowed, seen that it was, at least, someone else's fight; leave it with them and not demean herself.

But all hope evaporated when Addie filed up onto the grandstand with about twenty others. She was the first introduced. "Mrs. Will Austin," Ina Pilcher spoke to the scattered audience milling about.

Violet looked at the judge who sat by her, "Oh, dear God, please don't let her cuss or call those men names."

The judge smiled. "Addie believes in what's she's doing."

Violet turned questioning eyes on her husband. He was watching the grandstand and there was a bit of a smile on his lips. "You mean you approve of her doing this?" Violet shook her head and shrunk back into her corner of the buggy.

"Let's see what she has to say," The judge leaned forward.

Addie stepped forward, "Not quite," she corrected, sharply. "I am Addie Rose Fletcher—and Will is not named Austin, either. But I'm here because I think the time has come for women to have the right to vote."

A man shouted out, "Why do you ruin all our holidays with your carping?" It was Brice O'Dell, Clovis's son. "We can't let you vote. Women are shallow headed. It'd be the biggest mess you ever seen if women was allowed to run things."

"You know what Abraham Lincoln said about that?" Addie shot back. "He said, 'We may as well trust 'em; they been feeding us for years.'"

"Ain't the same thing," Brice spit back. "We're talkin' about runnin' the country, not makin' the gravy."

"Near as I can see, you haven't done all that great without women."

"It just ain't a woman's proper place,"

"Are you gonna shut your dammed mouth so I can make my talk." Addie stood on the top step of the grandstand, eyes blazing. "Or are you gonna show us a good example of what shallow is?"

"All right! Have your say and get it over with."

"I'm going to tell you a story." Addie dropped her voice. Maybe if they had to be quiet to hear her, they would think about what she said. "There was a woman in England who said that half of the population was women, and they, just like men, had to live under the law, but had no right to vote their opinion."

"Cain't hear you," Brice called out. "If you're gonna take our time, at least speak up."

"Come closer," Addie answered. "This woman in England found other women who felt like she did, and they decided to rectify the situation." Addie noticed he did move closer and so did a couple of others. "Well, people didn't like them. It meant change. Change in the way people thought about women. The suffragettes kept up marching and talking and disrupting, then finally some were put in chains and taken prisoner."

"Women in chains . . . did they go on trial?" Brice asked. The crowd had grown, and they were listening.

"No. Worse than that."

"What?" Brice pushed his hat back to his hairline with the stem of his pipe.

"The women only had one way to show how serious they were and how much they believed in what they were doing, so they wouldn't eat."

"No!"

"In other words, they were willing to die for what they felt was a serious wrong in English laws."

Brice pursed his lips, frowned as he looked past the grandstand to a dense forest that bordered the picnic grounds. Addie watched him. He was *thinking* about her story, she surmised. She had more to say; but it came to her, it would be best to stop. He was thinking and that was enough for now.

She stepped down from the grandstand.

The judge slapped his knee, and laughed out loud, "By George, that girl's all right." Violet, however, stayed back in the shadows of the buggy.

When Addie finished and another woman took to the podium, Violet leaned near the judge, "We have got to rein her in. This can't go on. I have an idea that just might work."

"Do what you feel you should." The judge patted Violet's hand. "But you're not going to hush that one."

CHAPTER 37

Will and Addie finally found time to go on the long-delayed trip to look up Stoner. They found him on the front porch of his farmhouse, just outside Corydon, Indiana.

Will walked up to the porch, realizing how old Stoner looked. "Will Stone? Stoner?" He figured quickly as he looked at him. His own father would be about the same age—approaching 50?

"You know me, but I don't place you." Will Stone stood up, held to the post of the front porch.

"You do know me, but I've changed a bit." Will extended his hand.

"We've all changed." Stoner stood, greeted them, and studied Will for a time. "Don't believe you were in the war—too young."

"No, I wasn't in the war. This is my wife, Addie Rose Fletcher. You knew me well when I was just a boy."

"My God, you ain't Fletch's boy?" He wiped his hand across his mouth. "Lawsy. He'd have to be a grown man now, I reckon."

"I am, indeed, Stoner. I'm Will Fletcher. I got my name from you."

"Well, you made a fine man. I used to bounce you on my knee. I can't believe my eyes. You were a fine boy, I know that; the light of your papa's eyes." He went back to his seat in the swing and motioned them to take chairs.

"Don't know as I would say that. He left us—me and Mama," Will answered.

Stoner looked down at the floorboards of the porch and moved the swing back ever so slowly. "I know that. I talked to him, coaxed him to go back, but he was one to follow his nose, and if he heard the sound of a train whistle, he couldn't walk away from it." He paused, then asked, "How is your Mama?'

"She's well. Married to a good man—a judge. He raised me just like he did his own son, Tom. Made no difference between us."

"That's good to know. I knew your mother remarried. Fletch told me she did."

The words fell on Will like a warm breeze. The very words he'd hoped for. Addie picked it up, too, and squeezed Will's hand, but said nothing. He felt like a hound on the chase with prey close in his sights. "Fletch told you? You've seen him? He's alive?"

"He was alive then. All of us who went through the war are alive on borrowed time. Fletch was a drinker. I haven't heard from him for a while."

"But how did you know my mother remarried?"

Stoner seemed to grow cautious and thoughtful. "Well, the war finally come to an end and I started home, but he said had some unfinished business, so he took another route home.

"By way of Corinth, Mississippi?" Will ask.

Stoner looked surprised. "You know about Corinth?"

"Some—not all."

"Well, yes, we left that whole place in terrible ruins—us and the rebs—all fightin' over two railroads that cross there. That's where I got the typhoid; it's gonna put me in the grave one of these times. Anyways, Fletch went there after the war but didn't stay. Then he decided to go back home and try to make peace with your mother. But funny thing; the day he landed there, he found out she married somebody else. Folks told 'im he was a judge.

"He came back!" Will breathed.

Stoner nodded his head. "He got on the train and come here to see me. He was in a bad way—drinking. Finally, my wife sent him kiting. She didn't want to keep cleaning up his messes. I ain't seen 'im since. He was a hard drinker. Wouldn't surprise me none to hear he was dead. You see, son, the war's still with us—a lot of us—and the liquor's a comfort."

"He came back," Will said again. It was all he had heard. "He wanted to come back."

"I think he always aimed that—at least in his mind. Not sure he sorted things out straight. I always thought your mother was the finest woman I ever met, but it was Fletch she loved."

"He wanted to come back," Will kept repeating.

"He told men in the Army he had a wife and boy at home. In his mind, it was kind of his bedrock."

"Tell me, Stoner, when he went to Corinth, was it to see a woman?"

Stoner was silent for a long time, looking across the road at his cornfield.

"Well, yes, it was," he said in almost a whisper.

"Liela?"

"Yes." He nodded.

"Thank you, Stoner. Thank you so much. You've helped more than I can ever tell you. You're making the pieces add up. I'm glad I found you. I'll never forget you coming home with my father when I was a boy."

"Them was the happy times," Stoner smiled and seemed to look inside himself. "Good times. I'm just glad to see how fine Violet's boy grew up to be. And with a pretty little wife."

"And we have a son, too. We call him 'Willie'," Addie said.

"Like you to stay for supper. I can get something together. Lost my wife about five years ago."

"No, we have to get back, but it's so good to see you again."

"Don't you two be strangers. You just get on that train and come and see ole Stoner."

On the train ride home, Will was all enthusiasm.

"It's good you found Stoner and learned a little about your father but, Will, you still don't know where he is."

He turned on her as if she had insulted him. "Everything has changed, Addie. Don't you see, everything has changed? He *wanted* to come back to us. I was twelve years old when my mother married the judge. He might have looked for me, but he couldn't because my mother had just remarried. Don't you see?"

Addie watched him for a bit, feeling with him his empty hunger, the missing piece that could never be filled. She wished she could comfort him, but she didn't know how. "I'm sure he looked for you. I can't imagine he wouldn't. Think of your own son."

"When I think like that, it makes me furious, because I can't imagine anything that would make me leave my son—and my father did, just that."

"So did you find Stoner?" Violet ventured, sitting in her favorite chair in the parlor. A soft breeze flowed in from the east window, the sounds of summer in the air.

She took the baby on her lap, feeling very apprehensive about what her son might have uncovered.

"We saw him," Will said. "We saw Stoner. Not well. The effects of typhoid still with him, but he was very happy to see us." Will smiled. "He only remembered me as a child."

Violet wanted desperately to know what Stoner knew, but feared to hear it, so she kept her attention on the baby, bouncing him and bringing up giggles from time to time.

"To begin with, Mother, my father was very much alive after the war. He went to help a family who had cared for him when he was wounded."

She steeled herself for what she almost knew would come next. "A family from Corinth, Mississippi?"

Will looked at her and continued cautiously. "Yes, but Mother, he came back to us. He was here—just after you married the judge."

Violet caught her breath. "Oh, Will. No. He came back!" Tears came to her eyes.

"Stoner said he found out you had had him declared dead."

"Oh, my God," she whispered. What had she done! Her hands began to tremble. What had she done!

She handed the baby to Addie, too shaken to hold him, and stood up, went by the fireplace, her back to them. "No. No, this is too fanciful. I don't believe it. It's some big story Stoner told, and you want to believe it."

"There's no reason not to believe him, Mother."

When they left, Violet sat for a long time by the cold fireplace. Stoner. She closed her eyes, they were all young again, she and Fletch and Stoner. All the world was new, life a joyous promise. They laughed and played at life. And life was real, and she was in love. She knew Fletch was, too. She suspected Stoner loved her, but he never said anything. Tears traced down her cheeks.

She got up, shook it off. The tiny clock on the mantle chimed four times. The judge would soon be home. She went to her room, closed the door, stared at the floor, and shook her head. "No, no," she whispered, and tears she couldn't stop spilled down her cheeks "Oh, Fletch, what have I done?" She dug deep in the back of the bottom drawer of a massive mahogany dresser and found the little velvet pouch. Inside the pouch, she found the ring Fletch had put on her finger. She slipped it on, turning it around on her finger in the darkening room. The dull, hard ache of loneliness filled her, the bitter ache of a heart broken. She could hardly see the ring through the mist of tears. Then she sighed deeply, resigned, removed the ring, pushed it back into the pouch, and returned it to its secret place.

Two hours later, she sat at the dinner table, opposite the judge, composed, perfectly groomed, and discussing the success of her monthly afternoon tea.

CHAPTER 38

Violet had been thinking for some time about the problem with Addie.

She explained to the judge over breakfast that she thought she had an idea that would work. She would take Addie to St. Louis and get her some special outfits from Girolamo Giuseffi's design house in St. Louis. "At my Christmas Tea, I'll ask her to pour tea at the table—make her the center of attention. And she will be complimented on how lovely she looks . . ." Violet dropped a spoonful of jam on a thick slice of bread and spread it about.

"Do you honestly think you're going to steer Addie away from that mission of hers?" The judge asked. "She really believes women should vote."

"I don't mind that she has convictions. I'd just like to soften her ways. Show her a pleasanter way to live."

He smiled and took a sip of coffee from his favorite mustache cup. "Well, my dear one, I wish you luck with your little scheme, but she is quite committed."

"Yes, but she's a mother now and," she looked at her husband and frowned, "I don't like that you think I'm 'scheming.'"

Addie had to admit, it made her feel rather elegant sitting in the new Harvey railroad dining car, with its white linen table clothes, china plates, and gleaming silver. It was lovely being served by a bright, young girl in a starched uniform while watching the countryside slide by as she and Violet traveled to St. Louis.

Violet had been unusually attentive the last couple of weeks, keeping Willie for her so she could get rest, and making strange comments about the best color for her to wear. Then came the offer of a three-day trip to St. Louis and shopping. Tired and exhausted caring for the baby and keeping up with her pie business, three days' rest sounded like Heaven. She left Willie in the care of her sister and the blessings of her husband.

The next day, the shopping trip Addie expected became something she could not have fathomed. They sat at one of the many tables that lined an elevated runway. Chandeliers sparkled above the long walkway, and before them were glasses of wine which seemed always to be filled by waiters moving with almost invisible stealth.

A skinny, young model walked by wearing a plum-colored suit, with a long, fitted jacket and a ponderous, wide-brimmed hat, plumes jutting out one side. Next came a girl wearing a full-skirted taffeta dress in navy blue, a high neckline, and leg-o-mutton sleeves with white lace at the neck and wrists. The models kept coming, walking with purpose, not looking right nor left. Finally, a model walked before them wearing a wondrous creation with a bell-shaped skirt that draped in folds across the front, edged with fringe, which allowed several tiers of lace to show below. It was emerald-green satin with white lace. Addie followed the model, mesmerized at such a lavish dress.

Violet leaned across the table. "The dresses are so lovely; you want to create an occasion just to wear them."

With that comment, a lot of things came clear to Addie. Was this why Violet had parties, teas, and held her position aloft in the community? Were they based on a desire to make a place to wear fancy dresses, or was it something else? Sometimes, Addie suspected her mother-in-law was something other than what she seemed, a woman who wore a mask.

Violet reached across the table, and touched her hand, "I never had a daughter to dote on and spoil. I want you to make the selections you like, and we'll have them made up for you in any color or material you want."

Addie, who was simply overwhelmed, finally made her decisions, at Violet's prompting, and ordered the emerald-green creation—although she couldn't imagine where in Amsley she would wear it. She picked another to be made in rose taffeta, and the suit made up in pearl grey with the hat to go with it. Then she went into a private little room with a fancy, gilded chair and was fitted for the selections she had made.

Violet seemed jubilant as they stepped out of this glamorous room with the runway, onto the busy city street. The fashion house offered patrons carriage rides back to their hotels if requested.

It was mid-afternoon when they walked into the hotel lobby. Violet turned to Addie and said, "I have a surprise for you."

"I have already had a year-full of surprises in two days, Mrs. Austin." She could not call her mother. She had only one mother.

They went down a long hall to a magnificent room full of sparkle, crystal and chandeliers, with windows on three sides overlooking an outside garden. The room held five small round tables with bright, white tablecloths and set with gleaming silver service.

"This is called the Garden Room," Violet said as a young waiter seated her and then started toward Addie—who had already seated herself—so he took the napkin stuffed in a crystal goblet, shook it out, and placed it across Addie's lap.

"Isn't this a glorious place? Nothing like this in Amsley," Violet's eyes sparkled.

"Have you been here before?" Addie asked.

Violet's expression changed. She gazed across the room, her eyes became misty. "Yes, once," she finally answered and then grew very quiet.

In the silence that had fallen between them, Addie wondered why Violet should take the time to do all this for her. What was the reason? Was it really that she had missed having a daughter to dress up and pamper, or was it something else?

The waiter brought a large china teapot with roses on the side and a three-tiered serving tray to their table, on which were tiny sandwiches and bite-size pastries.

"I have never worn a hat like the one we ordered." Addie tried to bring Violet back to the enthusiastic person she had been at the salon.

"Oh, you'll be gorgeous in it. You should be getting all of your things within the month, just in time for the holidays."

Addie smiled. She would have to become acquainted with this new self she was going to be.

Addie, dressed in her new finery and carrying Willie, arrived early for the Christmas tea at Violet's house. She took him upstairs, put him down for a nap, and came back to the dining room. The long table was set with Violet's most delicate china. Each month, Violet held tea and invited a different collection of women. She was the undisputed leader in these rarefied circles.

"You look like the grand lady." Violet stepped back, and smiled at her daughter-in-law. "I want you to sit at the head of the table and pour tea this time. You are a vision, a pretty young thing in the latest fashion. The ladies will be entranced."

"Pour tea! What's there to pouring tea?"

"Well, quite a bit. You ask about their health and their family, and anything else you might know about them, while pouring just the right amount into the cup and asking if they use sugar. Then invite them to enjoy the tea sandwiches."

Addie nodded, thinking she had been pouring coffee into cups at the Dining Car Café since she was ten.

At the head of the table, where Addie was seated, was placed a large ornate silver tray, which held an equally ornate silver teapot. In front of that was a tilted warmer stand to keep tea ready for refills. "When you have served everyone and need to replenish the tea, you carefully tip the warmer and refill the tea pot. It's not so much in the doing as the finesse of maintaining command as a hostess, while efficiently refilling the main service."

At promptly three o'clock in the afternoon, they arrived with perfect punctuality, neither late nor early.

The first cup she poured was for Lily Marshall, tall, willowy, and overly powdered. Addie's mother had told her that ladies sometimes would put a thin layer of flour in a pan and bake it until it turned ivory, then use it to powder their faces. Addie thought Mrs. Marshall had not baked it enough because she didn't look ivory; she looked ghostly. Before Addie could ask the silly questions Violet had suggested, Lily Marshall said, "I'll take two sugars, and where is your darling little boy?"

"Upstairs napping, I hope."

"He is simply the light of his grandmother's life."

"Yes, I know."

As the others were seated, Violet stood, wearing a satin dress, with an elaborately draped and folded skirt that swept up into a bustle in the back—one of eight dresses in varying shades of violet, from lavender to boysenberry she had ordered in St. Louis. "Tea drinking is an ancient ritual. We make a pot of tea when life is stressful. We serve tea when someone is not feeling well. We take tea together to share friendships and enjoy each other's company or if there is reason to celebrate as I have today. Many of you have daughters, which is a cherished possession. I have that in my son, but he presented me with a beautiful woman I can cherish as a daughter as well. She will serve today as your hostess."

They clapped and Addie felt her face turn hot. She had never been made the center of attention before, and in the company of these particular women, whom she knew were the most notable and admired ladies in town, she felt embarrassed.

Ethel Ward came next, a large woman, in her third year as a widow and now allowed to wear a solemn grey dress with white lace at the neck and wrist. "Violet always makes that speech," she whispered as Addie poured her tea, "but when my husband died, I drank tea, hoping it would help. It didn't. I come to her teas because it gives me a chance to dress up for something again."

"I am sorry about your husband. I remember when he died," Addie said and offered her the sugar bowl.

"You do? You are a sweet, thoughtful young girl . . . not at all what

. . ." she stopped abruptly. "Will is lucky to have you," she finally ended. She touched Addie's shoulder, moved on and took her assigned seat in time for Sarah to serve tiny sandwiches from a huge silver tray.

Jane Carlton waited as Addie poured her tea. "I suppose this grand creation you're wearing is from that fashion house in St. Louis Violet talks about."

"Yes," Addie whispered, mesmerized by what Jane was wearing. It was a dress, covered from neck to hem with tiny bow ribbons in every imaginable color. Addie could not help thinking, as she stared into the woman's bosom, of a flurry of butterflies landing on her honeysuckle bush. "I don't go to places like that," Jane was saying. "I design my own clothes."

Addie looked again at Jane's concoction. There seemed nothing appropriate to say to that. She looked again at the dress and then asked, "Sugar?"

"No. No sugar."

Nellie Bridger waited patiently behind Jane. Addie wished there was some way to escape. She was forced to admire her mother-in-law. No woman in the room was so elegantly dressed, no woman ever was, and Violet knew it. It was her role as she saw it, and she played it to scrumptious detail. She knew everyone's particular ailment, the names of their children and grandchildren, and their private worries and asked about them.

Finally, when all had been served tea, Sarah brought in tray after tray of sandwiches and dainty dessert morsels. Inevitably the talk got around to the train wreck and the mystery of why a train that made the same run every day should inexplicably jump the tracks. Everyone had an opinion. Now, a year and half later, no one had any concrete evidence to back up their theory.

"It had to be that someone was asleep or drunk when it was time to throw the switch and—" Ethel Ward was interrupted when the judge came through the front door and into the dining room.

"I am sorry to disturb you charming ladies and your conversation while you're sitting at tea, but I need to tell you something that has happened. Two girls have gone missing. One's about 18 and the other younger, maybe 15."

"Oh no," Lily Marshall's hand flew to her mouth. "Who?"

"Pearl Bennett and Pansy Ross. Do you ladies know them?" The judge fiddled with the hat he held, awkward in this feminine domain.

Ethel Ward flipped her black fan open, looked down into her teacup, and began to fan herself, certainly from habit rather than being too warm on this winter day. "I know who the Bennett girl is. Most of us know of her."

"I have seen her on the streets, but have never had occasion to pass any time of day with her." Jane Carlton added cautiously. "I don't know the other girl."

"Maybe they just ran away to frighten their parents," Violet suggested.

"Could be," the judge acknowledged. "Could be anything, but they've been gone since day before yesterday. Both parents thought the girls were at the other one's house for the night, but when the second night came, Pearl Bennett's parents began to get worried and started looking for her. Addie, your sister, Mary, seems to be the last to have seen them. They were in the Dining Car Café. No one has seen them since."

"One time that Ross girl wanted to try out for an Amsley Players presentation, but—" Nellie stopped, apparently not sure how to continue. "We didn't have anything for her."

Ethel Ward kept enthusiastically fanning herself, but her expression would have been the same if she had raised the lid on a bucket of rotten fish.

"I don't want to put a damper on your pleasant afternoon," the judge said, "and there may be no problem, but at this point, two young women appear to be missing. We have men all over the county searching for them. Just wanted you to know about it. Now, if you'll excuse me, I'll leave you to enjoy your tea." In the quiet that followed, they heard his footsteps resounding on the stairs.

Later, when the last of the ladies had made their deferential good-byes with gracious thanks for being invited, Violet sat by the fire sipping on one last cup of tea. Addie sat in the other chair, holding Willie, who was slowly waking from his nap.

"Addie, did you like the ladies that were there today?" Violet asked.

"They were certainly kind to me. "

"Which one did you admire the most?"

Addie looked at her mother-in-law, puzzled. Where was this going?

"I don't know. That's hard to say."

"How about Nellie? She already knows you," Violet prompted.

"She's all right."

"Is she one you would want to be like?" Violet persisted. "One that could be set up as an example for you?"

Addie was feeling deeply uncomfortable. "I think I'd just as soon be myself and not copy anybody. But if you want me to say who is an example for me, I'd say my own mama is nearly a saint."

"Yes, your mother is a fine woman, but think about it. These women are the most excellent ladies in town, character of spun gold."

"They're ornaments!"

"Ornaments!" Violet's attitude changed abruptly. "Look, I'm just trying to help you. You are spirited and smart. This is the way I would guide my daughter."

A fire was building in Addie. Violet wanted her to act like someone else, and that meant there was something wrong with her as she was.

"I know your mother had a hard time," Violet continued.

"Yes, my mother," Addie cut in, "she's the woman I admire the most. She is worth something. She taught us to think—yes, even the girls. Maybe not to pick up the right spoon or fork, but nobody in our family, not even the girls, live to be window dressing for somebody else."

Violet leaned back in her chair, "I know about taking care of your own responsibility–that is, when Will's father went to war, I needed to teach school to take care of us. But when I married the judge, I took up a position appropriate as his wife. This is what I am trying to tell you."

"I'm never going to be that kind of woman." Addie let Willie slide down to the floor to play. "I am glad I can make and sell pies and raise chickens and grow apple and cherry trees and make my own clothes. I can never be one of those helpless women. And I think women should be able to speak their mind. So now you have my mind."

"I love you, Addie, and that is why I ask you to move away from this woman thing that is constantly in the papers and interests you so much. It's something that can only do you harm."

That night at dinner, the judge turned to his wife and asked, "And how is your plan working to 'ladyfy' our young Addie Rose?"

Violet closed her eyes and shook her head. "I'm afraid it's hopeless."

The judge cupped his hand over Violet's, and looked out the window, smiling.

CHAPTER 39

Addie Rose wandered through the cavernous rooms on the ground floor of their new house. She had never imagined living in such a grand place. Rain pounded hard at the windows. It was the fourth day of rain in a week of grey days, which matched her mood, battling morning sickness in a way she had not experienced when she was expecting Willie.

She slumped down at the kitchen table. An uneaten slice of bread, spread with blackberry jam before her. Through a glass door, she looked into the dining room; that room and the kitchen were the only rooms furnished in the house. She had been appalled at the cost of it all, the long table, twelve dining chairs, and the breakfront, buffet and pie safe, but Will had insisted. Light glistened off the damask wallpaper from a wide chandelier. She took a bite, then pushed the plate away and carried her cup of hot tea into the empty parlor. She sat down in one of the two chairs, the only ones brought from the little house, and wrapped herself, cocoon-like, in a quilt before a dancing fire. The other furnishings Will had ordered from a craftsman near St. Louis would be shipped in three months.

On the day they had loaded up the wagons with the few meager things they would take to their new three-story brick home, Addie walked through the rooms of the little house before she left; the home they came to after their honeymoon and the house where little Willie had been born. A lot of living had gone on in those two years. She would always love the little house.

Now fighting nausea, she watched rivulets pouring down over the glass of the front window. The tea tasted good, and somehow calmed her. Will had kindly taken care of feeding her chickens, which now had a temporary roost along one wall of the carriage house. Nested deep within herself, she heard someone at the front door. She roused, went through the broad entrance hall and opened the door.

"Mary," Addie looked past her sister at the blustery rainy day. "What are you doing out on a day like this?"

"I need to talk to you about a couple of things."

"Come into the kitchen, and I'll make you a cup of tea."

"No, don't bother. I know you're not up to serving someone else." Mary drew a deep breath and continued. "I wanted to tell you first, Addie. Well, I told Mama—but you're next. I'm engaged. Andy and I want to be married in June."

"That's wonderful. You have been seeing Andy for . . . how long?"

"Two years. Almost. But there's another thing."

Addie turned to her sister, "What is it?"

"The women, as soon as warmer weather comes, are planning to stand on street corners and ask passersby to sign a petition to send to our senator."

Addie nodded, smiled, and pulled the quilt tighter around her.

"We've missed you at our meetings," Mary continued. "I just wanted to know if you are in agreement with this and maybe willing to do it?"

"Of course, you know I'll do whatever's necessary. I'm sorry I've been so sick this time, I haven't thought of much outside myself."

Mary stirred the dying embers and added a piece of cedar log, which caught fire quickly.

"There's not much happening now anyway."

They watched as the flame flared and crackled. Mary glanced at Fletch and Violet's wedding portraits on each side of the fireplace. "I see Mama and Papa have arrived, even if the furniture hasn't."

"Yes, it won't come for three months. It's being specially made."

"Oh, my. How nice. But," Mary hesitated, "this is why I really came, and I feel awkward about asking. I was wondering if you would offer your beautiful new home for our wedding. It will be warm—June, summertime, and I also would like Will to give me away. And we would like the judge to marry us. Right there, right before that fireplace."

Addie brightened, her hands coming out of the quilt in a single clap, excitement eclipsing nausea. "We would be so honored. I can't, of course, speak for Will and the judge, but I am sure they would love to share in your happiest of days."

"And you will be my Matron of Honor, of course."

"Mary, I will be very pregnant, then. I don't know."

"That's never stopped your before."

Addie laughed. "I think I'll do it. Let their mouths fall open. And we'll make you a spectacular wedding gown."

"Well, Addie, that's another thing." Mary leaned forward in her chair. "This is a once in a lifetime event for me. I'd like to go to St. Louis to that fashion designer who made your dresses and have my wedding gown made. What do you think?"

"Let's do it. This will be the grandest wedding! Will will love that. He likes 'grandest' things."

After Mary left, Addie's enthusiasm for furnishing their house took on a new meaning.

She watched steam build on the windows, as the fire put out more heat, and imagined her sister on Will's arm coming down the long stairs into this room. They had a lot of planning to do. She pushed back from her quilt. Mary would certainly invite the women they worked with to win the vote for women. She smiled. That could make for a very interesting and entertaining mix.

The day the furniture arrived to fill the parlor and the single downstairs bedroom, something else arrived. Will and Addie sat in the nearly empty parlor, surrounded by crates. They had a problem.

A letter for Will from Amy Fletcher had come to his office. Addie took the letter Will handed to her and read it.

Dear Will,

   I hope you are all right. I wish I could come see you and talk to you about something. I have just turned 18-years-old. I have lived most of my life—at least the life that I remember—in the care of Reverend Hollister, but I am grown now. I don't have any family in this world but you. Would you let me come to live with you and Addie?

   I like her very much and your little baby, but I want to be with you because you are my brother. I would work very hard doing the things you want me to do if you could please let me stay with you. I would not be any trouble at all.

                                             Your Sister,
                                             Amy Fletcher

Will looked at Addie with a pained expression. "This can't happen."

"We have to do . . . something," Addie said.

"If I bring her here, the illegitimate child of my father by another woman, it would be the biggest insult to my mother."

"Yes. But Will, if you tell her she can't be a part of your life, you will have abandoned her and all that means—just as your father abandoned you."

"What of that big plantation? She owns it. Couldn't she hire someone to work it and maybe stay with her?"

"I don't think that will answer her need. You of all people should understand what she feels and wants. Besides, I can't see her taking the reins to run a big plantation, managing laborers and help, overseeing the financial part."

Will looked at Addie, rocking little Willie and realized that not all women had the mettle of his wife. *Addie Rose Conyers could run a railroad if the need arose*, he mused as he picked up a hammer and began prying crates open. One by one, the pieces filled the parlor and dining room. They worked into the night placing each piece where they wanted it . . . then moving it . . . then replacing it. But this heavy question hung over them: what to do about a young woman who had already been abandoned once.

The next afternoon, after the other lawyers had gone home, Will sat in his office, Addie's words ringing in his ears: ". . . abandoning her to loneliness as your father did to you." Still, he couldn't push her in the face of his mother, his lifelong ally and support—sometimes his only ally.

It was a beautiful April afternoon, with the freshness of spring in the air. Maybe if he walked over and watched the trains arrive and leave, something would come to him.

Will stood outside the old depot, lost in his own thoughts, and then he decided to stop in the Dining Car Café;, maybe order a cup of coffee and some apple pie.

"So you're losing another daughter to marriage?" Will said to Cora Conyers, his mother-in-law.

"Yes, things will be different, but my girls do have a right to their own lives."

Will looked at her curiously, an idea taking shape. "Would you be needing help when Mary leaves? I imagine she will not help so much after she's married,."

"I haven't looked that far, but yes, I will certainly miss her help." Cora seemed thoughtful, a little sad.

"If I found someone to take her place, could she live with you?" Will could hear the eagerness in his own voice. He didn't want to press Cora, but he had to find a solution to this situation with Amy.

"I don't know about that. Who is it? What are you talking about?" Cora sat down at the table opposite Will.

"If I paid her room and board, and she served as your helper here, would you consider it?"

"I'd still have to meet her before I decided on that."

When Will got home, he was bursting with excitement to tell Addie his new idea.

"I think I've worked it out! Amy can live with your mother and help her at the café. With both you and Mary gone, she's going to need help, and we can watch over Amy. My mother never goes to the café."

"But Amy will certainly be at our house sometimes. You know that."

"Yes, but I think this will work out."

Amy Fletcher stepped down from the train onto the wooden platform, gripping her bag in one hand, and a pillowcase sack hung over her other shoulder. Will stood just outside the depot door, filled with doubt, fear, and even guilt. How was he to relate to her, or even care for her, almost a stranger, yet linked by blood?

He walked hesitantly toward her. This was it. No going back. His life would never be the same again. This innocent person, a living presence of his father's betrayal, would be in his life forever.

When she found him, her eyes lit up and she walked briskly toward him, newly adorned, he noticed, with the grace of young womanhood.

"Will, I'm so—" She stopped, tears crowding out her words. She tentatively hugged him. When he stepped back, he saw her smile beaming as tears traced down her cheeks.

"Ah, well, Amy . . . Addie's mother . . . you'll probably be working for her, as I explained in my letter—and living with her."

"Yes." Her eyes widened, questioning. "But I thought I would live with you."

Will picked up her bag, "For now, this might be better." He led her to the door of the Dining Car Café, where Addie and Willie (who was now a toddler) and Cora greeted her.

"This is my mother, Cora Conyers," Addie said, as she embraced the girl. "My sister will soon be married, and Mama needs some help. We hope you are comfortable taking her place. Mama plans to give you my room, with the same bed I shared with my sister. Then you will help out Mama, just as I did."

Amy seemed puzzled at first, then turned to Cora. "I think I would like that. Addie's just next to being my sister." She turned to Willie, "And I'm already an aunt."

"Come on, honey," Cora said, "Let's go in the kitchen. That's where the fun is. Do you know how to make pies?"

"No, we had a housekeeper who did all the cooking. Mrs. Hollister didn't do any of that."

"I'll teach you," Addie said. "And Mary will teach you to make bread. Mama can teach you everything else. She's a good teacher."

Amy turned beseeching eyes on Will. "When will I see you?"

"Almost every day. I work only two blocks from here and I often come here for lunch. Cora takes very good care of me. And besides, I just live across town."

"And up a hill," Addie said.

"You have another house?" Amy asked.

"Yes, you'll see it—in time." Will stumbled over the words, seeing years and years of problems before him.

"This is all very exciting. A family! " Tears brimmed her eyes again.

After they took Amy to Cora Conyers's house, got her settled and started home, Will said, "It is going to be impossible to keep from my mother the fact that Amy is living in this town and who she is."

"Maybe, my dear one, but you did the right thing," Addie patted his hand.

CHAPTER 40

It was a proper day for a wedding. The June morning promised to do its part. Soft summer sunshine and a light balmy breeze flowed through the open windows of the house, which was decorated from stair banister to mantelpieces to windowsills with greenery from the nearby woods. Chairs were neatly lined in rows before the fireplace; the ornate settees and plush chairs now ornamenting the periphery like a gilded picture frame.

When the decorating was done, Addie turned to her sister, "What do you think the guests would say if they knew the last people to sit on these chairs were the despicable suffragettes?"

They both chuckled.

By one in the afternoon, the lane up Cameron Hill was lined with carriages, buggies, surreys and hacks, all delivering guests. Ladies were dressed in their grandest finery, full skirts with draped and folded overskirts, straight skirts with bustles, some with parasols, and all with fans dangling from their wrists.

When the time came and Nellie Bridger began the wedding march, guests left their seats and went to the entrance hall to share the moment of the bride's long walk down the circular stairway on Will's arm. Adorned in her designer silk wedding gown, Mary was a vision, the like of which Amsley had never seen.

After the ceremony, the guests followed the bride and groom to the lawn and found seats at tables, dressed in white linen and arranged before a long serving table overflowing with food, with a cake placed in the center.

By the fourth toast, tongues loosened a bit, and little Jimmy Rodell, who had drunk enough courage, stood up by his table, addressing the crowd: "Andy, you know you married one of them mouthy suffragette women that rode into the deer hunter's camp. You know that? She ain't gonna be no kind of woman for you. You know what I mean. They don't like men."

Will clanged a fork against his goblet. "This is not the place for that, Jimmy. This is a wedding, and you're not going to ruin it." Roy and Alex, Addie' brothers, came quickly to stand beside Will. Then the judge stood.

Mrs. Ethel Burgess rose, "I'm one of those women, and Jimmy, I got eight children."

Lily Marshall stood also. "I'm one and I've been married 43 years."

Nellie Bridger said, "27 years of marriage."

Rodell shrugged. "I'm not sayin' nothin' more, but everybody knows what they are."

"Enough, Jimmy," Will said.

"You're talking about my sister, Rodell," Roy said. "I'm not having it."

So Jimmy Rodell sat down, but he refused to raise a glass for any of the dozen toasts that came afterwards.

Will, seated with Addie at the front table, had a case of nerves. Besides Jimmy Rodell, Addie's mother had brought Amy with her to help serve. Violet knew everyone in town; Will knew she would certainly spot a stranger. What if his mother should ask who she was?

By the time the bride and groom were hustled off into their decorated carriage, Will relaxed a little. His mother hadn't noticed Amy. Sipping a little wine, he watched Mary standing up in the open carriage, throwing her bouquet, and he laughed when he saw who caught it—Nola Fitzgerald.

It appeared the guests were having a good time and wanted the party to go on after the bride and groom left. Most went back to their seats. Will joined his mother and the judge at their table, poured himself another glass of wine and smiled. The first big event in their new house had been a huge success.

Violet turned to him, nodding toward Amy. "Who is that young girl, Will?"

"Someone Cora found to help her. Both her daughters are married now. She needed a helper."

Violet frowned, saying nothing.

The judge stood up, rubbed his forehead. "I think I'll go in; I don't feel well." He looked down at Violet. "You stay on and . . ." With that he grabbed for the back of Violet's chair and fell, collapsing hard across her lap; the wooden chair cracked as the judge's dead weight crushed down on her.

Roy and Alex rushed to the judge, lifted him up, and laid him on the grass under one of the cedar trees. He seemed lifeless. Violet was wrenched with pain and terrified as she looked at her husband. Alex volunteered to get the doctor. Will tried to calm his mother.

"Is he still breathing?" she lisped through her own pain. Willie toddled over and lay down beside his grandmother, but Violet hurt too much to notice.

Roy took the judge's pulse and nodded toward Will.

"We're getting help," Will whispered, holding his mother's hand.

"Where are you hurt?" Addie asked.

"My leg," Violet cried.

"Can you move it?" Cora wanted to know.

She winced, tried and found that she could move, but she cried out in pain.

The doctor finally arrived and went first to the judge, who was flailing his arms about uncontrollably.

While Will, Roy and Alex moved the judge into the house and the downstairs bedroom. Addie went to prepare a makeshift bed on the long settee in the parlor for Violet. Amy came and knelt down by Violet. "Would you like some water, ma'am?"

"Yes, please."

She came back and held a cup to Violet's lips.

"What's your name?" Violet whispered, wincing as she turned away from the cup.

"It's Amy, ma'am."

"You have a southern accent, Amy."

"Yes, ma'am. I grew up in Mississippi."

Violet grimaced as she tried to raise herself up to look at the girl, but couldn't. "Corinth, Mississippi?"

"Yes, I was born there. Do you want some more water?"

"Might you be Amy Fletcher?"

"Why yes, I am. That's just who I am. Here ma'am, they're ready to take you in and get you more comfortable."

Soon after the doctor arrived, he came to Violet and took her hand. "The judge had a stroke, Mrs. Austin, but he is coming around some. Doesn't know where he is or what happened. We'll have to wait to see how he does. Now let's look at you." He determined she had no broken bones, but he said she might have dislocated her hip. "We'll have to wait a couple of days to see how you're coming along."

He turned to Addie. "Put compresses on her hip and I'll give her morphine to sleep. Sleep is a great healer." He looked again at Violet. "I'll see you both tomorrow." He reached for his bag, slapped it closed and touched Addie's shoulder as he left.

In the early greyness of dawn, Violet woke from the foggy haze of morphine. She still ached everywhere. Finally, pale light filled the room and before her, hanging on the wall by the fireplace, was the great picture of Vachel Fletcher looking down on her. His lips seemed to be smiling at her.

"Fletch," she whispered, "I met your daughter yesterday."

CHAPTER 41

The judge recovered from his stroke. He declared he had no memory of how he got to the house or that he had had any problem. Violet used a cane and still complained of pain when she walked. Will had insisted they remain with him and Addie, under their care, but they wanted to go home. Yesterday, Addie had taken them to their own house and enlisted the aid of a home nurse.

Addie felt the quiet of the house. After wedding plans, the wedding itself, the presence of others who needed care, and now waiting out the last days of her pregnancy, she, surprisingly, felt alone. She had received a note from her sister, Mary, that there would be a meeting of the suffragettes at her house. It was a warm August afternoon. Why not go?

Ina Pilcher stood by an old rocker that Mary, the new bride, had brought from her mother's house, a relic from their old Baltimore days. Wearing spectacles and dressed in gray widow's weeds, Ina held a paper in her right hand and addressed the group, which Addie noticed had grown to a sizable number. The women, seated in a circle, were dressed in somber grays and black except Lily Marshall, young Clara Vickery, and Addie, who stood out like bright Christmas decorations.

Mary brought out a pitcher of tea and glasses on a tray. She went back into the kitchen, then returned with another tray, stacked with cookies.

"We have two important things on our agenda." Ina looked over the top of her glasses. "One is local, but the other, I guess you could say, is international. The local is, of course, the Old Settler's Picnic. In the past we have made speeches from the grandstand."

Nellie Bridgers, took three cookies from the tray. "That was not successful. The hecklers ended up cheapening our message."

Lily Marshall, in an ivory-colored dress, heavy talcum on her face, a fan lying across her lap, looked like a ghost had joined the circle. "They make us a sideshow."

The women murmured their agreement. All could remember being ridiculed.

"We could create stations here and there for people to come and talk to us and to sign the petition," Lily suggested.

"Won't work," Jane Carlton shook her head. "We'll have to mingle in the crowd to get these petitions signed."

"I'm sorry to interrupt, but where do those petitions go?" Clara Vickery, perhaps eighteen, with wide, brown eyes and long, copper-colored hair, was a newcomer, Addie surmised.

There was quiet about the room until finally Ina spoke up, "Well, Clara, that's the second thing on the agenda, and it should answer your question."

Addie felt a strange sensation tighten around her girth, but it passed, and she continued listening.

"There are two groups working across the country," Ina explained. "Used to be one, but they split. We need to associate ourselves with one of them, Clara, add names on petitions to add to all the others. It's the only way to have a significant voice."

"The National Woman's Suffrage Association is based in New York," she continued. "It is devoted exclusively to getting the female vote. The other is called the American Woman's Suffrage Association, and it's for universal suffrage, irrespective of race, color or sex."

Addie caught her breath as a sharp pain stabbed through her. She held Willie on her lap with one arm and gripped the chair with her other hand.

"The split was because of the effects of the Civil War," Ina said. "The American Woman's Suffrage Association aims at former slaves getting the votes as well as women, but what it comes down to is black men getting the vote." Pilcher tapped the back of the old rocker with the paper she held. "Women'll still be ignored, black and white."

Ethel Burgess (who, everyone knew, followed Elizabeth Cady Stanton with almost reverent devotion) said, "Mrs. Stanton is a leader with Susan Anthony for the one in New York, the National Woman's Suffrage Movement. We should align with them."

Another pain gripped Addie, and she let Willie slide down from her lap to stand before her. She knew her labor had begun, and she didn't know what to do. Then another harder pain took her breath away. Addie leaned back in her chair and closed her eyes. No one was paying attention. Then another pain came. She gripped the chair arm. *What am I going to do?*

"The New York group wants petitions that will force a bill in the state legislatures," Ina explained. "That's where the petitions come in, Clara. When we have enough states that have passed the bill, it will force Congress to present a bill and vote on a constitutional amendment to give women the vote."

Clara sunk back in her chair. "That sounds like a mammoth amount of work—and it could take years to get there."

"Indeed," Ina said, "but we have decided that this is the generation to carry out the mission."

"I move that we join with the National Woman's Suffrage Association. No matter what has happened in history, it's always women who are left out," Ethel opened her fan, vigorously employing it as if the subject was closed. Jane Carlton seconded.

They voted unanimously for the motion.

"Now let's talk about how to present our case at the picnic," Mary said.

"I have to go home or . . ." Addie cried out. "My baby's coming—faster than the last time with Willie. I'm not sure I can get home."

They all turned to her. Mary came quickly and took her arm. "We'll put you in the bedroom."

Ethel helped Addie to her feet. "I've birthed eight babies myself, sweetie, and helped out with many more. You'll be fine. We'll just get you to Mary's bed and get the doctor."

"And Will," Addie whispered, "and my mother."

In bed, the hard pains locked in and held her time and again, but in the groping maze, she was aware of women coming to her, and Ethel holding her hand, talking to her each time a pain came with words honeyed and soft as a hymn. She heard Will's voice somewhere, saying the doctor was on the way. Then she saw her mother, who kissed her forehead. But the baby was coming. Then Ethel Burgess took over, and Addie gave birth to a baby daughter.

Undaunted by this business of childbirth, Ethel laid the infant across Addie's stomach and looked down at her. "You did *real* good, honey, real good. It's a little girl, and this girl's gonna to vote. You know that, don't you? She was born in a suffragette meeting."

CHAPTER 42

"Who is Otis Tolbert?" Amy asked.

Will sat opposite her, having lunch at the Dining Car Café. "He's a lawyer, an associate like me, in our law firm."

She leaned forward, her expression deadly serious, and lowered her voice. "He doesn't like you."

This was not exactly a surprise to Will. "Oh, and how do you know that?"

"I heard him talking in here to some of the roundhouse men. When I heard your name, I began to pay attention. I don't think he knows who I am." She paused, timid about saying, "your sister."

"He said you want to stand above everybody, that's why you built that big house up on the hill. Oh, Will, he has what Reverend Hollister used to say—a hateful spirit."

Will smiled and cut into a piece of cherry pie. "He thinks I get privileged treatment because the judge started the law offices, and I'm his son. But we know I'm not the judge's son." Will took a drink of coffee and shook his head. "When Otis loses in a trial, he falls back on the idea that he is given unwinnable cases and ranked second fiddle."

"He was very convincing, Will, when he talked to those men."

"He should save his convincing talk for the juries."

Amy toyed with her napkin for a minute, then looked up. "What was our father like? You felt a loss I never did. I never had him to lose, but I wonder sometimes what he was like."

Will decided it was best for Amy to hear the better things he could tell her. Somehow, and surprising himself, he wanted to protect her. Maybe it was akin to protecting the child he once was. "My father was exciting!. He lived a bigger-than-ordinary life, full of ideas and how to make things happen, how to fix things. He could put an entire train locomotive together. Can you imagine that? He made you happy to be around him. He was the light of my life, but he lived for the moment, and I suppose he lost interest in me—and my mother. It's better, Amy, you never knew the joy he could bring and feel the emptiness when it was gone."

"My mother loved him," she answered.

Will nodded. His mother loved him, too. But what did she feel now?

"I know the loneliness, Will. My mother died when I was a child. She left me."

Will felt a warmness growing toward the girl. He reached out and took her hand, a gesture that surprised them both.

"Yes, of course. It was thoughtless of me to say that," he said.

As he watched her, he recognized something. His work had consumed him, been the balm that comforted him, filled his life and affirmed who he was, but Amy could not have that option. Addie would understand this difference very well.

CHAPTER 43

Will woke to a howling gale at the windows, roaring around the corner of his upstairs bedroom. The room was dark except for a few feeble embers in the fireplace and a thin light from a lamp on a table, centered outside the bedroom in the wide hallway. He went across the hall to the nursery, to be sure both children were snug underneath their covers.

Then he peered out the window at the end of the hall. A blizzard raged, piling snow along the outside sill. He stared sleepy-eyed at the two other closed bedroom doors and the steps leading up to a landing, outside the dormer rooms on the third floor.. He realized that, for the first time, he could not go down Cameron Hill to work, a trip that usually took twenty minutes, but today would be—treacherous.

He grabbed a coat and went downstairs to stir embers in fireplaces, add wood and build a fire in the big kitchen cook stove. He opened the front door. Sharp frigid air poured past him.

By midday, the house had warmed throughout, but they all hovered near the cook stove in the kitchen, Carrie in a cradle and Willie playing on the floor. Will decided to go into his office and read up on a case they would be trying in early November.

But as he walked through the hall an idea came to him.

He went to the kitchen and picked up Willie. "Little man, I'm going to show you a little trick." He carried him up the stairs, placed him on the top step, belly down, put his little fingers around the baluster spindles of the stair rail, and showed him how to move down, sliding on his belly one step at a time, changing his hold from one spindle to the next. Will felt the boy tremble under his hand as he began to move slowly down. Close by his side, Will helped with each step. But then the boy began to feel the adventure of moving, slipping over each step, until he was laughing.

Addie hurried into the hall, "What are you doing? He's too little to do stairs. I've been so careful about that."

"No need to be careful now. He knows how to go down without falling."

Willie decided this was great fun and wanted to slide down again, so Will took him to the top of the stairs. "My father taught me to do this," Will called down to Addie. "It works fine if you take time to teach the child how to do it.."

Addie stood, horror in her eyes, hands clutching her throat as she watched her son gleefully slip down the stairway. When he was on the ground floor again, she picked him up and hugged him close, but he twisted out of her arms, wanting to go again.

"No," Addie said, "that's enough!"

When the children were down for their naps, Will came out of his study, went into the kitchen, poured himself a cup of coffee, and sat down at the table where Addie was making raisin pies and persimmon pudding for Ina Pilcher.

" I thought Mary's wedding was especially nice, didn't you?" Will asked.

"It was lovely; everyone said so."

"And everyone remarked on our beautiful house?"

"Yes, Will, they did."

"Why not have Thanksgiving dinner here at our house and invite all of our families, along with the lawyers I work with and their families, too?"

Addie put the three pies in the oven, and turned. "Your mother sitting at the same table with Amy Fletcher?"

"My mother discovered who Amy was before she'd been in Amsley a month. The judge has always had the dinner at his house and even invited the partners and associates," Will continued to push the idea.

"He's not that well now." Addie was thoughtful, then added, "He might appreciate it. At least for this year. And what about Otis Talbot? You say yourself he's no friend," Addie said.

"Oh, most assuredly we'll invite Otis Tolbert."

Addie turned away but Will caught her knowing smile. She was so quick. She saw just the person he was aiming at.

"And if that goes well," he went on. "What about holding an open house before Christmas and invite everyone?"

"Everyone?" Addie turned abruptly after she put the persimmon pudding in the oven.

He looked past her, at the gray, snowy day outside. The cozy smell of baking pies filled the room. "Sure, we'll put an invitation in the paper."

"Really, Will? The whole town?"

"They'll come. They'll want an excuse to come to this house. I see buggies drive up Cameron Hill, slow the horses as they go by, circle and go back down. They'll come and it will be a spectacular. Our house and our party will be on their lips for days. You'll see."

"No doubt about that," Addie sunk down in a chair.

And then they turned, horrified. Willie was standing in the kitchen doorway, up from his nap, his eyes dancing, his face fairly glowing as he pointed to the stairs, "I do."

Will's quiet plan, which he had not really verbalized to Addie, was to make his home known for grand entertaining, like the Campbell house they saw in St. Louis, and this Thanksgiving dinner would be a trial run. He still winced when he thought of the cramped and ungracious meal they had had when he and Addie lived in the little house. That would not happen again. He would never forget Otis Tolbert's dismissive attitude.

Thanksgiving dinner was an enormous success with their families, as well as Oscar Jamison and Clemet Sampson from the firm and their wives. When everyone had gone home, and Addie was upstairs putting the children to bed, Will walked into the parlor. Only the light from the fireplace filled the room as he stood looking at his father's shadowy portrait. "No one could have done better," he whispered. "Not even you."

The only thing . . . Otis Tolbert had not come.

Thoroughly satisfied with the success of Thanksgiving, Will placed an invitation in the paper two weeks before Christmas.

> Mr. and Mrs. William Fletcher would welcome anyone stopping at their home on Cameron Hill for refreshments and holiday cheer, four to eight o'clock in the evening of December 10.

The next day, he and Addie with the children went searching across the two wooded acres on the back of their property for Christmas trees. When they found the right ones, Will notched them for Addie's brothers to come with a wagon and bring them to the house.

Addie made a dozen apple and a dozen cherry pies, as well as long pans of her famous chicken pies. Her mother, Cora Conyers, and sister, Mary, brought in trays of confection delicacies.

When the day came, it was a bright cold winter day with only remnants of snow hugging the roadside. As Will and Addie dressed, he came to face her. "Addie, there's one thing I must say. There'll be people here of all opinions, people you don't agree with and don't agree with you. Please do not start on that woman thing and please, please do not cuss at anyone."

"I will not change my opinions. You know that, but I'll hold my tongue for you—for tonight."

He had been right—everyone came: from the preacher to Will's law partners; the farmers from whom Addie's brothers bought meat and produce to supply the Dining Car Café; people from Amsley and the countryside. Will had made a point to invite the sheriff and all the deer hunters Addie had insulted, to show there were no unaffectionate feelings remaining between his wife and the hunters.

The house, which always seemed so spacious, was packed with guests freely imbibing cider and wine while jostling plates filled with food, for which the Conyers family was famous. Above the din, Nola Fitzgerald sang carols with Nelle Bridger pounding away at the piano. Finally, Will caught sight of Otis Tolbert moving through the room. Will tapped Addie on the shoulder and they hurried to him. "Glad you could make it, Otis," Will put out his hand.

"This is quite a place you've built for yourself, Fletcher." He finally clasped Will's hand and smiled. But there was no smile in his eyes. "Looks like half the county is here. You planning to run for political office?"

"Nothing like that. I just want to share my good fortune with friends and see them having a good time on this happy season."

Addie studied Tolbert. There was pettiness about Tolbert, envious of Will's talents and prosperity.

"Well, now that you're here," Will said, "the party can really begin." He turned to Addie. "Have Sarah bring the children down. We'll be lighting the candles on the trees."

"Looks like you have everything just about perfect, Fletcher," Tolbert said, after Addie left. "A pretty wife, a grand home, a son and a daughter, success in your father's law firm."

Will ignored him, as Addie and Sarah brought Willie and baby Carrie to join the party. Willie thoroughly enjoyed being picked up and passed from one guest to another, the center of attention. Carrie was more interested in lights than people.

Will called everyone who could find a place to stand to crowd into the parlor while he and Addie lit each of the two trees with three-dozen candles. When it was done everyone clapped, including Willie.

Will called them into the hall to show off his son's new found ability to pull himself up the stairs as well as slide down. The guests watched. Then finally at the top of the stairs, Will picked up his son and told him to wave goodnight before he was taken off to bed.

Before Will came back to the party, Nola was leading them in singing "The Holly and The Ivy" and "Deck the Halls." The candles would burn for only an hour before being extinguished. Guests stayed on, however, as Nellie and Nola livened the party with "Rollicking Band of Pirates, We," the new Ragtime music, with Christmas carols mixed in occasionally. Finally, at 1:30 in the morning, Will and Addie closed the door on the last of the guests.

Addie, exhausted and ready to drop into bed, hurried up the stairs, and checked the nursery. Carrie was sleeping soundly. Then she went to Willie's room.

He was gone!

She thought he was hiding from her and played along, expecting him to giggle and jump out, trying to surprise her—a game they often played. She looked in all of the upstairs bedrooms—still nothing.

"Will, where is Willie?" Then she heard a muffled cry coming from somewhere up the third-floor stairs—to the unfinished rooms. And she saw him. Lying on the landing. Eyes wide in terror, trying to cry but gagging, arms reaching for her, for her to help. "Willie, baby, what is it?"

He was gasping and convulsing, his lips were blue and beginning to bloat. His mouth was open, but no words came out. She put her fingers down his throat to make him heave up what he had swallowed. "Willie, what did you put in your mouth?" But she saw it. He had found the pan with carbolic acid the workers were using to clean windowsills in the unfinished dormer rooms.

"Will, go for the doctor," she screamed. "His face is swelling,"

She watched in anguish as his face bloated and he kept trying to cry out, but only choking sounds came from his throat. His eyes spoke the fear and pain he was feeling.

When Will arrived with the doctor, little Willie had lost his fight. He lay lifeless on their bed. "Oh, my God," Addie sobbed lying beside him, "Oh, my God! No, no. This can't happen. My darling little man." She hugged him desperately to her. "It can't be. This can't be." She looked helplessly at the doctor. "He was alive and playful a few hours ago and . . ." She choked on the word.

Carrie in her crib was shrieking, feeling something had gone fearfully wrong in her safe little world. Will, tears streaming down his face, brought the baby to her mother, who held both her children to her, unwilling to give them up, not the live one, not the dead one.

Will threw himself on the bed, put his arms about his wife holding their two babies. Their babies, their own little world, had fallen horribly to pieces in just hours.

The clock downstairs chimed four times. It was the middle of the night, he sensed, but time now had slowed, flowing endlessly, apart from anything real. At the wide window, the night was black, the world sleeping, their ordered lives untouched.

Finally, Addie gave the baby to the doctor and carried Willie, limp in her arms, down the stairs. Carrie was still crying, but her mother hardly noticed. Addie laid Willie on the kitchen table, as she would some object she would later take to the basement. She sat down by her dead son, staring at him, stunned and paralyzed of thought. She was outside herself, in a strange, surreal place. Across from her, Will's head was buried in his arms on the table, his shoulders heaving.

She looked at the tiny body before her, unseeing, unfeeling, her tears drying. She shook her head. Her children were upstairs in their rooms asleep. Will was at his office and this before her had nothing to do with her—a feverish nightmare.

The funeral was a thing that progressed seemingly on its own. Distantly, Addie noticed Will, a person overwrought and broken. She sleepwalked through it, a body present but a spirit frozen.

CHAPTER 44

They came back to the house after the burial. Will sank down into
a chair before the fireplace, too heartsick to talk. Behind him,
Cora Conyers, Addie's sister, Mary, her husband, and Violet talked
low, but he didn't hear what they said. Didn't care to hear. Addie had
gone upstairs to bed, he assumed. It was stunning. Willie gone. He
couldn't get his mind around it.

Addie came to the parlor, stood before him, eyes red, and hair
streaming wildly about her face. Thank God for Addie. He couldn't
stand this without her.

"I will not live in this house!" Addie screamed like a madwoman.
"If we'd stayed in the little one, we would have our Willie."

"Addie . . ."

"This *damned* house murdered my son! I hate this house! I hate
you for building it!" She shook with rage.

"Addie," her mother came to her. "You're not yourself. You can't
say such things to Will. He's hurting . . . "

She pushed her mother aside, staring down at Will. "My baby is
lying in the ground, in the cold ground tonight, in a dark box because
of this cruel house."

Will stood and reached for her, knowing this was not really Addie, but she turned on him, pounded on his chest, her eyes glaring hatred.

"You had to have this grand, showy place. Are you happy now?" she cried.

"Addie . . . I wanted this place for all of us—Willie, too."

"I want to hit something," she ran fingers through her disheveled hair. "I want to beat something, the walls, the chairs, all of it . . . I want my baby back! I want Willie back. It was your house that took him, Will Fletcher."

"Addie," her mother held her. "You don't realize what you're saying. He was Will's son, too. He's grieving. Don't do this to him."

He felt Violet's arms around his shoulders and her lips touch his forehead.

Addie ignored her mother. "If you want to live with me, I will be in the little house where we started. I will not stay here. Everywhere I look I see Willie's little face. I simply can't stand it!"

He watched, helpless and defeated, as Addie brought things downstairs she would need for her and the baby.

"If you're determined to go," Andy, Mary's husband, said, "I'll hitch up a horse and Mary and I'll go with you. Start a fire."

Will went to the front door wanting to stop her. "You're taking my other child, Addie," he cried out. "Do you understand what you're doing? Can you do that to me?"

Carrie was whimpering in the bassinet that sat by the front door. Addie picked it up, opened the door and turned to Will. "You have your house."

He sat in a chair he had once been so proud to place in the entrance hall, hearing again the terrible resounding vibration of the front door closing on him. Tears dropped on the jacket he still wore from the funeral.

Finally, he went back to his place beside the firelight.

Had it only been two days ago this nightmare had begun? Two days from hell. He had lost his son, now his wife and daughter, and the house he once loved left him with ashes in his mouth.

Why, he thought, when he glanced up at the portrait of his father, must he always lose what he loved? The gods seemed forever ready to snatch away what he wanted most to hold.

Addie, back in the old house, sat down on the bed where she and Will had begun their life together, where Willie had been conceived. She lay back, fell into a deep well of sorrow, and shut out the world. The next day, Cora Conyers slipped into Addie's room, where her daughter lay in the dark, unwilling to talk to anyone. She gathered her up in her arms and held her close and whispered, "You must eat something, and Addie, remember you have another child."

"I know, Mama."

"I'll fix you something." Cora soothed her daughter's tangled hair.

"I don't want anything."

But Cora left her and soon the little house was filled with the aroma of fried ham, biscuits and brewed coffee. Addie came into the kitchen, shoved her hair off her face and slumped into a chair. "Your cooking always smells so good, Mama."

"First, you eat, my darling girl, then we'll talk." Cora put a plate of food before her and sat down with her own.

"It tastes good," Addie bit off a piece of biscuit. "Don't remember eating much. I feed Carrie, rock her to sleep, and go back into the room. The comfort of darkness."

"Addie," Cora began, fondling the handle of a hot cup of coffee, "can you say that the house in Baltimore where we lived was responsible for your father's death? He fell down the stairs. It was a tragic accident." She reached across the table and held her daughter's hand. "And so is this. Will did not cause Willie's death." She spoke soothingly. "No one did."

"He taught Willie how to negotiate stairs."

"He taught him that to save him from falling down the stairs. It was a terrible accident. An accident. Will is heartbroken."

Addie Rose looked at her mother, a woman who worked long hours, raising four children alone. Her mother could be angry, had the right to be—*should* be, but she wasn't. Addie studied her with a new awareness, that of a mother now, an adult herself, and felt overwhelming love for a woman she felt was almost a saint.

"It's Will's showplace!" She spit out. She was not her mother, and she knew it.

The next day Cora Conyers drove her horse and buggy up Cameron Hill. When Will opened the door, he stood before her, haggard and somber. She read the question in his eyes: Why had she come?

"I brought you some chicken dumplings and bread just out of the oven." He nodded and took the basket. She followed him into the kitchen.

"I want to talk to you, Will." She opened the basket and began to set the food out on the table while she talked. "You may not believe me when I tell you this, but Addie needs you. She *is* stubborn; how well I know that. But I know she needs you."

"I don't think so." He shook his head, turned and walked into the parlor.

Cora followed him. "She wanted to strike out at something. Someone. That's not our Addie. You know that." Cora had never seen him so defeated. "And I think you need her, too." She was not exactly certain where she was going with this. "Maybe," she added.

He stared down into the fireplace. "She blames me for our Willie's . . . How can I ever get through that? I don't think she ever wants to see me."

"But she does. Gather up some things, Will, and go with me. Wouldn't you like to see Carrie?"

Will followed as Cora opened the door to the little house where Addie had retreated. Addie Rose looked surprised when she saw him, but quickly averted her eyes.

"I came to see Carrie," he added quickly. He had felt awkward and unwanted many times in his life, but never so much as now.

Addie, hunched inside a shawl she hugged about her, stared down at the floor. "The baby's awake in the crib."

He brought Carrie out into the room and held the baby to him as he rocked her. Cora sat with Addie across from him.

Cora disappeared into the kitchen and, soon, smells filled the little house with the warmth of a home.

Finally he decided to say it. To risk saying it. "I want to stay here, Addie."

"The house belongs to you," she snapped. "I can't stop you."

"That's not the point." The baby squirmed in his arms. "You can refuse."

"It's your house. I don't care, one way or the other."

"I'll make my nest there on that couch. I won't intrude, Addie, I promise you that. And I'll be gone mostly . . . at work. But Carrie's mine . . ."

"I know. I know."

Cora bustled into the living room as if she were at the Dining Car Café. "I have prepared food for you . . . either of you, in case you get hungry. I'll stop by tomorrow, Addie. Help you with Carrie." She glanced at Will as she took her leave.

Will gazed at the closed door, wondering if he, too, should go, but it was warm and comforting here and going to the house on Cameron Hill would be unbearably silent.

The next day, in the gray, rainy afternoon, Will sat in a rocker in the little cottage they had lived in when they were first married, numb to the world around him, tears coming from time to time. Addie lay in her bed, seemingly unaware of anything but the abysmal emptiness and grief he knew she felt. He was roused from his lethargy when a knock came to the front door. He answered it, and found two women standing under umbrellas as rain poured down over them.

"Please come in," he welcomed them, thinking they had come as some sort of mission of comfort. "How kind of you to come and on such a bad day." He ushered them into the parlor. He knew them both, Bonnie Winchester and Martha Wilson. He had been in school with Martha's son. "Let me get you some coffee. Warm you up."

"No, thank you." Martha was wrapped in a dark green cape with fur trim around the collar that she held tightly around her. She sat primly on the edge of her chair. Bonnie wore a black slicker and kept it buttoned up as well, even though the flames in the fireplace kept the room warm. Both women wore their hair parted in the middle in the style of Mrs. Lincoln. "We have come especially to see Addie Rose," Martha said.

"But you are welcome to hear what we have to say," Bonnie added.

"I'll get my wife."

After they were seated, coffee poured, Addie came in to join them, and Will retired to the bedroom, but left the door open.

They immediately stated their business. "We are women, and there are many others, who have talked of your behavior, your unseemly behavior . . ." Martha's voice was crisp.

"Unwomanly," Bonnie chimed in.

"We have watched you with disgust as you flaunted yourself and screamed and even cussed at menfolk," Martha continued. "That baby child was taken from you for a reason, Addie Rose Conyers. You may not see it, being as brazen as you are, but the rest of us do. That child was taken from you as a penance for your actions and your insults to good women and mothers who know their place."

"Going out among men," Bonnie picked up the gauntlet, "wanting to have rights that have always been theirs. Showing yourself when you were with child, disgracing yourself and shaming your fine family. Didn't you think there would be retribution for that?"

Addie gasped and fled into the bedroom; her eyes wide, horror-stricken.

Will went past her into the parlor. "You are to leave this house now, this very minute, and never come back or speak to my wife in that way again!" he shouted.

But they didn't move.

"We are very tender now; our hearts are aching, and you come here with your cruel remarks. Addie only spoke for what she thinks is right—and I agree with her. Our baby died because of a terrible accident, something no one . . ." Words stuck in his throat, tears poured down his cheeks. "We are heartsick. Can't you understand that? You sit there in your vicious judgment. Take your things and leave now!"

They stared at him, stunned, unmoving, a puzzled look on their faces, apparently assuming he would understand them.

"*Get out*, I said!"

Finally they reached for their purses. Will went to the door, opened it and held it for them to get their umbrellas open.

"Just so you know, I think my wife," he said, as they stepped over the threshold, "is the straightest-thinking person I've ever met."

Once the door closed, Addie came out of the bedroom. For an instant they looked at each other, both crying. Then she ran to Will and into his arms. They stood holding each other, anguished, tears streaming down their cheeks. Addie laid her head on his shoulder. "Thank you," she whispered.

As he looked past her into the little kitchen, holding her warmth against him, he knew they would go on. A little of the old joy flooded his heart. And he knew, too, that nothing else that might happen to them could be worse than this, losing their little Willie.

CHAPTER 45

It was incomprehensible to Will that life outside the sorrowing little world he and Addie lived in, went on as usual. But winter began to fade into brisk spring days.

One morning in March, when he had just started his day's work, Clemet Sampson brought in a woman, highly agitated, and seated her across from Will's desk.

"Mrs. Eckert, this is Will Fletcher, and I believe he's the lawyer that could do the best for you." Clemet glanced at Will. "Sadie Eckert has come to us. Her husband needs representation. She'll tell you what she needs."

"My man's been accused of murdering two people." She was almost too jittery to sit still in her seat. "They come early while we was still abed and took 'im off to jail. He never done such a thing! You got to help him. I jist don't know which way to turn." Sadie Eckert hugged hard a brown shawl pulled around her shoulders. Her dark hair fell loosely about her face, a face that might have been pleasing to look at once, before work and worry had worn away its beauty.

Will looked passed her to Clemet.

"A little over a year ago," Clemet began, "two girls went missing, just disappeared. We all remember it. One of the deer hunters was out with his dog yesterday morning, and the dog began to sniff around in a spot with an indentation in the ground. Then he growled and pawed at the dirt until the hunter started to pay close attention. He knew something must be down there. He went home, got a shovel, and discovered one of the girls in a shallow grave. He and the dog found the other one close by. Both had been shot."

With that, Sadie Eckert began to wail hysterically, "He never done it!" She clasped her hands together as if begging, looking to Will. "He ain't got murder in him." Tears streamed down her gaunt face. "What if they find him guilty, take 'im away and kill 'im? You have to help us," she pleaded. "I am just so scared, Mr. Will." She buried her face in her hands. "Oh, God, help me."

"Why did they come for your husband, Mrs. Eckert?" Will asked.

She sat, hands over her face, shaking her head, saying nothing. Black crescents of dirt lodged under each fingernail.

Clemet put his hand on Sadie's shoulder, "Why don't you wait in my office. Try not to worry too much; we'll do all we can to take care of you and your husband. There's no proof of anything yet." He escorted her out of Will's office, but Clemet soon came back and sat in the chair Sadie had vacated.

"When the girls went missing, there was a lot of gossip among the neighbors on the farms that one of the girls was involved with a Delmar Eckert. Sadie is his common law wife. He has a number of children by her, but was apparently carrying on an affair with a young neighbor girl, Pansy Ross, and some said, her friend Pearl Bennett."

Clemet paused to seemingly organize his thoughts. "Since those who knew him cordially disliked Eckert, he was accused of some kind of foul play in regard to the girls' disappearance. He denied having any knowledge of their whereabouts. Pansy's father didn't know much about it. Said he thought she'd been trying to get away from Eckert, but Eckert had continued to harass her. Still, it was just gossip and nothing came of it. Just suspicion."

Will looked up at Clemet. "And you want me to take this case? Eckert looks guilty as sin to me. A revenge killing—a rejected, obsessive lover."

"He deserves counsel," Clemet insisted.

"Do you think I am ready to try a double murder, Clemet?"

"I do, Will. It won't be easy."

"You're right about that. Looks like a loser to me."

"Maybe, maybe not. With this case, you'll test yourself. You'll never know what you got in you until you move into the fray."

Will shrugged. "All right, I'll take it. I guess I should say 'thanks' for throwing a big case my way."

"We'll see about the thanks later on. There's a lot of anger out there over these murders. Might get kinda testy."

After Sadie left, Will decided to go to the jail and meet the primary suspect in the case—and his new client. The jail, a red, brick building that had once been a house, provided an apartment on the second floor for the sheriff and his family. Sheriff Eckles ushered Will through two cluttered offices on the ground floor, down a hallway, into a large room, divided into holding cells. Only one was occupied. Delmar Eckert.

He was a short, square man, in his late forties, Will judged. Eckert was stretched out on a cot, arms over his head. When Eckles and Will approached the cell, he sat up immediately.

"You that lawyer Sadie got?"

"I'm Will Fletcher, and yes, I'm to represent you."

"I never done it. Never killed nobody—ever, and that's the God's honest truth."

"I'll just leave you two to talk," Eckles said, and disappeared down the hallway.

Will drew a chair up and sat down outside the cell. "I want you to tell me what you know about the murders and what you know about these two girls. Anything."

"I don't know a thing. Only knowed them by sight. That's all—and just one of 'em. Didn't know the other 't all. The Lord strike me dead right here if I'm lyin'." He put his hand over his heart.

"You'd better not lie to me if you want me to have all I need to get you off of this charge. Remember that. No lying," Will leaned forward trying to make eye contact with Delmar Eckert.

"I ain't no more involved in them murders than you are. Don't know a thing."

"Now let's back up a bit, Delmar. I think you did know the girl, Pansy. Quite a few people have said you had a relationship with her. Maybe you're not remembering everything, a little scared now. Memory, a little fuzzy. You want to try it again?"

Eckert rubbed his hand across his mouth and stared down at the floor. Finally he did look up and faced Will. "I'm gonna tell you how it was. She was always fiestin' around me—like she had, you know, kindy a yen for me. Weren't none o' my doin', her comin' after me. Folks saw it and thought . . . well, they saw it wrong. She was just a flirty kid to me. I never paid her no mind. I got Sadie and the young'uns, you see."

"Yes, there's Sadie." Will stood and looked him over. "I'm just getting started, Mr. Eckert. We'll be talking quite a bit. Need to speak to some others."

"Them folks that are sayin' I killed Pansy . . . or whatever her name was . . . you can't believe all that. They full of gossip. You're my mouthpiece, *you* gotta believe me. I never done it."

Will reached through the bars to shake Eckert's hand, which caught him off guard, but awkwardly he fumbled for a handshake. "We'll have to sort out the gossip from the facts, Mr. Eckert. If you remember something that happened to have slipped your mind today, be sure and tell me when I come back."

"Sure. Sure thing, Mr. Fletcher."

Will walked through town, out to the railroad tracks and the depot. As he passed the Dining Car Café, he smelled Cora's cooking and it occurred to him he should stop in and see Amy when he finished at the Roundhouse. But if he needed to know the town gossip, he decided the railroad men were as good a place to start as any.

The Baltimore and Ohio Railroad Roundhouse was a massive expanse of a building, with a single track leading into it and two locomotives back-to-back were in for overhaul. A half-dozen or so men worked on one, and a couple of men were bent over a long work bench along the west wall, engine parts spread out before them.

Henry Hoskins, the foreman for the B. and O. Roundhouse, came forward to meet Will and held out his grimy hand. "Will Fletcher, what brings you here?"

"I'm Delmar Eckert's attorney." Will caught a flicker of what could be amusement in Hoskins' eyes, and then it quickly passed. "I'm working on that double murder. Been some talk and it led me here. Seems the railroad men knew of Eckert and one of the murdered girls."

Hoskins smiled, nodded then called back to the workers. "Mr. Fletcher, here, wants to hear what you might know about Delmar Eckert and the murder of them girls."

The men ambled over, stood about in a loose circle, curious but guarded, lawyers being an unusual commodity in their lives.

"Eckert's my client." Will tried to break the ice. "I'm sure you've heard the girls were just recently found—murdered. Eckert says he barely knew the one named Pansy and didn't know the other one at all."

The men laughed, but were still unresponsive. Hoskins pulled his cap off, scratched the back of his neck, a little smile playing on his lips. "You need to speak up, men, say what you know."

"Well," Omar Burton began. "He knew Pansy well enough to get her half drunk, bring her in here Saturday nights, after the men's payday. He'd prostitute her. Took a dollar from us to get at her."

The others were stone-faced, evasive, some looking out the grimy east window, apparently cautious about speaking up.

"Anybody else gonna tell what they know?" Hoskins prodded.

Clint Russell nodded but avoided looking at Will. "That's what he done. Used her ever' Saturday night. We all know it." Then Russell punched Rob Stuart's arm. "Ain't that right, Rob?"

"Russell ought to know. I saw 'em in line," Rob answered.

"Yeah, right there along with you."

They all began to laugh.

"Eckert's lyin' to you, Mr. Fletcher," Hoskins said. "He knew that girl Pansy and he used her and murdered her. We all think so. He's a piece a scum, that one."

The men murmured their agreement.

"I heard that the girl Pansy was trying to get shut of 'im but she couldn't," Hoskins said. "Thought he owned her. You know, fixated like. But I can't say about the other girl. Never saw her."

Will thanked the men for their time and left. His spirit plummeted. He had his first big case, a double murder, and he was going to lose it. Eckert was rotten. A jury would hate him, guilty or not, and they'd hang him. He hated him, too, and he sure looked guilty. No wonder Clemet wanted to dump the case on him.

As Will left the Dining Car Café, it occurred to him that it would be of value to talk to the girls' parents. Maybe he'd go out there tomorrow and find out about Pansy's life. As it happened, however, when he got back to his office, a very impatient and irate Virgil Bennett was in the waiting room, the father of Pearl, the other murdered girl.

He stood as soon as Will came in and confronted him. "I come here to see who's prosecuting that Eckert and I find out your *defending* the bastard!"

"I'm his lawyer," Will answered. "I'd planned to pay you a visit tomorrow. Let's talk in my office." He motioned down the hall.

"You're not gettin' nothin' from me to help that man. He murdered my little girl," Bennett spit out as he sat down across from Will. "You better see to it he hangs."

"Why don't you tell me what you know about Pansy and your daughter? And the best you can about what they were doing before their disappearance?" Will leaned back in his chair, his fingers making a steeple over his lips, waiting for Bennett's story.

"Well, Pearlie mostly lived with her ma and me, but sometimes she works for people." Bennett pulled off his cap and put it in his lap. "She'd been workin' for that rich old lady, McKee, in town. Old lady's in a wheelchair and got to be waited on. Pearlie's been livin' in there with her."

Will nodded. If Eckert had such a hold on Pansy and maybe Pearl, how could the parents not know? "And Pansy? What about her?" Will prodded.

"Pansy's ma died about five years ago. There was four young'uns. The oldest boy, he run off. Joe Ross, Pansy's old man, farmed out the two young ones to some kin down in Missouri. Kept Pansy to keep his house."

"So she had a father around?" Will pulled a paper over before him and made a couple of notes.

"Yeah, you could say that I guess, but he's an oddity. Off to hisself. I reckon Pansy went her own way when she wanted to."

Will was getting the picture. The girls were perfect prey for the likes of Delmar Eckert.

"He killed my Pearl and that Pansy, sure as I'm sittin' here, and there ain't no way in hell you're gonna get him off and I'm sayin' you better not."

"You suggesting I lose the case—on purpose?"

"I'm just tellin' you, he's gonna pay one way or the other."

"That's a threat, Mr. Bennett. I think our conversation has come to an end." Will abruptly stood. Bennett took the cue, slapped his cap on, and started to leave but turned in the doorway. "I'm just tellin' you, Fletcher . . . you know what I said."

"It'll be hard to forget." Will pushed his chair back, ready to walk Bennett out if he didn't leave on his own.

On the way home, Will stopped off to see Flora McKee, the "rich old lady" Bennett said his daughter worked for, and as it happened, a longtime friend of his mother's.

"Will," Flora said, when he was ushered into her parlor by the latest hired girl. "What a surprise. Would you like a cup of tea or coffee, maybe?"

"No, no, Mrs. McKee, don't trouble yourself." She sat in her wheelchair, hair snowy white, lap robe warming her knees. He had known her all his life. "I wondered what you could tell me about Pearl Bennett, the girl who worked for you."

"You're on that Eckert case!" Flora McKee said. "That's all the talk everywhere—newspapers, too. Town's got him guilty, hung and buried, and the trial hasn't started."

"That's true." Will found a chair and sat down.

Mrs. McKee smoothed the quilt across her lap. "Delmar Eckert did come to the house sometimes and Pearl went out and talked to him. He always stayed on the porch. Are you sure you wouldn't want a cup of tea, Will?"

"No, I really need to get home."

"Pearl used to say it was her beau when I chided her. Once he came and she said they'd broken up and she wanted him to leave her alone. I was heartsick when I heard what happened to her. That fine young girl, her whole life before her. I didn't have a minute's trouble with her."

Will kissed Flora McKee on the forehead. "Thank you, my dear lady. Do you think you could testify if I called you?"

"Well, of course, if you need me, but I can't help you much with that Eckert."

Will immersed himself in the case, taking apart each element, each detail, and studying it until he knew what every possible answer or explanation could be, but his old doubts began to plague him. He lost sleep. Addie was no comfort; she believed Eckert was guilty, believed the jury would hang him and that Will had made a mistake by taking the case.

He rode up Cameron Hill, to their house that now sat vacant. He unlocked the door and, immediately, unbidden images of Willie confronted him. He sat by the cold fireplace under the portrait of his father. But for the first time it came to him; he was on his own journey and whatever his father had done, it had nothing to do with him. It put iron in him.

The trial was set for May 6, four weeks after the preliminary hearing, at the courthouse in Sutton's Point, the county seat, and eight miles north of Amsley. Will arrived early and found the big grassy square on which sat the massive two-story, wooden courthouse, lined on all four sides with buggies, wagons, and carriages. The lobby outside the courtroom teemed with people waiting for the show. *Half the county must be here,* Will thought. He slipped in through a side door and took the place where he had been seated when they had empaneled the jury.

Courtroom doors opened behind him, and the crowd flooded in, filling every seat.

The case had caught attention far beyond the newspaper at Amsley. Reporters were here from Cairo, Paducah, Springfield, Chicago and St. Louis. The case had it all: discovered bodies, sex, betrayal, prostitution, murder, and a defendant easy to loathe. Reporters and their readers were bloodthirsty for the kill.

Delmar Eckert had been brought to the courthouse on horseback from Amsley, with three armed guards riding on each side of him. He was led in and seated by Will.

District Attorney Jackie "Honey" Linwood, a forty-year court-room veteran, headed the prosecution. Will had seen him in action. He got his nickname from his honeyed Georgia accent, and he knew how to woo a jury with it.

Ole "Honey" first called to the stand Henry Hoskins, foreman of the Baltimore and Ohio Roundhouse who testified about Eckert's nefarious pimping business using the murdered girl, Pansy.

Will was on his feet, "That is irrelevant and overly prejudicial."

The judge was quick to overrule him.

On cross, Will asked Hoskins the first of two questions, "Do you believe Delmar Eckert murdered those girls?"

"Objection. Calls for speculation." Linwood drawled.

"He can answer," Judge Jacobson responded.

Hoskins answered that he did, and then Will asked the second question. "Isn't it true you never saw him wield the alleged murder weapon?"

"Well, it ain't so much that. It's just like him. He ain't no good."

"Mr. Hoskins, you have no personal knowledge of Mr. Eckert using the weapon, so you have not personally witnessed anything involving the murder of the girls. Correct?"

"Well, no, but . . ."

"Thank you, Mr. Hoskins."

Hoskins was followed by a parade of prosecution witnesses, mostly railroaders, and to a man, they backed Hoskins testimony.

Honey called Virgil Bennett, father of one of the murdered girls, whom everyone knew was itching for the kill. Honey knew it would pump up the drama.

Again, under cross, Will asked each one the same two questions he had asked Hoskins, and even with Virgil Bennett he got similar answers.

Finally the prosecution rested its case.

Will called Sadie Eckert to the stand.

Every eye was on the forlorn little woman, wearing her black

Sunday dress as she walked slowly to the witness chair. Timidly she looked out at the crowd, then down at Delmar Eckert, and lowered her head. As she was sworn in, not a sound was heard throughout the courtroom.

Will was nervous. This testimony would be crucial. Sympathy was with her. He must go gently with this one. Reporters were poised to start writing.

"Did your husband drink, Mrs. Eckert?"

"Yes."

"Much?'

"Pretty often. Yes."

"Did he get violent when he drank?" Will asked.

He held his breath waiting for what could be, from Sadie, a damning statement.

"No, he jist got quieter and quieter when he was a-drinkin'."

Relief melted down through Will.

"Was he ever violent with you or the children? In any way?"

Sadie lowered her head and said nothing for a long moment. Will's heart quickened. This was key testimony. She looked out into the courtroom, centered on Delmar, and finally answered softly, "He never was like that."

"Thank you, Mrs. Eckert."

Honey Linwood was kind, too, but soon his questions became probing. "Mrs. Eckert, we all 'preciate you comin' here at such a hard time. But evidence of your husband's character would indicate he had a propensity for violence, does it not? It is a relevant negative character trait, is it not?"

Will was on his feet. "Your Honor, I object."

"Let the witness answer, counselor," Judge Jacobson admonished.

She repeated that her husband was never violent, and she said she didn't know anything about what her husband did on the nights when he left the house.

Reporters were madly scribbling every word.

Sadie was excused. As she walked down the aisle to the door, she looked neither right nor left, nor was there even a rustle of paper to break the silence.

Will was exuberant. Her testimony was the most believable, most valuable, and thankfully not damaging.

After Honey gave his closing arguments, it was Will's turn.

"The prosecution has done a most excellent job in one area: They have painted a graphic picture of a man with a flawed character. Eckert has freely admitted to all they have said, but not murder. They have showed Eckert as a user and abuser, a man who betrayed his wife, a man who likes his drink and his women. But at no time or place was he ever seen by anyone to be violent.

"Delmar Eckert is not being tried for his character. He is being tried for murder, the violent and horrendous act of murder, of robbing two young women of their right to live out their lives.

"The prosecution has *proven* nothing.

"What actually links Delmar Eckert to the murder of those two girls? No evidence whatsoever exists. It's precisely the fact that they have no evidence to link him to the murders that they have filled this courtroom with bluster and rhetoric, a smokescreen showing off Eckert's flaws and shortcomings. Most would agree, his behavior is despicable. But despicable or not, it is a fact separate and apart from what he's charged with—the violent act of murder. No evidence exists to prove he is guilty because he didn't do it.

"The prosecution has *proven* nothing."

As he talked, Will kept his eyes on members of the jury. Some were intent on his every word, some took notes, some glared at Eckert with unabashed hatred. They despised the man. Will did, too, but he had come to doubt that Delmar Eckert had in him the hard grit to kill.

He continued his closing: "His wife said he is not violent. She said when he was drinking, he becomes quiet." Will's eyes searched the jury. "And Sadie Eckert has every reason to use this opportunity, this very public forum, to seek revenge. But she chose to be . . . truthful.

"The girls were killed, as best can be determined after being so long in the ground, by gunshot. The Eckerts have guns on their farm. All farmers do. When the girls went missing, Delmar Eckert was the immediate suspect. The sheriff searched the farm for the murder weapon, but Mrs. Eckert said none were missing, none were out of their usual place, and nothing she'd seen had blood on it. To date, no murder weapon has been identified. Wouldn't a murderer want to get rid of the instrument of his crime?

"Of all the words and emotions that have filled this courtroom, there are just two facts to remember. Delmar Eckert is not being tried for his character. He is being tried for murder and there is no indisputable evidence to tie Delmar Eckert to this heinous crime.

"Members of the jury, the prosecution has proven nothing."

He turned to the judge. "The defense rests."

The jury was out a day and half, coming back just before lunch on the second day.

The judge looked at the verdict scratched on a piece of paper, and handed it back to the bailiff. The spokesman for the jury stood.

"We, the jury, find the defendant, Delmar Eckert, *not* guilty."

The courtroom erupted into screams for justice. Wadded paper, pens, apple cores, or anything else loose, came flying through the air, raining on Eckert and Will. Newspapermen were writing furiously. The judge pounded the gavel again and again, but the crowd would not calm. They would not have it. Above the gavel, shouting and bedlam, Virgil Bennett screamed, "You killed my girl and you're not gettin' off for it!"

Still the gavel rang out, but to no avail.

The newspapers heralded William Vachel Fletcher, the young lawyer from Amsley, Illinois, as gifted for winning a "not guilty" verdict from a jury when everything pointed to the defendant as guilty. True, there were night riders passing by his house, yelling obscenities, and a window was shattered by a rock at the house on Cameron Hill. But overwhelmingly, the papers had praised him as a talented legal genius who won a case thought to be lost. Letters and telegraph messages came to him, begging for help with other hopeless cases.

Then one day a letter came to his office from Paducah, Kentucky. Standing by his desk, he unfolded it, assuming it was another frightened defendant begging for his help. When he read down the page, his hand trembled.

And he slowly sat down.

CHAPTER 46

To Mr. William Fletcher,
    I saw your name in our newspaper, the Paducah Record. Congratulations on your success. My brother's name was William Vachel Fletcher. Any relation?

Claude Raymond Fletcher

Almost nothing could have lifted Will Fletcher's spirit to a higher precipice, coming off a successful defense in a hopeless murder case, than he now enjoyed—nothing except this. He debated whether to show the letter to his mother, and finally decided she would know if it was a hoax or not.

Violet held it for a long time after she finished reading, then looked up. "This is Fletch's brother." She rubbed two fingers across her forehead. "He and Fletch didn't get along." She handed the letter back. "From what I surmised—Fletch didn't say much about his family—they planned for Fletch to take over the family business. But Fletch had other notions—building railroads and engineering trains. I got the impression Fletch was the favorite son, and when he left, they were angry and hurt. They turned their back on him and he did the same. Fletch did mention once that his brother was going to do what the family told him to do, and take over the company. They're third generation tobacco brokers."

"The wonder of it. Paducah!" Will shook his head, amazed. "Not seventy miles away." Maybe the answer was there. Immediately, hopes soaring, he made plans to go to Paducah.

Will found a long warehouse facing the Ohio River with wide lettering across the top of the second story: FLETCHER AND SONS. He walked through a bay door into the cavernous warehouse. It was partitioned into open stalls filled with tobacco, different names over each stall. At the distant end of the vast warehouse he saw an office, a door with a glass half-top on which was printed "Claude Fletcher." Will came to the door, knocked, and opened it to a cubbyhole of an office.

He extended his hand to the man behind the desk. "I'm William Vachel Fletcher." The man was small of stature, with grey hair and glasses. "I'm here because of your letter. You ask about my relationship with a Vachel Fletcher. You said he's your brother."

Claude Raymond nodded and paused before parsing out, "Yes." He motioned for Will to have a seat.

"I, too, am interested to know if we are talking about the same person and, if so, where he is now," Will added. Both men were hesitant, taking each other's measure.

"Can't help you there. He's been gone a long time from Paducah." Claude Raymond pushed the paper he was working on aside and dropped his pen in an inkwell. "And I'll tell you, not much missed."

"Maybe we're not talking of the same man."

"Perhaps not." He looked across at Will. "I see your name in the papers now and then. You've cut out quite a reputation for yourself."

"Thank you for your kind words. My interest is about the William Vachel Fletcher you know." Will pulled the conversation back to the main purpose. "I believe he's my father."

"My sympathies to you."

Will steeled himself for what might come next.

Claude Raymond stood up, adjusted his glasses and said, as if reluctant to put it in words, "He was my brother."

"'Was'?"

"Gone. Dead, probably. He was a hard drinker. Hurt in the war."

With this, a certainty was beginning to crystallize in Will. "He was a railroad engineer. Left us, my mother and me, before the war. Deserted us."

"Sounds about right." Claude Raymond sat down and leaned back in his swivel chair. "We knew he married some Yankee woman. Vachel was a disappointment to us, heartbreak to Mother. Never could make anything stick. Some people can't, you know. If you're his son, you're apparently not cut from the same cloth."

Will felt the contempt behind his words and trembled. He hoped Claude Raymond didn't notice his breath coming faster. Hearing all this was like an assault—but a familiar picture taking shape. The old heartsickness weighed on him again, but it made him all the more determined to find this man, to know him for himself.

"Father set a lot of store in Vach," Claude Raymond went on, "Mother, too. He was to work with Father and then take it over." He gestured about the warehouse. "It's been good to our family."

Will looked about, trying to memorize what might have been his father's life.

"Was your father infatuated with the railroads?" Claude Raymond questioned.

"Yes."

"Did he work as an engineer on the Southern Illinois Railroad?"

"That's who he worked for when I was a child."

"And he left you?"

"Yes. My mother likes to think he left because of the war and was killed . . ."

"Poor woman." Claude stood and reached for a bowler hat on a nearby rack. "Let's take a ride." He called for one of the men to have a carriage brought around. "I have something to show you. Afterward, I'll show you around the wharf and our business—the business your father couldn't wait to leave and chase his dreams."

They stopped at the edge of a cemetery on a rise above town, overlooking the Ohio River. Claude Raymond walked with a cane and labored a bit as he climbed to a site under a pine tree. It was a plot of ground within wrought iron fencing. He opened the gate and Will followed.

Among other markers, there were three graves, all with tall white markers, rounded at the top—Bonnie Fletcher, Benjamin Fletcher, and James Fletcher.

Will stopped, read each name with their birth and death dates, frowned, and looked at Claude Raymond. "They all died within a few days—a week's span. Who were they?"

"Vach's family—wife and two children. Flu killed them. Russian flu."

Will stared at the markers."My God, another family!" He tried to comprehend what was before his eyes. Stunned, he stopped for a minute, put his hand on a marker to steady himself, to absorb it all. He started to mention Amy and his father's family in Corinth, Mississippi, but decided not to. "Did the influenza take the whole family?"

"Not Vach. The mean ones always survive, don't they? There was a baby girl who survived, too. "

"A girl? Where is she?" Will asked.

"She's here in Paducah. Grown now; married with a child of her own."

"Did he desert her?"

"Not exactly. My wife and I had no children, so we were happy to take the little thing—and Vach wanted to leave."

"And?'

"And he did. We've never heard from him again."

The same story.

"Her name is Frances," Claude Raymond volunteered. "She was a little over a year old when he left. We're the only parents she knows."

Will looked down at the three graves. This was an entire *chapter* in his father's life he never suspected. "You said 'wife.'" Did he . . ." Will hesitated, not sure how to ask. "That is, was there a marriage?"

"Oh, yes, lovely wedding. Bonnie was much younger than Vach. Can't say it was a happy union. Vachel could never quite put away the bottle. And I thought, for some reason, she wasn't the girl for him. Just my opinion."

"And it was after the war, you say?"

"Oh, yes, sometime after the war."

As Will took Claude Raymond's arm and helped him down the long slope, he realized the woman in that grave had lived and died and never knew she was not legally married.

Claude Raymond walked with Will down to the waterfront, where rows and rows of tobacco barrels were lined on a floating pier, proudly showing off the vast business he presided over.

"Could I meet this—Frances?"

"Certainly, I'll take you to her house. And you'll meet Mother, too. She lives with Frances and her family now. Up in years, you know. My father passed away some time back."

They walked up to a white colonnaded house set back off the busy street. Once inside the house, Claude Raymond took him to a small room, a library off the dining room, where a woman sat with a book open across her lap. She had snow-white hair, dressed in black, with a sparkling broach at her throat. Claude Raymond introduced him: "This, Will, is my mother."

She stood up and when she faced him, Will was astounded. She was an older version of Amy, her unknown grandchild from Mississippi. It came to him he was not only looking at *his* grandmother—but Amy's, also. He said nothing. Why should these good people know about Fletch's other family in Corinth.

Then Frances came into the room, and he was speechless. She could have been his twin, but she also resembled Amy.

Claude Raymond leaned close and whispered, "Any doubts now?"

"No—can't say I do."

Frances turned to him and extended her hand. "It's a pleasure to meet you. A famous lawyer. A celebrity here."

"Not quite that. I've been fortunate."

"Talented, I'd say."

Claude Raymond's mother had gone back to her chair. "What brings you to our house?"

"He's following up on a business deal and was intrigued with our common name."

"What is it?" she asked. Bright brown eyes belied the wrinkles in her face.

"Will. That is, it's William Vachel Fletcher."

"Claude, you need not hide why he's here. He looks just like Frances. Vachel told me he was married to a Yankee girl and had a son. I'm betting you're that son?"

"Mother's hard to fool," Claude Raymond said.

"I see that." Will smiled down at her, charmed by her sharp intuitiveness.

"That makes you my grandson," she went on, "in fact, my only grandson. Frances has been my only grandchild."

There was a long awkward silence. What could he say?

"The offspring of Vachel and the Yankee woman." She pronounced.

Was it a question or a statement? It felt as if he should apologize. "It appears so, Mrs. Fletcher."

"Mrs. Fletcher!" She closed her book and put it on a side table. "I'm your grandmother, William Vachel Fletcher. Come sit closer so I can get to know you. You did turn out to be a fine-looking man."

He pulled a chair near her, and she took his hand.

"My only grandson," she repeated.

Will looked into those quick dark eyes.

He had found Fletch's mother.

CHAPTER 47

In the rail car going home, Will was lost in himself, hardly noticing the boisterous family seated across from him. Lush green countryside seemed to roll by outside his window; and with each stop, passengers hurried to get off as new ones came on. This haze of activity played out before him like a stage play.

The trip to Paducah had been more than he ever expected; meeting Fletch's family, his new family, a family of tradition and success. Meeting them had enlarged his life, enriched it. Will had only known distant grandparents in Pennsylvania, his mother's family, he'd seen only twice. But the whole episode in Paducah had been sharply painful. Another family! Another child left behind and still no clue where William Vachel Fletcher was now. Was he even alive?

Besides trying to absorb all he had learned, another question plagued him: What should he tell his mother? She knew he went to see Fletch's brother, Claude Raymond, but how could he tell her that her husband had not only produced a third family; he had actually "married" the other woman. Each time Will came back, with more information fitting into the puzzle, it added disappointments and heartbreak for her. Maybe she had it right all along; just believe the fantasy that her husband died in the war. But another thing troubled him; he wasn't sure what the legal status would be for a man declared dead and later remarried. Had his father broken the law?

As the train jolted along on the rails, he made a decision. He would tell his mother he had met Claude Raymond, and yes, Fletch had gone back to his family and even worked in the family business for a while, but tired of it and left. It was all true and believable. He would visit her tomorrow and tell her that. And only that.

The first part of his plan fell apart when he arrived home and Violet was there waiting to hear all he had learned. At dinner he played down the visit, giving her the sketchy summary he had planned.

"So you met this Claude Raymond Fletcher of Paducah, Kentucky?" Violet asked. "What did you think?"

"He was very cordial. Runs the business now. "

"And others in the family?"

He paused. Careful now. "I met Fletch's mother—my grandmother . . ." He started to mention his half-sister but stopped. "There's no doubt who we are talking about now, Mother. Nothing ambiguous— like Corinth."

Violet studied Will. "What else did you learn?"

"Not much. Fletch lived there for a while, but no one knows where he is now."

"He's working on some railroad." Violet opened her napkin and spread it across her lap. "William." She was tentative."I know Fletch. I learned him long, long ago. There's no malicious intent in him. For him, the siren call is a train whistle. Fletch is exciting. Life with him is like being at a wonderful endless party, but there is the other side, when the sunshine goes away . . . "

"That sunshine has gone away for many people," was Will's fast retort.

"So you *did* learn more?" Violet was immediately on his remark.

"Will," Addie finally spoke up. "You're forcing your mother to simply pull information from you. Why wouldn't she want to know about Fletch's family?"

"The man plowed a path of pain through everybody's life he touched. You may say life with him was like a party but . . . I'm sorry to have a father like that," Will blurted.

"Fletch is Fletch," Violet said. "Now what is it you think I shouldn't hear?"

Addie settled Carrie on her lap and began to feed her but finally spoke up. "Will, you have to realize that women are strong. They're not some delicate flower. They can handle it."

"Well . . . believe me, I find no joy in telling you this, but Vachel Fletcher not only lived through the Civil War; he married another woman and fathered three children by her."

"Married!" Violet froze, as if someone had slapped her.

"Yes, married."

"Was there a wedding?"

"Yes, there was . . . a wedding."

Violet caught her breath, leaned back in her chair. Will saw the rise of her chest, the attempt to control herself; saw she was staggering as she heard this.

"That woman lived, married and died, and never knew she was not living in a legal union," Will added.

Will watched his mother swallow and reach for a water glass. He knew she had not counted on this.

"Did you meet this—wife?"

"She's dead. Two of the three children are gone, too. Buried in a cemetery overlooking the river—very peaceful place, an enclosed section for the Fletcher family."

Violet's hand shook as she set the water glass back on the table. "So he left after they died?"

"Yes, except for a baby girl—Frances. He left her with his brother, Claude Raymond. Told them he'd leave her for a couple of months, but he never came back."

Tears traced down Violet's cheeks. For a long time she sat quietly. Finally she looked up. "How did . . . they die?"

"The Russian flu. Seems the family was on an extended business trip to Europe when the epidemic hit."

Violet fished in her pocket for a handkerchief, wiped her eyes. "Oh, Fletch!" she whispered as she looked away.

Finally she turned back to Will. "Was this trip with the tobacco business or the railroad?"

"Tobacco," Will answered.

Violet glanced at Carrie, on Addie's lap as she fed her. "The surviving child, what of her?"

"She is grown now. Strangely, she looks a little like young Amy from Corinth. And they both look like my father's mother. The one I just met."

"And this . . . this mother?"

"Yes, I met my grandmother."

"Grandmother!" Violet echoed, and heaved a sigh, tears still spilling down her cheeks. Will had never seen his mother show jealousy.

"A nice enough lady," Will continued. "A bit of a schemer, I think, and she, like you, tends to excuse his faults."

Violet shook her head. There was nothing to say.

"Not his brother, though," Will added. "Claude Raymond sees him for what he is or was—an unfeeling drunk."

Violet slumped back in her chair.

Addie cleaned the baby's face and let her down to walk about the room. Addie left the table to serve coffee as the meal ended.

"I despise the man," Will finally said.

"Will . . ." Violet put her hand on his arm, as if she wanted to stop him, but there were no words left to excuse Fletch.

That night, back in her own home, Violet sat alone in her parlor, moonlight streaming through the open window, soft warm air and summer night sounds filling the room. She had asked Will to take her home, she needed desperately to be alone and fight her way through this fresh wound.

There was nothing that would excuse Fletch this time. She had harbored the dream, perhaps a romantic illusion, that whatever Fletch did, down in the depths of his heart, he loved her. Only her.

But this! He had come back. And she had married someone else, too, she quickly told herself, still wanting to excuse him. But still—another family! She leaned back, gripping the chair arms, steadying herself. Will's words had fallen like heavy stones on her long-held hope. Another woman. Another family. A European trip. A successful life she had not expected.

Her romantic dream shattered that day. Now she saw it plainly; she was only the first of others he had lied to and left.

She suddenly felt old.

CHAPTER 48

W hen Will got back to his desk the following Monday morning, it was cluttered with letters and newspapers. He smiled when he read newspaper accounts about Amsley's young, gifted lawyer. Somehow, though, it made him feel like an impostor. He couldn't believe those grand words were for him. Before he got through half of the letters that had accumulated, he heard excited voices in the waiting room.

Hershel Hanover, the barber whose shop was just below the law offices, was out in the lobby. Will hurried out to see what was going on. Everybody was hovered about Hershel. "They found 'im this morning. The body was a mangled mass, some parts between the tracks. Other parts all about." Hershel waved his arm. "It was an awful sight they said."

"Who, Hershel? Who was it?" Will asked.

"Well, it wasn't anybody but that Delmar Eckert. The very one you got off from doing murder."

"Eckert?" Will almost gulped the word. "You mean he's dead?"

"Dead, I guess! The train run over him and torn 'im up in pieces. He's probably drunk and never knew where he was or what hit 'im."

Will settled into one of the waiting room chairs and dropped his head in his hands.

"You may've got that Eckert off that murder charge," Hershel shot at him, "but that don't mean he wasn't guilty. God's got a way of makin' things right."

Will stared, unseeing, down at the wide oak floorboards. Amid the praise that had been poured over him, Will had vaguely discounted the people who thought justice had not been served. The furious words of Virgil Bennett still rang in his ears; words he screamed at Eckert after the jury found him not guilty: "You're gonna pay for this!"

Will raised his head, looked up at Hershel. "Were there any other tracks or footprints at the site?"

"Never heard nothin' 'bout that. Sheriff'll be lookin' into things like that, I s'pect."

The sheriff didn't wait too long. Virgil Bennett was brought in that afternoon and charged with carrying out his death threat.

Clemet Sampson stuck his head in Will's office. "He wants to see you, Will."

"Who?"

"Virgil Bennett. He wants you to represent him. How 'bout *them* apples?" Clemet pushed his glasses up. "He thought you were Satan's brother after the Eckert trial."

Bennett, a huge hunk of a man, balding and bewhiskered, raged around his cell like a caged bull. "You got to get me off! I know you can do it. You got a man off, guilty of sin and murder, and I ain't done nothin' and you know it, Will Austin."

"Fletcher," Will corrected him.

Bennett shrugged.

"You did yell a threat at Delmar Eckert when the verdict came down, saying he was not going to get away with it," Will reminded him. "Everyone heard it. That's why they brought you in."

Bennett sat down on the narrow cot in his cell. "No matter. I never done it."

For the next two weeks, Will studied the site of Eckert's death and interviewed Bennett's wife, his two sons, neighbors, and anyone else he thought might have something pertinent to tell. The more he looked at the whole picture, the more he became convinced that Virgil Bennett had nothing to do with Delmar Eckert's death.

That, however, did not make him feel confident.

"The irony of the whole thing is," he confided to Addie as they sat at dinner the night before the trial, "I thought—and I still think—Delmar Eckert was guilty, but he got off. And I am sure Bennett is not guilty, but I don't think he will l get off no matter the evidence."

"You can only do your job, Will. You can't control what people think."

He shot her a wistful look. "I know."

It was a sultry June morning, the air soft and close like a storm was brewing, and indeed, dark clouds lay on the western horizon. The courtroom windows were pushed high to let in fresh air. Handheld fans were vigorously employed throughout the room by the curious and, in some cases, vindictive onlookers. Newspapermen were there for the sequel to the sensational Eckert case. It made good copy.

The court couldn't find him guilty for lack of evidence, but fate took a hand and meted out punishment. It lifted the case to a new and more dramatic level—divine retribution. And Sadie Eckert was there with her five children, perched on the third row behind the prosecution.

The trial was back in Judge Jacobson's courtroom, but the lead prosecutor—a rail-thin specimen, somber in a black coat, a gold watch fob draped from his belt to a pocket watch—was C. Bradley Van Dyck. Van Dyck stood before the jury, pursed his lips, rubbed his chin with his bony fingers and began to lay out his case, explaining what he planned to show.

Then Will stood and spoke to the jury. "No matter your personal bias or the words of a grief-stricken father that echo in your memory, we must at all times be guided by evidence. I will show you that it is impossible for Virgil Bennett to have murdered Delmar Eckert, if indeed he was murdered, or—and more likely—he met his death by faltering along a railroad track at the wrong time."

The day grew warmer, and by 11 o'clock, men had shed their jackets, and their white shirts were soaked with sweat. Distant thunder rumbled on the hot stagnate air. One by one, witnesses were called to the stand. They answered the questions put to them by both Will and Van Dyck, and then they were excused. But as they responded to the inquiries of the prosecutor and the defense attorney, the case began to take a form that everyone could see. It hung on one set of facts that seemed to Will to be unassailable: Bennett's wife and each of his two sons, under separate questioning, had said that they always got up at five in the morning; the men went to their chores and afterwards sat down to breakfast, about six o'clock. Eckert had fallen before the wheels of the Illinois Central, speeding to its 4:45 a.m. stop in Amsley.

Will called Bennett's oldest son to the witness chair. "State your name, please."

"Alvie. Alvie Bennett." His fingers clasped and unclasped nervously, trying to manage his hands."

"Do you help out on the farm, Alvie? Do chores?"

"Yes."

"Do you have horses on your farm?"

"Yes, course."

"If you wanted to get to town as fast as you could, which horse would you use?"

"That'd be ole Madge."

"Alvie, have you ever been to the Eckert farm?"

"No, sir."

"You know where it is?"

"Yes, I do."

"If you or anyone decided to take ole Madge, ride to the Eckert farm, meet up with a person, shove him in front of a speeding 4:35 Illinois Central locomotive, then ride back to your farm in time to do the usual chores at five in the morning could it be done?"

"No, sir, it wouldn't work. Too far."

"And you, your brother and your mother all testified separately that your father was at home on that morning, doing the chores as usual."

"Objections," said the prosecutor. "Counsel is leading the witness."

"Overruled." The judge leaned forward, steepling his fingers as he listened.

"He was with me that morning, doin' the milkin' like always." Alvie was emphatic.

Van Dyck grilled Alvie, trying to get him to admit to lying to protect his father. He put forth the idea that Bennett could have been out all night, maybe met Eckert somewhere with his dark intentions fully plotted in his mind. Still, nothing could refute the clear timeline.

On the third morning, the case was given to the jury. The judge gave them instructions, and as they were about to file out for deliberations, a loud unexpected wail tore through the formal ambiance of the proceedings.

"He didn't do it!" Emmett Eckert screamed. The twelve-year-old son of Delmar ran down the aisle. "Don't make that man out guilty! He never did nothin' to my Pa." Emmett stood before the judge's bench, beseeching. Then he turned to look at Virgil Bennett's wife, still sobbing.

"Son, what do you mean, interrupting the court like this?" Judge Jacobson's sonorous voice boomed over the proceedings. "You don't realize what you're doing."

"I do so, and I ain't gonna let that man be accused of somethin' he don't know nothin' about. I killed my pa! I done it, and I ain't sorry."

The judge looked down on the tattered boy, whose face was twisted into miserable pain. "Why are you saying these things? Your father was found innocent, and this man may be as well. You're destroying your own life."

"Cause I done it! I see his woman crying over there. My pa used to leave my ma sobbin' like that. He'd go off with them girls he liked, and my ma would set in her chair cryin'. If she yelled at him about leavin', he'd hit her. Hit us, too." Emmett looked up at the judge. "He weren't innocent. He were mean and he were guilty."

The courtroom buzzed with conversation, all order gone. The judge banged the gavel and mostly brought back quiet. He looked at the jury and asked them to return to their seats.

Sadie Eckert ran down the aisle, put her arm around her son's shoulders and looked up at the judge. "He don't mean what he said.

He's had a lot with his pa's trial and now his death. Don't listen to 'im, judge. He never done nothin' like that."

But Emmett shook her off.

Again bedlam filled the courtroom, until Emmett began to speak, then it just as quickly stilled.

"I and my pa, we went a coon huntin' like we did some nights. I knowed he'd get to drinkin', and he did. It was gettin' toward morning, and we was walkin' home alongside the railroad track, and I heard the train a comin', and an idea come to me. Something that'd fix all he done to us. So's I got on his other side and gave him a hard shove, just as the train rolled by."

"Oh, my boy, don't do this! " Sadie screamed, tears pouring down her cheeks.

"And I killed them girls he used to go see. It was me that shot 'em . . . with my rifle."

"No, son!" Sadie Eckert collapsed to the floor.

"Someone see to this woman," the judge said.

Will was on his feet. "Your Honor, I request you declare a mistrial. Reasonable doubt."

"Mr. Fletcher, I appreciate the consequences of this confession. I understand reasonable doubt, counselor. Bailiff, take this young lad away. We'll need to talk to him further about what he says."

The judge looked toward the jury members, most of them desperately fanning themselves.

"Your task would be an impossible one with this exculpatory evidence before you," the judge said. "I declare a mistrial."

CHAPTER 49

The newspapers had a field day. The sensational Eckert case, which brought front-page coverage from St. Louis to Chicago to Louisville, Kentucky, and all the little towns between, was still good copy. Along with its salacious details of abduction, sex, infidelity, and murder, came an equally riveting, surprising conclusion. And the key to it all was a twelve-year-old boy!

Throughout the coverage, the name of William Fletcher was proclaimed across many counties as the young lawyer in a small firm who could see through it all. He saw a man, news print proclaimed, whom everyone thought to be guilty, who was, in fact, innocent, and the second man he defended who appeared to be seeking revenge was not guilty either. Will was touted as a lawyer whose stellar talent belied his youthful appearance.

The first paper to broach the idea was the *St. Louis Post Dispatch*. It suggested through an editorial opinion that "we may be witnessing the rise of a political leader. Would voters not want someone with such keen insight representing them, and using their legal acumen for the greater population?" The idea came out again in two other papers, as well.

Will folded the papers up and, rather than dropping them in the trash, decided to hold on to them for a while. He pushed them to the back of his lower desk drawer.

That Sunday afternoon, after he, Addie and Carrie had had dinner with the judge and Violet and were ready to leave, Will helped Addie into the carriage and handed up little Carrie, now a busy toddler, to her mother. "Before we go home," he began tentatively as they moved out onto the street, "let's drive up to our house on Cameron Hill. Do you think you would like to see it?" Glancing her way, he ventured. "Maybe?"

Addie didn't answer. He turned to her. She was staring straight ahead.

"I go up there sometimes," Will said softly. "I go in, walk through the rooms. There was some vandalism after the first trial."

Addie still said nothing.

"We'll have to think about more room as Carrie gets older," Will continued.

"I'll try it." Addie blurted. "Don't expect anything." She looked down at the floor of the carriage. "I'll try, Will."

He reached over and touched her hand with his. "That's good enough."

Inside the house, Addie stood for a moment, deciding whether to go on. Will took the baby and reached for her hand. She walked slowly through the wide rooms. The furniture was covered, but dust coated the tables and mantels, and cobwebs tangled through overhanging lights. It looked neglected. They came to the foot of the stairs, and she stopped. She pulled her hand from Will's and put it on the stair banister. She drew a deep breath. Addie started up, up to the bedrooms. Her breath became sharper, remembering. It *was* a magnificent place. She couldn't deny that. She had always thought so . . . before she came to see it as a deathtrap.

They came to the closed door. Willie's room. She shook her head and they moved on to the room that was once Carrie's. Will took the baby to the south window of the nursery where she could see the cedar treetops and the long vista to the town, Amsley. He let the toddler down to explore in the room and he turned to Addie.

"We were happy here once." Will was watching her, giving her space to understand how she felt in this desolated house full of nightmarish memories.

"Yes," she said finally, and then feeling drawn, she came into his arms. For a long time they held each other. She felt something of the quickness of youth stealing over her, remembering a time when there was vaulting confidence and supreme joy, before the dark, hurting season came into their life.

"There's something I haven't told you, Will," she whispered against his cheek. "You have been so occupied."

He held her away from him a bit, "Yes? What?"

She felt as she looked at him some happiness that she hadn't known for a long time. "We are going to be parents . . . again."

"Really?" She watched a smile slowly play on his face, absorbing this news. "When?"

"About February."

He shook his head, as if in disbelief. "This is wonderful."

They both looked down at Carrie, who had found the toy box and was pounding the floor with a wooden block.

"But it will not replace Willie," Addie said quickly. "No baby can replace Willie."

"No. Never." He took her in his arms and held her close. "But Addie, we will never be without Willie. We'll think of him every day of our lives. He'll always be with us."

She nodded her head, lying against his shoulder. "Always, but my sorrow is not so much for me or for you. It's that Willie didn't get to have his life."

Driving home, Addie was quiet, and Will knew this was not the time to say anything. She would have to resolve this in her own way. He knew her pride would not let him talk her into anything.

As they sat up in the bed that night, before he blew out the lamp, Addie said, as if a new thought came to her, "It was Willie's house, too, wasn't it?"

"Yes. It was the only one he knew."

She smoothed the sheet that lay across her lap. "We'll need to get the house cleaned, Will, and the yard is overgrown. The cedar trees should be pruned a bit."

Will said nothing as she talked.

He had his Addie back.

CHAPTER 50

" There is something soul satisfying about restoring a beautiful house
to its original sparkle," Mary said as she sat down opposite Addie
at the kitchen table. They had spent the day at the house on Cameron
Hill, preparing it for Will and Addie to move back.

"I suppose if 'restoring' means clearing away two years of cobwebs
and dust, you're right."

"Has it been two years?"

"Yes," nodded Addie. "But it seems eons ago I lived here. Lived
this life. I feel I've been in another world,"

"Grief is like that."

"And I've lost touch with what has happened with the Suffrage
work."

"Can't say much has happened. Women all over the state have been
holding conventions. Working to get signatures, enough to present a
bill. We did get one thing. The age of a girl to give consent to have
sex has been raised from ten to fourteen years."

"My God." Addie stood up after polishing the dining room table
until it gleamed. "What does a fourteen-year-old girl know?"

"Will you march with us in the July Fourth parade next week?"
Mary asked.

"No. I don't think so."

"Not, I hope because Will's mother disapproves."

"No. Nothing like that. My heart is not in it yet. Besides, Violet is staying close to home now. The judge is ailing, and she has trouble walking since the accident."

Addie stood under the big clock on the bank corner—across from Herschel Hanover's Barber Shop, Will's law office above, on the second floor—waiting for the Fourth of July Parade to begin. The sun was warm on her shoulders as she held two-year-old Carrie, Will by her side. She heard the band rounding the corner. It passed by, followed (as usual) by Civil War veterans—a smaller number each year, Addie noticed. As they went by, Carrie joined in the clapping and cheering. Will put her on his shoulders. Two more floats—wagon beds dressed up with paper decorations and signs—glided by. Then the suffragettes, three rows of women in white blouses and black skirts, "VOTES FOR WOMEN" sashes across their chests, marching in cadence with the band music. Mary was in the front row, carrying the sign as they chanted: "Let the truth be shown, that woman has as many rights as any man has known. Let us help her win the fight, while we go marching together."

Addie felt a pang. She should be out there, fighting and parading. Only the mildest of clapping greeted them, and there was one catcall.

Will looked down at her and smiled. A welcome, soft breeze poured over her, and she felt a comfortable gratitude that he was no longer her adversary in this struggle.

"Sorry you're not out there?" he asked, adjusting Carrie, who was completely caught up in the carnival atmosphere going on around her.

"I'll join the fray later." She touched her expanding belly.

He looked back at the parade for a moment, then turned back. He smiled at Addie and said, "I didn't think motherhood would still that fighting blood."

Just then an open carriage rolled by; a man waved to all while a young boy tossed wrapped, hard candy to the crowd. On the side of the carriage it said, "Make Elkanah Parks your Representative. Send him to Springfield next fall."

As the parade came to an end, they walked down Main Street, past Lemuel Price's Hardware store, Zelma Olsen's Dressmaking shop, Carl Meek's ice cream parlor, to an irregular patch of grass across the street from the Baltimore and Ohio Roundhouse. Elkanah Parks stood in his carriage speaking to a group of people gradually gathering around him.

Addie turned to Will. "Shall we go hear what he has to say?"

Will nodded, "Briefly, I guess, but I already know."

"Workers have no knowledge of what it takes to run a company," he was saying. "They can't understand that the demands they make would destroy the very company that puts bread on their tables. They are short-sighted, ignorant of the need to keep costs down . . ."

"Let's go," Will said and took her arm. "We should go to the café, see if Amy has some apple pie."

"Apple pie on the Fourth of July? What a good idea," Addie said.

The depot and the café were both decorated with red, white and blue bunting across the front. As they were ready to mount the steps of the Dining Car Café, the north/south 11:40 Illinois Central ground to a stop. A dozen passengers stepped down onto the platform. A couple of men dressed in black suits followed Will and Addie into the café. Inside, most tables were occupied. The 12:30 Baltimore and Ohio to St. Louis would be along soon.

Amy hurried to them. "Happy Fourth! Good to see you. Can I get you something before I wait on those two men back there? Looks like they're really important dressed like that."

"Coffee and apple pie," Will said with a smile.

Will cut into his pie, looked across at Addie, held the fork up and smiled, "To my apple pie bride. This is where it all started."

Just as they took their first bite, Mary, still wearing her "VOTES FOR WOMEN" sash, came in with her husband, Andy, and sat down. Amy, they noticed, was having a very animated conversation with the two men at the back table, then she turned and pointed toward Will.

"What could they want?" Addie said.

"Will is known far and wide now," Andy said.

"A local celebrity," Mary added.

"Hardly," Will looked embarrassed. "I've been fortunate."

"Oh, Will, accept it. "You're clever and you're a celebrity," Addie teased.

Will didn't have time to respond before Amy came back to their table.

"Those men over there asked if I knew Will Fletcher," Amy was talking to Will but still looking back at the men. "They came from Springfield to look you up. Shall I introduce them to my famous brother?"

Will glanced at them briefly. "I suppose. Probably have some unwinnable court case."

Amy brought them to their table, both dapper in fashionable suits and stylish mustaches.

"Sorry to intrude, but we're surprised at our good luck of finding you so easily," one said.

"Please join us," Will said.

The other man extended his hand to Will. "Alden Bayles," he said, "and this is Asa Starwalt. We're from Springfield. "

"Since you are obviously celebrating the Fourth with your family, I'll get right to the point—why we're here to look you up." Starwalt began. "We're looking for a candidate to face off with the Republican contender for a seat in the State House next fall."

"Someone with youth and appeal. Someone with a name, a little stature," Bayles added. "Your name has come up. We wanted to meet you. Offer you the opportunity."

Will looked up, stunned, speechless, then finally said, "I am honored to be considered, but I'm just now getting my law practice established. That's demanding in itself. I'm not sure I want to leave it now. Even if I did decide to accept your offer, I'm not sure I have the makings of a politician."

"We understand you'd want to think it over, consider what it would cost your practice." Bayles looked at Addie, pregnant and holding Carrie in her lap, "And your family."

Will nodded. "I'll think about it." He stood and shook hands with both men. "I will."

Starwalt explained, "The thing is, we need some legislation that will settle this thing about the miners. Give them a voice."

A train was pulling in and drowned out what they said, "You give it some thought," Starwalt called over the train's shrieking brakes. "We'll be in touch." They nodded to Addie and those at the table and went back to their own table.

"What's this about the miners, Will?" Mary leaned forward to speak over the train as it pulled out.

"Miners are on strike because the mines are a hazard to work in," Will answered. "There are salt, lead and especially coalmines throughout the state. The miners work mostly with pickaxes. Sometimes, mines collapse. Miners get trapped or killed or maimed. Their families are left destitute because, if a miner dies or can't work, the owners are done with them. The miners have demanded the mine companies put in safer structures, but the owners brought in strikebreakers. Many of them were former slaves who had had trouble finding work and were eager to take the place of the white miners. This has created animosity in all directions—owners and miners, blacks and whites. "

"So what would they want you to do?" Addie looked skeptical.

"Well, legislation could force the mine owners to provide more safety in the mine shafts and require the miners to go back to work if their demands are met."

"Will, you must run," Mary said. "They need someone like you for the miners."

"And for the women too," Addie said.

Will was quiet, distracted as they went through the rest of the day: the picnic at the Old Settlers grounds, with music and speeches on the grandstand; suffragettes combing through the crowds, persuading people to sign their petitions; and fireworks across the lake.

Late in the night, moonlight streaming across their bed, Addie awakened and found Will gone. She slipped into her robe and went downstairs. In the parlor, he sat in the semi-darkness, beneath his father's picture.

She sat down by him, put her arm around his shoulders and held him. Neither spoke. Finally he said, almost in a whisper, "I don't know if I should run for that office or even if I can do what it means to fulfill it. There's no one to tell me."

She smoothed his rumpled hair, reached up and kissed his cheek. "The answer is not with me or in that canvas with paint on it. It's in your own heart. Do you have something you want to give to the people who need help?"

"I don't know, Addie."

Will stood before her at the breakfast table, as she fed Carrie scrambled eggs. "I have decided to run."

She smiled at him. "I was sure you would, and I'll help you, but I guarantee you'll hear from the suffragettes as soon as they learn the news."

Will looked at her, amused. "I would expect that."

CHAPTER 51

On July 20th, the house on Cameron Hill was filled with everyone Will could think of to invite, including the sheriff and deer hunters. Just because they'd had Addie locked up was no reason to exclude them from a possible vote.. He had telegraphed all the newspapers that had carried accounts of the Eckert and Bennett trials, saying he had an announcement to make and that it would be of interest to their readers.

"That's casting a wide net, Will. Several of those newspapers were even in other states, a bit beyond your district," Addie pointed out.

"Name recognition everywhere can't hurt."

He was right. They all responded quickly.

A week later, the parlor filled with reporters, Will stood under the portrait of his father and began. "I have decided to become a candidate for the office of State Representative of the 15th District."

Everyone applauded and then one of the reporters spoke up. "What kind of plans do you have, if you should get that seat?"

"One of the foremost is to present a bill to help the disenfranchised miners in the state. No current laws protect them. Safety is not a priority with mine owners, as all of you well know."

Wendell Cross, editor from the local *Amsley Record* newspaper, raised his hand but began speaking immediately. "Your wife is known to all of us as being passionately in favor of women getting the vote. Are you running to suit your wife?"

There was a flutter of laughter around the room.

"This is not my wife's campaign," Will corrected the editor. "In fact, she refused to help me make this decision. And yes, it has come to my attention on occasions that my wife does have a strong opinion on that subject."

More laughter.

"Will, now, you've known me a long time." Wendell Cross would not sit down. "You bypassed my question—politicians like to do that—so I will ask you this: If you are elected, will you push legislation to give women the vote? There's a lot of people out there, even if they wouldn't admit it, who are strongly opposed to it. You know that, don't you?"

"I've seen the opposition firsthand, Wendell, but there are other issues."

Wendell sat down; his question unanswered.

"That's about it, gentlemen. On the subject of my wife, she's also known for her apple pie. Mrs. Fletcher and I invite you to join us for some coffee and pie."

The next day, Otis Tolbert came into Will's office and spread a copy of the *Amsley Record* across his desk. There was a two-column article splashed on the front page of the paper about Will's announcement.

"Can't get out of it now, Fletcher. They'll hold your feet to the fire."

"You're probably right, Otis."

"Your law practice is going to suffer. Of course, with two big wins, you may feel you've got enough celebrity to rest on your laurels, so to speak."

"Nothing is stopping you from running for an office if you want, Otis."

"That's not for me. I'll leave that in your camp, Fletcher."

Three weeks later, the *Amsley Record* announced that candidate William Fletcher would hold a rally at the Old Settlers Picnic on

August 15th. Addie read the announcement to Will. "It ends by saying, 'Will Fletcher is our own hometown boy, now running for the State Legislature.' It says to 'go out and give him your support . . .'" but then she stopped. "Look, Will, right beside it is an article about that train wreck that happened three years ago. It says some of the claimants have received compensation from the railroad, but most of them have not."

"That's right. The railroad processes the claims through our firm. When they pay out a claim, we send it to the recipient and then close the case."

"What can be done?"

"I've written letters to the Baltimore and Ohio home office about the lagging payments."

"And?"

"Usually a letter comes back saying the claims are being processed and the payments will be forthcoming, but nothing happens."

"How many claims were there?"

Will thought for a moment. "As I remember,33. The railroad says payment is coming, but in some cases, it hasn't. In fact, most of them."

Addie looked out the dining room window. Will saw that disapproving look on her face when something was not aboveboard. She turned to Will. "What are you going to talk about when you make your big speech up there on that grandstand?"

"You'll see." He kissed her cheek and left for work.

The picnic grounds—always alive with activities on this local celebration dating back from before the Civil War—was filled with people. Concessions lined the back of the grounds, a small forest of pine, cedar and oak trees behind them. The smell of frying fish and barbequed pork floated in the air. For two cents, children could ride a pony along the edge of the wooded area. Rows of benches were lined up before the grandstand.

When Will arrived with Addie and baby Carrie, people in the crowd cheered and flocked around him. They made their way to the grandstand and Addie took her seat with Carrie behind him.

"Ladies and Gentlemen," Will began, "thank you for the invitation to speak today."

People who had not found a seat on the benches moved closer, until a dense crowd stood before the grandstand, some even milling around the side and back to get in better earshot.

"I was asked to seek this office to provide a voice for those who have no voice. I'm sure you know I mean the miners—the salt, lead and coal miners. The conditions they work in are deplorable. The mines are notoriously unsafe. We have heard of the horrors of collapsed mines; miners trapped many feet below ground. If they survive, they are often maimed. If they are disabled, they are of no use to the mine owners, and their families are left in deep poverty.

"I'll introduce legislation that will force the mine owners to shore up the mine shafts, make them as safe as possible, and not abandon families when a miner loses his life."

A voice boomed over the crowd. "You ain't gonna put up a bill to give women the vote, are you, Fletcher? We all know about that wife of yours."

Will did not answer for a moment.

"Well, are you, or aren't you?" The man persisted.

"I'll bring that issue to the floor." It was a matter-of-fact answer.

"I knowed you was running for that office just to promote them women."

"That is not true," Will shot back.

"Yeah, yeah."

Life was chaotic as Will became more and more immersed in the campaign. He went to his office at Austin, Sampson and Jamison a couple of days a week, but he carried no caseload. He went by train, sometimes buggy, to county fairs, store openings, sale barns, band concerts, village fish fries or barbecues, to make an appearance, pass out handbills, and talk—a short speech or a long talk, according to what the town fathers had requested.

It wasn't any more peaceful at home. One morning when they came downstairs in the semi-darkness of dawn, they found a row of buggies lined along the road up Cameron Hill.

"I'll not open the door till I have my coffee," Will said. "Whatever they want, they'll still want it after I have my eggs."

For many mornings, a steady stream of men came to the house and found their way into Will's office. Behind closed doors they made personal requests, offered money for special consideration, demanded self-serving legislation be put forward if Will should be elected. Some threatened; some complained.

CHAPTER 52

Mrs. Ina Pilcher had called a meeting of the suffragettes, and Addie offered her house. Usually, Will's callers were in the morning, so Addie suggested two o'clock in the afternoon. The women had not met since the Fourth of July and Old Settlers events to count the signatures each had collected. Maybe with what they had, combined with lists from women in the other counties of the 15th district, they would have enough signatures on petitions to plead for a bill to be drafted and put to a vote. With Will running, they were sure they now had a candidate on their side.

Mrs. Pilcher called the meeting to order. Besides Ina Pilcher, Addie and Mary; Hattie Powell, Ethel Burgess, Sylvie Scofield, and Alice Farrell also came. The meeting had barely gotten underway when a knock came at the front door. Addie excused herself to answer it.

"Sheriff?" She was a bit taken aback. "Will has someone in his office just now, but you are welcome to sit in here and wait." She motioned to a chair just inside the parlor door.

He looked around the room, recognizing immediately the same group he had hauled into jail for riding into the deer hunters' camp.

He harrumphed, and then said, "You women go right on with your meeting."

"We certainly intend to, Sheriff," Mrs. Pilcher countered.

Her attitude evidently didn't set well with the sheriff because he broke in, his attention finding its focus. "Listen to me, Miz Addie Fletcher, if your husband is gonna get into this woman thing, I'm not gonna support him. There's a lot of serious things that need tendin' to before we get to petticoat government."

"Sheriff," Addie Rose spit back, "Will's got lots of ideas, and petticoat government is just one of them. "

The sheriff stood up, his face reddening. "I'll sit out here in the hall, till Fletcher is available."

The *Amsley Record* carried another story related to the train wreck three years previous. It was a story based on an interview with one Lyle Gill. He had lost his crop when the railroad car jumped the track, dumping his soybeans along the embankment and into the creek. The Baltimore and Ohio Railroad had not paid out his claim, which he said had been determined in court by agreement on both sides.

"I got a letter," he explained in the interview, "from the railroad saying they paid out all claims through the firm of Austin, Sampson and Jamison. I asked about it over there at the law office, and they said they had not received the payment. My crop didn't get to market that year, so it was hard to start up the next summer. It's been mighty slim pickin's since I lost that crop. I'm still wonderin' where my money is."

The next week, Addie sat in the parlor reading the *Amsley Record*, the lace curtains floating out on the light breeze, cooling the night, as the room glowed yellow with lamplight. She called out to Will, who was working in his office: "Have you seen this? It says here that Emmett Eckert, twelve years old, was found guilty of first-degree murder of his father. It said he was not tried for the murders of the two girls found in a shallow grave, even though he had confessed to those murders. 'Young Eckert,' it says, 'was sentenced to Reform School until he reaches 21, and then he will finish his thirty-year sentence in prison.'"

"That boy didn't have a chance in this world. He had a father that was first in line to teach him the vices of adult men," Will answered back.

"And, Will, there's another article about that train wreck. You should come and look at this." She handed it to him when he came into the room. "Who is interviewing these people?'

Will took the paper and read it out loud.

> Jenny Dunbar remembers the day very well. "The train began to sort of shudder, then the cars jammed one into the other, and we were all screaming as the cars, like dominoes, began to topple sideways off the track and slide down that ravine, baggage and passengers falling on top of each other. We all thought we were going to die, right then. I hurt my back and broke one of my wrists as I tried to push up somehow. I've never been the same since." When questioned about the compensation she was awarded by the court, she just shrugged and shook her head. "What compensation?" she said. "I'm still waiting."
>
> When asked where she thinks the money went, she says, "Who knows?" Not to me. I'm always told it is being processed."
>
> The law firm that tried more than 30 of the cases is Austin, Sampson and Jamison and is responsible for distributing money paid out by the Baltimore and Ohio Railroad. One must ask, "Where is the money?"

On a Friday in late September, another story appeared in the paper. Will had gone to work to look over his mail and to pick up some more handbills the printer had delivered. Clemet Sampson stopped by Will's office, spread the newspaper out across his desk and sat down. "I don't know who's doing this, but it puts the firm in a bad light. We've got to get to the bottom of it."

Will began to read the article.

Frank Skinner was one of those injured in the train wreck. He relates what happened: "I was thrown into the aisle and hit my head. Doctor later said I got a crack in my skull. Knocked me out. Don't remember a thing till I come to lying on the grass stretched out. I had a terrible headache that wouldn't quit. I 'member that. I's in the hospital a good while. They said I was lucky I wasn't dead."

It was determined by the courts that Skinner would receive money from the Baltimore and Ohio Railroad. According to Skinner, it was more than a year after the wreck that the case came up because, he says, there were so many, but the railroad was required to pay his hospital expenses and compensation of $2,000.

"Don't look like I'm gonna see any of that," he said.

When asked what he thought happened to the money, he said, "I'm not sayin' outright what I think, but it looks like that money might a got waylaid somewhere into somebody else's pocket." When asked if he thought the railroad defaulted or if there was embezzlement somewhere along the line, he said, "Alls I'm sayin' is, something's not right."

When pressed to say if he thought there was embezzlement going on, he answered, "That's a good word for it, I'm a thinkin'."

Clemet looked at Will when he finished reading. "We've got to put a stop to this. The firm can't distribute money it hasn't received."

In early October, the most damning of the articles hit the paper. It was a letter to Editor Wendell Cross:

> This letter is addressed to all the people whose claims from the Baltimore and Ohio Railroad have not been honored.
>
> This information comes to this writer from good authority, and it declares that the money has been paid to the law firm of Austin, Sampson and Jamison and has been held in the firm's account at the bank. However, funds have been drained off it to finance the political advancement for one of their partners, William Fletcher, now campaigning for a seat in the state legislature.
>
> You who are waiting for your settlement, this, my friends, is where your money has gone.

"My God, Will. This is a lie. And outright lie." Addie stormed when she read it. "What are you going to do?"

"I'm not sure, yet. I'll refute it in the paper, of course,"

"But people like to believe the worst. You know that."

He looked down, dejected.

"This will destroy your campaign," Addie said.

"Campaign? It will destroy my name, my reputation, my practice. I'll most certainly hear from the state bar. They'll conduct an investigation. The campaign is the least of it." He shook his head, in despair. "The question is, who would do such a thing? It's 100 percent a lie."

"Elkanah Parks's campaign people? Your opposition in the race?"

"Possibly," Will leaned back in the chair, his arms crossed, "but if it were him, these articles would be appearing all over the 15th district. They're not."

"That's true. They're just local, as far as we know."

"Clemet Sampson is going to talk to Wendell Cross about who's planting these lies." Will said. "I don't know whether he'll get anywhere with Wendell. I know Wendell is scrupulous and won't want to reveal his sources."

"But if he's so scrupulous, he wouldn't want to print lies, either.

CHAPTER 53

Will continued his campaign, assuming the destructive articles in the paper to be limited to his county only. He was to learn otherwise. He and Addie took the train to Harrisburg, in Saline County, where he knew there had been mine explosions.

They were met at the depot by the mayor and taken in his carriage to the steps of the great courthouse. "This is where you'll be making your speech after the chowder is served," the mayor explained.

Addie looked up at the monumental four-columned structure, which seemed to rise from the grassy square, three stories tall, like a mountain from the valley floor.

"Making a speech standing before this, Will," she whispered, "would overawe any audience."

It was Harrisburg's chowder festival, an annual celebration at summer's end. In an open plot of ground—just off the square that enclosed the Saline County's magnificent courthouse—a dozen, great iron pots simmered over separate fires.

"Everybody brings to town their sweet corn, onions, carrots—you know, the bounty from the gardens," the mayor proudly explained. "They put it in the chowder pots to cook all afternoon."

Near the grounds where the chowder slow cooked was a farmers' market with vegetables, watermelons, and strawberries, and beyond that, another long table held cakes, cobblers and cookies.

The day was warm, and Addie's cumbersome body quickly made her weary. The mayor found a seat for her while Will walked through the crowd, passing out handbills and talking to one and then another of those waiting for their chowder.

Saline County had a coalmine, as did the adjoining county, Gallatin. Both had histories of disasters. The combination of airborne coal particles, flying free when pickaxes hit veins of coal, and the lanterns needed for light created an extremely flammable situation, as did the lantern flame if a pocket of gas was released. Many times, family members stood by the mouth of the mine helpless and terrified, while their fathers or husbands were trapped deep below ground, fearing the worst, and often, when the shaft was finally opened, realizing the worst. Will counted strongly on the votes from this county and Gallatin.

From time to time, Addie would see someone whisper to a nearby friend and point toward Will. He stopped and talked with the loafers on benches along the wooden sidewalk in front of stores. The band was forming up on the courthouse lawn beside the steps where the mayor had said Will would give his speech.

As the afternoon wore on, the band—all in white uniforms, instruments gleaming in the sun—played with enormous enthusiasm. The smell of chowder filled the air, and Addie smiled as she watched frisky children come by the boiling pots of chowder, asking how long it would be before it was ready to eat. Tray after tray of cornbread was brought to the tables. Addie leaned back in her chair, rubbed her hand across her thickening stomach, and thought about what a lovely day this was.

The band continued its concert as lines of people formed, carrying their own bowls and spoons. Chowder was ladled out to all the comers.

The concert ended and people sat eating their chowder on the courthouse lawn, along the edge of the wooden walk in front of stores, or in their buggies, parked along three sides of the square.

The mayor escorted Addie and Will to the top step of the courthouse portico. Addie took a chair to the side, while the mayor introduced Will. She was nervous for him. Had these people heard of the damaging articles in the Amsley paper?

"Gentlemen. And ladies, too," Will began. "As the mayor said, I am a candidate for a seat in the State House of Representatives, your representative in the 15th district. I want to mention some things that I feel need to be addressed, and I know that you will very much understand why we need these laws passed. Something must be done to make the mines safer. The mine owners will not move on this unless a law is passed that will make them lawbreakers and force them to conform. We also need a law that will require the owners to share some responsibility for the families left when a miner loses his life or can no longer provide."

There was applause. Addie breathed a sigh of relief. They were with him.

"I know what the owners say: 'If you want to be a miner, you agree to the risks.' But that's not good enough," he continued. "And there are others who need a voice: field laborers, mill workers . . ."

A man with a bushy beard pushed through the crowd, and stood in front of the others. "Is it true you're traveling all over these counties with a train ticket, passin' out sheets of paper with your name on it, and it's all paid for with the money that ought to a-gone to them that was hurt in that train wreck in your county?"

Will stepped forward and Addie thought he was going down to punch him. But he stopped, didn't step off the portico. "That article was completely false, a lie. The railroad has not paid out claims to everyone, only a few because . . ."

"If you took money from them people that was hurt, shame on you," another put in.

"I don't know who's behind those accusations," Will protested. "They're lies. You notice they didn't have the courage to sign their name."

Addie thought Will should not get involved in the back and forth with a couple of people. He had important information he needed to tell them about what he would do.

Another man pushed out in front. "I hear that the real reason you're going to Springfield is to make a name for yourself gettin' women the vote."

"I wouldn't want that kind a name!" one man deep in the crowd yelled out and everyone laughed.

"I'll end this talk now." Will apparently saw he had lost them. "My goal, if I'm elected, is to help the miners, your own families. That's who I'll work for. And field laborers and mill workers. There's much to be done; I think you'll agree. But I need your help next November."

There was a smattering of applause.

Will walked down the three steps and took Addie's arm. The crowd parted and they made their way to the mayor's carriage. The meeting had been a disaster.

Will had taken the train to Effingham to speak at a men's prayer breakfast. He would later travel to Charleston several counties away from Amsley to address a banquet sponsored by a chapter of the Masonic Lodge. The next day, he would go to Vandalia for their annual fall festival. "There'll be hot air balloon rides," he told Addie as they watched the train screech to a stop by the depot. "Remember those?" He tipped up her chin, kissed her goodbye, and boarded the train.

After she saw Will off at the train station, she went to see Violet. The lady was pale from being inside all summer, but as always, impeccably dressed in her signature color. With a faltering step, she led Addie, with Carrie, into the parlor and found her rocker, now a permanent nest.

"I'm sure you have read the vicious articles coming out in the paper," Addie said. "I wanted to hear what you thought." In truth, she wanted to see how she was handling it.

"The firm is not at fault," Violet declared. "But it upsets the judge. I don't allow the paper in the house now. I haven't told him of the others. So much of his life was bound up in that firm and now . . . why don't you come with me."

With some effort Violet lifted herself from the chair and led them into a downstairs bedroom. The judge was propped among the pillows, eyes closed, mouth agape, fingers curled over his chest like waxy claws.

Violet leaned close to him and spoke. "Addie's here. She brought little Carrie to see you."

He roused, looked toward Addie, eyelids heavy. He didn't seem to recognize her at first. His eyes closed again and then with a deep sigh as if it required prodigious effort, he opened them and tried to pull himself to a sitting position against the high mahogany headboard. He caressed Carrie's head.

"Addie," he whispered, and a wan smile appeared on his lips. Then weariness seemed to overtake him, his eyes closed again, and he settled down in the pillows.

"Maybe we shouldn't disturb him," Violet whispered.

Once seated in her rocker, she asked Sarah to bring them tea.

"How do you think the campaign is going? Is he well received?" Violet asked.

"He seems to be, but Will shouldn't have gone into politics. He's a good lawyer but not a good politician." She had not voiced her opinion to anyone, especially Will, but she thought his mother would agree. She let Carrie slide down from her lap and go back to her grandmother.

"I notice," Violet began, "the older Will gets, the more he becomes like Fletch."

"I doubt he'd be pleased to hear that."

Violet chuckled, "I am sure he wouldn't. Fletch couldn't resist something new. Many men find their calling, stay with it their life through, but Fletch always saw a new, bright, shiny world that needed to be conquered."

As they finished their tea, Addie said, "I'll ask him to stop by and tell you how he fared with these latest audiences."

Addie stood and Violet forced herself up from her chair.

"Don't bother. We'll see ourselves out." Addie took Carrie's hand and went to the door.

Little Carrie sat in the buggy seat beside her as Addie started home to prepare for the monthly meeting of the suffragettes. An idea came to her, full-blown and so appropriate, it seemed a surprise even to her. Her mother had always seemed the greatest example of the powerlessness of women, left to do endless work as a consequence of a man-made the plan. But now there was one before her, a most pathetic creature, and an innocent victim—Sadie Eckert, widow of the murdered and unfaithful Delmar Eckert.

She turned to her daughter. "Let's take a ride, Precious. Shall we pay a call on the widow Eckert?"

Addie walked up to a white, weather-beaten, clapboard house, chickens scurrying out of her path, and knocked on the door. Sadie opened it part way and peered out. Her arms wet and soapy to her elbows, hair straggling over her face, two small children peeking shyly around her skirt.

"What do you want?" Sadie pushed her hair back with a soapy arm. "I cain't take no more washings. Got more'n I can do now."

"It's not that."

"Well, what?" Sadie scowled.

"I'm part of a group of women who work to get women the vote. We help women, too, who are going through a hard patch. I expect you know what I'm talking about."

"So, them rich women in town is talking about Sadie Eckert. Feelin' sorry for that Eckert outfit, are they?"

"They're not feeling sorry for you, Sadie, in the way you mean, but I think you could use some help."

"I reckon I could, but I don't noise it around. Everybody's curious. Looks at us like we're some kind of people with a bad disease when we go to town. They point at us and whisper." She opened the door wider. "You're here, might as well come in."

Addie led Carrie along as they followed Sadie. "Sadie, there's a meeting at my house today. I would like you to come with me. You'll see you've got friends. Women have to help each other."

"Lawz," She looked about the dingy kitchen. "I never thought to go to town today." She pushed back a lock of her straggling hair. "Got the young'uns here."

"Bring the children. My little girl'll be there."

She looked down at the floor then finally back up at Addie. "I guess there ain't nobody here to say I cain't."

Addie waited while Sadie got herself and her two little girls presentable (as Sadie called it) to go to town and the meeting. Addie looked about at the squalor of the room. At one end, Sadie had a two-tub set-up to do washing, a scrub board resting in one, and three piles of clothes on the floor beside the tubs. Addie considered the situation. What had Sadie herself done? What had she done to suffer betrayal, public humiliation, and heartbreak? In this situation, Sadie was sister to the two girls her husband had abused and her son had murdered. Addie couldn't imagine what it would feel like to see your child taken away to prison.

Finally Sadie was ready. "Miz Fletcher, I don't hardly know what to think, you comin' out here to my house to take me to your meeting." Addie watched as she and the two children packed themselves into the narrow buggy seat behind her and Carrie.

"How are your days, Sadie? How are you getting along?" Addie thought it a stupid question as soon as she asked it, but she didn't know what else to say.

"I don't think much. I wake up and the day goes along some way or another, and finally it's dark and I go on to bed. Then the next day comes. I just don't think. I just do the washings and I don't think . . ." Her voice trailed off.

Sadie sat overawed and wooden in a chair in Addie's parlor. Ina Pilcher stood before the fireplace and began the meeting. Fourteen women were sitting in a circle about the room, periodically stealing glances at Sadie.

Addie quickly stood. "I have a guest, someone who makes our cause and purpose self-evident and urgent. Sadie Eckert has lost her husband."

Sadie raised her hand. "No use in makin' it look good. Everybody knows the ugliness of it."

Now it seemed appropriate for everyone to make Sadie the focus of attention.

"Were you ever . . . struck?" Ina asked.

"Lawz, lots of times."

"Did you go to the sheriff?"

"Once, but then I got hit again at home and, 'sides, the sheriff thought I'd done somethin' and had it comin'.. That's way before . . ."

She didn't finish, nor did she need to.

Mrs. Pilcher explained to Sadie about the signatures and that they were needed so women could have the vote and demand laws to protect them.

Sadie listened, her head down.

"Would you like to sign your name to our petition," Addie asked. "Lots of women have."

Sadie leaned back in her chair, her head resting against the high chair back, the picture of weariness. The room was quiet, the women's eyes averted, waiting for Sadie's answer. After a long while she said softly, "I reckon there ain't nobody around now to tell me not to."

"No." The word reverberated around the room.

"Let me have that paper." She slowly scribbled her name and handed the paper back to Addie. "I never thought to come to town today and I . . ." Sadie's head bent low to hide the tears streaking down her hollowed cheeks.

"Sadie," Ethel Burgess said, "it's hard for a woman to take to the fields and make a crop, but that's what a farm means. Maybe you could find work in town and rent out your farm."

"Lawzy, I don't know," she shook her head. "Rent out the farm. What would I do then?" She lifted a teary face to Ethel. "I take in washin' now. And ironin'."

"We'll help." Hattie Powell came to her, sat down, and took Sadie's hand. "We'll help."

They squeezed into the buggy for Addie to drive Sadie and her children home. She then went to the depot to wait for Will's train.

He was glowing with the excitement of the trip. On the ride home, he talked continuously about the reception he received at each of the appearances.

"Nothing was said about the railroad claims?" Addie asked.

"It was never mentioned."

"So if Elkanah Parks were behind it . . ."

"It would be known and brought up everywhere. I thought of that, too."

CHAPTER 54

Beautiful Indian summer days filled October, with deepening yellow sunlight, brilliantly colored trees wearing their fall attire of yellow, rust, and deep red, inviting life outside under the sky. The judge in his soft voice asked Sarah if she might be able to help him to a chair on the lawn under the oak tree. With much advance planning, she and Violet managed to seat him in his wheelchair, bring him to the porch, and with a wide plank Sarah found in the carriage house, wheel him over the steps and into the yard. Sarah brought a chair out for Violet to join him.

He sat, eyes closed, as he basked in the dappled sunshine through the tree leaves, enjoying a warm gentle breeze. Without opening his eyes he whispered, "Have they resolved that problem with the railroad? The claims, I mean?"

Violet was surprised at the lucidity of his question.

"No, I don't think so. This is not for you to worry about."

He shook his head slightly. "It casts a dark shadow over my firm." He stopped, got his breath and went on. "How am I not to worry?"

"It's for Will and the other partners to take care of."

He seemed to lapse into silence, but she knew, no matter how weary he was, the firm he founded was his dearest accomplishment and never far from his thoughts.

Finally she said, "Will is coming over this afternoon. You can ask him."

"Hmm," was all he answered, and he seemed to fall asleep again. Then he opened his eyes and looked at her. "Violet?"

"Yes?"

"If I ask you a question, will you tell me the truth?"

"Of course."

He was very still for a long time, and when the words came, they were slow and hoarse. "Did you ever love me?"

She instantly averted her eyes. "Yes, of course. Would I have married you and given you a child if I didn't?"

"Hmm." He closed his eyes and rested his head on the high back of the wheelchair. "Do you love me now?" His voice was soft.

"Yes, John, I do."

He nodded his head, eyes closed. "Do you think I'll die before I see the trees turn golden again?"

"You're not going to die."

"We all die."

"Don't think like that. Every day is precious. Don't spend it with thoughts like that." She shifted in her seat and busily occupied herself with a cardboard fan ostentatiously waving a fly away. "Oh, there's Will now," she said, relieved of this line of conversation.

"So you're out taking the air," Will said as he came toward them.

Sarah got another chair for Will, who sat by the judge.

"Addie said your latest speaking engagements were successful," Violet smiled at her son. "No more harassment this time?"

"Maybe that has died down. It's been a month now since the latest article."

She shook her head. "Malicious, whoever it was."

"You need to take care of that, Will." The judge spoke, his eyes still closed. "Bad for you. Bad for the firm. Go to Baltimore. Find out why the B and O has not paid." He stopped and drew some labored breaths. "Say you'll have to take legal action if they are not forthcoming with those claims." His voice was barely audible. "You have to do that. You have to clear your name. You'll lose your license to practice law."

Again, the judge fell silent for a while. Then he said, "People will lose trust in the firm. Pressure the railroad to pay. It was decided in court." He stopped, licked his parched lips and leaned forward in his chair, growing a bit more animated. "Then when they pay," he stopped again and got his breath, then he continued, "put it in the paper." He rubbed his eyes that were still closed, then leaned back as if he had taken care of what was on his mind. Once again, he opened his eyes and turned to Will. "You've got to do that, son."

Will pulled his chair close to the judge. "I'll do it. The election's next week and I'll go then."

"Go now."

Before Will could answer, they saw Nola Fitzgerald walking across the lawn toward them. Violet glanced at Will. "She comes by often. I think she wants to know what you're doing—still carrying the torch for you," she whispered.

But Nola was not in a romantic mood. She was in a fury. She plunked the afternoon *Amsley Record* down in Will's lap. "Read that, William Fletcher."

Will took the paper and slowly read it aloud.

> Dear Wendell Cross,
>   William Austin is styling himself as Will Fletcher, but in truth he is Judge Austin's natural son. His mother was married to a man who went by the name of Fletcher at the time William Austin was born, but that man had gone off to war, and like so many young men, he never came back. Once the Fletcher man was gone and had been gone the right amount of time, Judge Austin persuaded the mother of his son to have her husband declared dead, which she did. The judge then quickly married the woman, whose son he had actually fathered . . .

"Will," his mother interrupted him. She motioned to her husband. "Don't read any more. He doesn't need to hear this."

But the judge roused. "Let me see that—the paper."

Will handed it to him, and he quickly scanned the letter, shaking his head. "Lies. Lies," he whispered and handed it back to Will. "Go on. Read the rest."

Will continued:

> Will Austin is a fraud. His name, his parentage and his morals. Everything about him is a lie. The old judge, who founded the firm where Austin works, is sponsoring his "natural" son for a seat in the state legislature, and is using money the firm rightfully owes the people who were injured in the train wreck.

"My God," Nola cried out, making impotent gestures with her hands as she stormed around behind the chairs, "they're making your mother out an adulteress and shredding the judge's reputation."

"It's all a damnable lie." Will scoffed.

Violet's steel composure left her, and she began to cry. "They say I was unfaithful to Fletch," she whispered, plaintive as a child. The sobs grew deeper. Will went to her and put his arms around her shoulders. She looked at him with the eyes of a wounded animal, and gave full vent to her tearful anguish.

"Who's behind this?" Nola demanded, as if Will were somehow keeping it a secret.

"I'm sure it's the people working for Elkanah Parks." He wasn't sure at all, but it was a good bet.

"If I knew who it was, I'd go strangle . . ." Nola stopped suddenly.

Violet's sobs stilled. They stared in disbelief. The judge slumped forward in his chair. Before anyone realized what was happening, he tumbled forward onto the grass.

"I'll get the doctor, " Nola said.

When the doctor arrived, he shook his head. "He's gone."

Will took his mother inside and sat with her. "It breaks my heart," she cried, "that the last thing he heard in this life besmirched his character. He was an honorable man in every way and to end it with those words falling on his ears, it simply—it makes me ill."

Will held Violet's hand trying to calm her. "It not only assassinated his character," Will said, "it was in a true sense an assassination of him, and it would not have happened if I had not run for this office."

Violet quickly turned to him. "You're not responsible for writing that letter, Will."

The effect of the letter impugning the character of Judge John Austin was minimal. According to Amy, most of the talk at the Dining Car Café leaned toward the opinion it was a political smear to defeat Will Fletcher, especially with the salacious epistle coming strangely just a week before Election Day. They had known Judge Austin too long and respected him too well to believe the lie. Still, it planted doubt.

Both Will and his brother Thomas stayed in their mother's home that night. The next morning Oscar Jamison, Clemet Sampson, and Otis Tolbert came to call and offer their sympathies to the judge's wife and to Will and Thomas. As Will showed them out, Jamison said quietly, so that Violet could not hear, "This may not be the time nor the place, and I don't want to add to your burdens just now, but the election is only four days off and you should know, the letter that appeared in the *Amsley Record* was circulated in all the papers that had covered the Eckert trial."

Will steadied himself against the door, as if he had been dealt a body blow. That it had hastened the judge's death, he had no doubt. His mother's grief was not only for her husband, but also the scandalous accusations about her. And now the absolute falsehood was spread far and wide.

"We'll just have to see," was Will's answer. "Either way, whether I win or lose, the last thing the judge said to me was to go to Baltimore, put pressure on the Baltimore and Ohio to pay their claims, and then publish the results in the papers."

Jameson extended his hand to Will and nodded. "Time enough for that, son."

Great with child, Addie considered not going to the funeral, but she considered, also, that that had not stopped her from her work with the suffragettes and everyone knew it.

Will stood before the long, oval mirror in their bedroom dressing for the funeral. "I have not slept much this night," he said, tying his string tie. "If I go forward at the service and speak of the judge who was to me everything a father should be, it will be said that he was really my father, and I am putting up a pretense. If I don't go up and speak, they will say that I'm ashamed to come forward and *that* is proof that I am his natural son."

Addie stood behind him, partially reflected in the mirror. "You'll know what to do when the time comes."

The white, wooden meetinghouse on Third Street, with its high steeple and tall slender windows where the judge had always worshiped, was filled to capacity. At least three dozen mourners stood in the back and some congregated on the steps outside. Will and Thomas sat on the front row, their mother between them. Violet, known for her self-possession and dignity, had been so distraught she could hardly leave her bed, now seemed a helpless, defeated little figure in black, crouched between her sons.

The parson mounted the steps to the pulpit for the service. Soon he asked if there were those who wanted to speak. Both Clemet Sampson and Oscar Jamison spoke at length, remembering when lawyer John Austin brought them into the law firm and served as their mentor. Others shared their tributes, and then Thomas came forward to speak, but Will sat with his head down. There was a lull after Thomas returned to his seat.

"Anyone else?" the preacher asked.

"Yes." Will stood. "I'd like to say something." He walked up, stood behind the pulpit and gazed across the sea of people who had known and respected John Austin, and he began. "We are all very sad to lose this great light that has gone out of our lives. When I was an eleven-year-old boy abandoned by my own father, the judge, as I always called him, came into my life and took up the role of a father to me. His guidance and his influence, along with my mother's, made it possible for me to know success. My heart is full right now, but I have no words adequate to express the appreciation I have for this man."

As Will looked out across the church and the multitude of people, he wondered if the author of the letter that had killed the man in the casket before them was sitting there in their midst, smiling inside at the damage he had done. As he spoke, he wondered, too, how many people believed he was judge Austin's adopted son. He didn't care. He had to speak the truth. "John Austin has never been anything but an honorable man—his entire life."

CHAPTER 55

On the day of the election, Will went for a walk in the wooded acres that bordered the back lawn of his house.

What would this day hold, or tomorrow, or the next when the results of the votes were in? Celebration or condolences? He hoped no more condolences. He had met an army of people in the last two months, people who cheered and applauded his plans if elected. But now, with the newspaper articles before them, would they still feel like applauding? He felt not the least bit hopeful, but he knew he must keep up the image of a winner.

Pale sunlight filtered through the dense tree leaves, brilliant in their fall colors, mixed with the deep green of the cedars. He sat down on a fallen log. Even if he won, how could he salvage his reputation—and his mother's good name? He missed the judge's good counsel already.

He watched a leaf, curled and crimson, drop from a tree limb and glide slowly in the cool breeze to the ground. He finally stood and ambled back toward the house. He would go to the courthouse and cast his vote. A crowd would be waiting, so he couldn't take Addie with him. It would open questions to her—and to him—about a woman unable to vote her husband into public office.

At the courthouse, a small crowd of men loitered about, having already voted. Ina Pilcher, Hattie Powell, and Sylvie Scofield were there looking for any sympathetic male who might sign their petition. Will nodded to them but went on.

"Who's writing them things down about you in the paper, Fletcher?" someone called out.

"Whoever it is, they're lying," Will answered with a laugh.

"You used to go by Austin, now it's Fletcher. How come you changed it?" another yelled, the question potent with implication.

"My father's name was Fletcher. He abandoned my mother and me, but that's my real name. You'll have to excuse me. Don't want to miss casting a ballot for myself." He laughed and waved to them as he went inside the gray, weather-beaten structure.

In the voting booth, he looked down the list and found his name under "Candidate, State Legislature, 15th District, Elkanah Parks, Incumbent," then "William Fletcher, Attorney." For a long time, he looked at it, his own name there, not believing. It felt strange to vote for himself. It felt as if it were just another name on the list, like the other candidates.

The next day, to be near the telegraph office in the depot, Will, Addie (with Carrie), Thomas Austin, Addie's sister, Mary, and her husband, Andy, waited together in the Dining Car Café, while Amy kept refilling their coffee cups. During the noon hour, Will's partners, Jamison and Sampson, came to have lunch and find out any late information that might have come in. Even Otis Tolbert came by. It would be at least a week before all the ballots were counted and reported, but there might soon be some indication from the early tallies as to how it was going.

Will went next door to the depot every hour or so, and by dusk, partial results from most counties had come in. It did not look promising. Elkanah Parks was running ahead two to one.

Tolbert clasped Will's shoulder before he left. "Can't tell yet. Need to wait for the farm votes to come in and the miners, too. They're sure to go your way."

Will thanked him for the encouragement.

The vigil continued through the next day, although only Addie and Amy were with him, and although not every ballot had been counted, it was clear that Will had lost the election. He finally decided to send a telegram to Elkanah Parks, congratulating him on his victory.

Will sat in a chair in the parlor, morose. He needed to go back to his office and at least see what needed doing. He had a law practice to take up again, but he had no enthusiasm for it now. The campaign had been intense, exhilarating, people constantly surrounding him at barbecues, fish fries, luncheons, and dozens of other events, the applause flattering, and now it was abruptly over. Done. And he had lost. He couldn't seem to make himself pick up the work he used to revel in.

Some invisible force had written lies in the paper about him, and the people, the voters, believed them. The judge had once said the most valuable thing you have in this life is your reputation. You can replace everything else, but if someone robs you of your good name you can't really put that back. Now his mother had been damaged— and the judge's life ended.

He was heartsick and, beyond that, humiliated at being so resoundingly defeated. He thought the voters had not so much repudiated what he wanted to do for them as they'd repudiated him personally.

Will went back to the silence of the woods again for a walk. It was quiet under the canopy of trees. He had not had time to face the reality of the judge's death, a man he had not accepted, but to whom he knew he owed much.

He needed Addie, but she was in the last weeks of her pregnancy, and he didn't want to unburden himself on her. She had suffered through the campaign and the malicious attacks on her husband. Back in his house, he stood by the fireplace and stared up at his father's picture. It stiffened his resolve. He had to succeed. He couldn't tolerate anything else. To fail would validate that his father had thought him irrelevant. He'd go to Baltimore as the judge had admonished. This was one thing in which he *had* to win.

Looking across his desk, Will saw that accumulated letters had been stacked in neat little piles. Who would have taken the trouble to do that? One caught his attention. The return address was "Illinois Bar Association."

He tore it open. As he read down the page, his heart pounded.

> Dear William Fletcher,
> It has been brought to our attention that accusations have been made that warrant an investigation. The accusations imply embezzlement. The funds in question were to have been paid by the Baltimore and Ohio Railroad to the firm of which you are a partner, compensation for injuries suffered by the many claimants and clients of your firm. The accusation alleges that you used those funds to finance a political campaign.
> We will launch an investigation into these charges as of January 4, 1889.
> Sincerely,
> Ethelbert Callahan
> President
> Illinois State Bar Association

"My God," Will whispered. He had expected something of this sort, but he'd pushed the idea away, hoping it would not come. But now it had. What if he couldn't prove the accusations were false? He would lose his license to practice law, maintain his life, and support his family. Where was the heaping praise he had basked in just a few short weeks ago?

He had to go to Baltimore. Everything that counted in his life depended on it.

Will walked down the hall, looked in on Oscar Jamison and asked him to join him in Clemet Sampson's office. Without sitting, he read the letter and told them he would have to go to the home office of the B and O Railroad, demand payments be made, and save himself from ruin and the firm from disaster. He had to clear his name. They agreed. He had no other choice.

CHAPTER 56

Baltimore, Maryland, 1888

W ill stood on the corner of Baltimore and Calvert Streets, across from the Baltimore and Ohio Railroad home office. Seven stories high, the final one sloping inward in the French mansard style, the building was topped with an iron filigree railing that surrounded an observation deck. Elaborate in stone carvings, hooded awnings over dozens of windows like a granny's gardening bonnet, the building covered a full city block.

Inside that building, Will thought as he stood surveying this grand edifice, was the solution he needed to get payment for his clients, salvage the trust of his law firm, redeem his good name, and protect him from losing his license to practice law. Everything in his life depended on it, and the solution was in there. But where?

He might have been awestruck at one time, but the task ahead drummed through him as he crossed the street and entered a spacious lobby; offices with dark doors and half windows lined the back wall.

Inside the front entrance, a skinny young man, with a high, stiff collar and a string tie, sat at a desk labeled "Information."

Will immediately launched into the explanation he had somewhat rehearsed in his head. "I am William Fletcher. The law firm of which I am a partner represents several clients who were injured due to a

Baltimore and Ohio wreck. Some have received the compensation the courts determined they should have but most have not. I need to meet with someone about this."

The young man looked up sharply. "Your name's William Fletcher?"

"Yes." *Was that the only thing he heard?*

Quickly the young man regained his professionalism and masked himself in formality. "You will need to go to the third floor. The Finance Department is located there."

Will turned toward the stairs.

"Just a minute, Mr. Fletcher. I have to send a message up for them to receive you."

He scribbled a note, put it in a little tube that whisked the message to a lofty mysterious place in the building. Presently, a message came back. "The elevators are across from the stairs. It has been my pleasure to assist you, Mr. Fletcher," he recited.

By the elevator, Will pushed the triangular button pointing up. Soon a brass-plated door opened, then a black metal safety door was pulled back accordion-style. A man in a maroon uniform with brass buttons sat on a stool before a panel of numbers.

"Which floor, please," the elevator operator said.

"Third."

"Thank you." He closed both doors, pushed a button, and the elevator glided up.

"Calling at floor number three." He opened the doors.

Will nodded, muttered the obligatory "thank you" and stepped out onto a plush rug. He walked over to another young man with a high shirt collar and string tie, who nodded a very friendly greeting.

"Mr. Fletcher? About insurance claims? Any one of the people in these offices can help you, but they are all with someone else right now."

"I'll wait." He looked around at the opulence of this magnificent structure, the fine offices, and his temper began to quicken. If the railroad was so affluent it could do all this, why was it defaulting on insurance payments?

One of the heavy wooden doors opened, and a man with a cane and bowler hat stepped out.

"Mr. Fletcher, I think Mr. Grogan is available now. Come with me."

Grogan met him with an open smile, shook Will's hand and motioned him to have a seat.

"How can I help you?" he asked Will.

Will went over his rehearsed explanation, and Grogan followed closely all that Will said. Will was prepared to hold his ground, even launch into a sharp line of attack if he sensed any attempt to avoid the issue.

Grogan looked out at the bright November day, apparently trying to decide what to say or do. "This is the situation, Mr. Fletcher. We had a president, the former president of the entire Baltimore and Ohio operation for over fifteen years, John Garrett. Did a sterling job. There was stability and there was growth, a climate of confidence and pride, a structure in place, and everyone knew his responsibility and performed well enough. And then the president died, suddenly—a heart attack. We have had two presidents since. Each served for a year. Their main fault, I would say, was they weren't Garrett.

"I am taking the liberty of discussing these internal issues with you, because it is helpful for you to understand the 'why' behind the disruption of payments."

"So now," Will responded quickly, a warm feeling of vindication washing through him, "can we expect the payments in a timely manner?"

Grogan smiled, apparently feeling Will's persistence. "We'll see about that."

"Mr. Grogan, I am not leaving Baltimore until I am assured this situation will be rectified. I understand the shock of an unexpected death. My stepfather recently died. Nevertheless, the trust of my highly respected law firm is being eroded due to these delinquent payments. I must press you to fulfill your obligations."

Grogan looked down at his desk and nodded. "I'll try to get this in motion, Fletcher."

"Today?"

"If not today, very soon."

"I will be a frequent visitor until our firm says they are receiving the payments. Are we understood?"

Grogan looked up, made direct eye contact. "You're a lawyer?"
"That's correct."

Will rose to leave. Grogan stood also. Then, as if a new thought came to him, he said, "I'd like to take you upstairs, give you a glimpse of the Baltimore and Ohio Railroad's future development. Maybe give you a more positive side of our company. "

Will felt this was a ploy to distract him from his mission. "Mr. Grogan, I already have respect for what railroads do for us, including the Baltimore and Ohio. Railroads have been part of my life since I was a child."

"I think you'll find this little trip interesting."

Will shrugged and followed Grogan to the elevators. "New fetish, you see; nobody uses the stairs anymore." Inside the elevator, Grogan said, "Sixth floor, Clarence."

"Yessuh, Mr. Grogan." Will was impressed with the deference Clarence showed Grogan. Maybe he *was* dealing with the right person. "Calling at floor six." Clarence opened the doors.

They stepped out onto a floor filled with much larger offices. Will turned to Grogan. "And what happens on this floor?"

"Everything. Everything that counts. This is where plans are made, dreams or visions sketched out to become reality." Grogan was as eager as a schoolboy to show off a new toy.

"Mr. Grogan," Will began, "before we go into one of these offices, I will tell you I am greatly impressed with the immensity of this organization and the running of it, but having said that, nothing is going to divert me from my task here. Can anyone help expedite these claims?"

Grogan stopped and looked Will over, probably thinking, this audacious young man doesn't realize who he's talking to. "Well, yes, there just might be." Grogan opened a door without knocking. It was an expansive room, corner office, fall sunlight pouring in from four windows on a paneled wall. On the other wall was the largest map Will had ever seen. It showed all the routes of the Baltimore and Ohio Railroad, noting even small towns. Grogan spoke in soft, guarded sentences pointing out various stations.

"So, Grogan, you have a visitor with you today, I see." A deep voice sounded behind them.

"Mr. Mayhew, I have been showing this young man our future plans. He's here about some delinquent claims due his clients. Name's William Fletcher." Grogan explained, then quickly excused himself and left.

Will turned immediately as the man reached for his hand. He felt he was being passed around from one to another. "I'm impressed with all this, but . . ." Will explained again for the third time in an hour what he needed from the company.

Mayhew listened and said, "This is something to be settled in the Finance Department. Mr. Curry's office handles the claims. That's on the third floor."

"Really? I was just on the third floor."

"Curry's your man. Go see him or Grogan. You've met Grogan, I see."

Waiting for the elevator to transport him once again to the third floor, Will absently turned to a large, rectangular bronze plaque on the wall opposite the elevator. There was a long list of names with raised lettering. While he waited, he perused the list until one struck a chord. He focused on it, ran his finger over the lettering, and read it again. "William Fletcher." He smiled at the coincidence and thought, *Maybe?* His heart began to pound but he held himself in check. There had been too many disappointments in the past, but just maybe—

When the elevator doors finally opened, and Will stepped inside an idea came to him. "Clarence, did you know a William Fletcher?"

"Why, yes, I shore do. Everybody does. One time something happened to him up there in his office. So's he's not here so much anymore. They took him down right there where you're standing in this elevator one morning, all laid out on a stretcher."

"He died?"

"Looked to me like he was gone, but they took him over to that Jarvis Hospital where them that fought in the war go."

"A military hospital?"

"I hear so. Calling at floor three."

"Clarence take me to the ground floor."

On the street, Will hailed a hack that was passing.

"You know where the Jarvis Hospital is?" Will asked the driver.

"Of course," the driver said with a little indignation. "It's where all them Yankee soldiers go."

Will was tempering his excitement. Even if the man, William Fletcher, Clarence spoke of could be his father, did he still live? Will was unaccountably annoyed that he might have died and he would have been cheated out of meeting him and seeing his eyes when he confronted him.

In the hospital, a thick-set woman in a nurse's uniform was seated at an ancient, brown desk near the door.

"I am looking for a man," Will said, "whom I believe was in this hospital. William Fletcher. Do you have information on him?"

She went to one of six file cabinets and thumbed through some papers. Will held his breath. He had no real reason to believe this man was his father, just because he had the same name.

"Yes, we did have a William Fletcher. He was released to go home four months ago."

"Do you have an address? I'd like to go see him."

She looked down at the papers in his file, a puzzled expression developing. "I can't understand this. It says Baltimore and Ohio railroad station, track 23."

"Track 23. He lives on a railroad track?"

She showed him the paper. "That's what it says." She looked at it again and shook her head. "Your guess is as good as mine."

Will went out to the long, brick depot at the railroad station, its many rail lines feeding past it, like so many ribbons. When he asked the ticket seller if he understood the address he had written down, he got a crisp answer. "Can't you see that I'm too busy to run all over this station? There's a line of people behind you who are waiting to buy a ticket. They're going somewhere. I'll have a porter take care of you."

Eventually, a porter did come, and Will showed him the address. "Do you have any idea what this means?"

"Why sure. It's a short spur of a track with a railroad car on it. A right fancy one too, I'd say."

He led Will to the steps of the railroad car. "Here you be," he said as he left.

Will knocked on the door and waited. Another young man with a high stiff collar and string tie opened the door. Will concluded this must be the dress mode of the Baltimore and Ohio employees. "Come in. If you could just have a seat on that chair near you, I have some papers for Mr. Fletcher to sign. We're almost done."

A man with snow-white hair sat at a ponderous desk, with a couple dozen cubbyholes stretching up above the desk. His back was to Will, signing papers and giving directions to the young man who had answered the door.

Will looked about the car, a railroad parlor car, paneled with mahogany wood, the long row of windows swagged in crimson velvet, edged with gold fringe and tassels. Near the desk was a game table, as well as another smaller table with two chairs and a well-stocked bar. In the center of the car, surrounded by two gold plush settees and two forest green-colored velvet chairs, was a small ornate table. Everything was ornate!

Will waited inside the door, disappointment filling him. The man had white hair and seemed older than Will imagined his father would be. The young secretary turned, nodded to Will as he went out the door.

Will stood, ready for his turn, but knew by now he had followed another hope that led to a dead end and hard disappointment.

The man at the desk rose, turned to face him and extended his hand.

Will froze. Those velvet brown eyes he'd seen so often, looking down on him from a canvas, were the same. His knees felt they would give way. And now those eyes were truly looking at him. His heart pounded in his ears.

He kept staring, stunned and speechless. The hair was not brown anymore and there were squint lines around his eyes; the features were not the sharp, lean ones of youth. But they were the same.

The man watched Will, puzzled. "Can I help you?"

It was so unlike what he had imagined. "I am Will Fletcher," he finally got out.

"Will Fletcher, you say." He smiled and laughed a bit. "The name has served me well enough; I hope you can say the same?"

"I am your *son.*"

William Vachel Fletcher sobered; his glib tongue fell silent. There was a visible withdrawal in his demeanor. He looked into Will's face for a time, slowly shook his head, looked away and then was drawn back. Something came over his countenance, like someone hurting. "Of course," he nodded and finally said, "you would be a man now."

Here before Will stood the very embodiment of his years of resentment and yearning, of disappointment and questions. And he felt nothing! Absolutely nothing.

"Come, have a seat." William Vachel Fletcher motioned to the two green chairs in the middle of the car.

The moment was awkward. Finally Fletch spoke. "How have you . . ." he stumbled, unable to say the words. "You must hate me."

Will's eyes leveled on Fletch, "Yes."

Fletch looked down at the carpet, saying nothing for a time. "There's a lot to tell," he finally said, "if you would allow . . ."

"I'm sure you do have a lot to tell. I do too. In fact, the story of my whole life, which you missed. But I have only one question."

"Only one?" Fletch seemed surprised.

"Why was I not worth your time?"

Fletch veiled his eyes and waited long to answer. "You ask me for an answer, and I have none. I have no defense. There isn't one."

"Other boys," Will began, stopped, choked up, then went on, "did things with their fathers. I must tell you, the man my mother married was all that a father should be, but, Mr. William Vachel Fletcher, he was *not* my father. He's part of the reason I am here. The last thing he said to me before he died was for me to go to Baltimore and resolve this problem."

Fletch seemed to regain his composure. He leaned forward, an inquisitive expression replacing the sober one. "And what might that problem be?"

Will took a breath, retracted his emotions to a professional level, and began explaining all that had happened, emphasizing the position of distrust it casts on his law firm.

"So you're a lawyer," Fletch responded, seemingly intrigued. "Yes."

Fletch cocked his head, rubbed his chin, his eyes brightened as he eyed Will. "You any good?"

Will waved his hand, dismissive. "I've had some success." What an arrogant question. "As I said, the man who raised me was everything a father should be. He founded the firm I work for."

Fletch did not react, which irritated Will. Didn't he comprehend the pain he had left behind? Didn't he care?

"The railroad will stand behind its obligations," Fletch said.

"They've indicated that before. I'll be here, Mr. Fletcher, until it is an accomplished fact." Father and son met eye to eye, taking each other's measure, neither wavering.

"It will take some time," Fletch answered.

Will watched his father, distrusting him. He wants *my* time now, and holding the money back for leverage can buy him that.

Abruptly Fletch changed the subject. "Do you have a place to stay?"

"I'll go to a hotel. I came in town early this morning on the train."

"I would be pleased if you would stay here—that is if you're comfortable with that arrangement." There was a question in his eyes.

"I would be comfortable enough to ask a lot of questions of you."

Elbows on chair arms, Fletch's chin rested on his clasped fingers, as he nodded. "Yes, you would feel that way."

They fell silent for a time. Scudding clouds had crowded out the sunny day, and now a soft rain pattered on the long row of windows.

"You live in this railroad car?" Will was impressed with the opulence, and yet it was nothing less than he would have expected of Fletch; it was—very like him.

"When it's necessary for me to go to another station, I have them hook this car onto a train going there—all the comforts of home, and I'm still working."

"You travel in style," Will commented. He looked about, "Where do you sleep when you're riding along and not working?"

"At the other end of the car. Two long seats face each other. They convert into beds. You might as well stay until we get this matter resolved about the insurance claims."

"I had planned to go to a hotel," Will said, unwilling to take anything from this man who had given him so much grief.

"As you wish," Fletched shrugged. "Have you talked to anyone over at the home office about this?" he asked formally, now as one professional to another.

"Grogan, Mayhew, and I was sent to Curry, but haven't seen him yet."

"You need to see Grogan." Fletch rubbed two fingers across his chin. "We'll take care of that tomorrow."

CHAPTER 57

As they sat in the lavish parlor car, rain streaked down the row of windows and drove against the car, rocking it slightly. Fletch put firewood in the little square, black stove and lit a fire. He came back, sat down, reached for a bottle, poured two whiskeys and put one in front of Will. There was awkwardness in the silence between them. Fletch reached for a drink. "You mentioned a judge Austin," he said, huskiness in his voice.

"Yes, he's the man who married my mother."

Fletch stood again, went to the window and peered out at the darkening day, his back to Will. "How is your mother?"

"She's recuperating from an accident and the death of her husband. The judge died last month."

Without looking back he asked, "Has she had a good life?"

"I would say so. Comfortable, certainly. The judge adored her."

Will fondled his glass, finding it hard to begin and yet determined to do what he had spent his life planning. "I have imagined this a thousand times, Fletch. The time I would find you. Confront you. I've searched for you, followed up any flimsy lead." Will was surprised at the quiet strength he felt once he started. "My mother said you died in the war, but I knew you didn't." There was a strangeness in

this for Will. The anger he'd carried was for someone in a distant
memory. The man standing by the window, his back to him, was a
person he didn't know. He resented it somehow, as though he'd been
cheated out of his revenge.

Finally, quietly Will continued. "I knew you left us before that. I
remember the disappointment when you didn't step off the train. I've
wanted to tell you how much I despise you for the damage you've
done. I loved you better than anyone on earth when I was little. The
happiest times were when you came home to us each weekend. Then
I came to realize you weren't coming home anymore, and the hurt
and hatred began to grow until the hatred was all I had. "

Fletch turned, started to say something, but Will held up his hand,
cutting him off.

"It's fueled everything I've done. I couldn't tolerate thinking I was
a failure and deserved no better treatment. Not worth my father's time."

Fletch's tired eyes turned on Will, eyes that seemed to have seen
it all. "I'm . . ."

But Will would not be stopped. His face felt hot, the hackles rising
as he poured out the venom he'd lived with. Thoughts of the judge
came to him, of his cool measured judgment, who would not have let
emotions rule him. His presence seemed to be with Will, even now
guiding him. It calmed Will a bit. "I guess, in a way, that's why I'm
here. You see, it's essential our clients—the injured passengers in
the B and O train wreck—get their compensation, but its more than
that." Will stopped, pondering whether he should tell Fletch about
the trouble he was in. Finally he said, "I ran for public office and . . ."

Fletch turned sharply, attentive. "For what?"

"I ran for State Representative from the 15th Illinois district."

Fletch raised his eyebrows and Will could see he was impressed.
"Did you win?"

"No, I did not win, and the Baltimore and Ohio Railroad is to
a great extent the reason. Articles came out in the papers implying
money had been paid by the railroad to our law firm, and was being
used to finance my political campaign. The Illinois Bar Association
is launching an investigation, and if I can't show that clients are

receiving their payments from the railroad, I could lose my license to practice law."

Fletch pursed his lips, came back and sat down, as if absorbing this new piece of the picture. With a glance roving over Will, he said, "Looks like you're somewhat backed into a corner."

"But the Baltimore and Ohio railroad has the key."

The tired eyes looked down at the floor. Fletch stroked his chin, "We'll see what we can do."

Will sat in one of the green chairs, rain drumming on the roof, the fire warming the parlor car. He thought, as he looked at his father, this man was no more than a stranger to him, no more than someone he'd talk to on the street or on a train.

Fletch reached for the bottle, and poured himself another glass.

"Do you know you have a daughter?" Will asked abruptly.

Fletch swirled the liquid in the glass and took a drink. "Frances? Certainly."

"Not just Frances. Amy?"

Fletch looked up, a question in his eyes.

"Amy? I don't know anyone named Amy."

"She was born after you left Liela."

Fletch put the glass down and looked, across the room at the rain drizzling down the windows, then back at Will, his attention sharp. "You met Liela?"

"She died, Fletch."

"Liela's dead?" He seemed genuinely astonished, the first emotion Will had seen from him.

"And then there was Reverend Hollister who took Amy to raise. He applied to the War Department for a veteran's pension to help raise your child. The War Department contacted my mother as the only family they had on record. That's how my search began. In Corinth, Mississippi, where Hollister lived, I learned I had a sister and I learned about her father, Vachel Fletcher, who was supposedly dead."

"Hollister." Fletch gave a joyless chuckle. "A busybody."

Outside, a train ground to a stop on a distant tract and another rumbled past. Rain peppered the top of the railroad car.

"Casper's dead " Will added.

"Liela and Casper, too!" Fletch leaned back in the chair and closed his eyes. He seemed to sink deeper in his chair.

Lights flooded the car as a train pulled in on a nearby track.

Fletch watched the train screech to a stop outside his windows. "I can never explain to you the horrors there—Corinth. Not for days— weeks. The thirst. Always the thirst. Water was muddy or contaminated by rotting flesh. I could never make you understand, or understand about Liela."

"Try me. I'd like to know about my father's life, when I stopped being a part of it," Will came back sharply.

Fletch did not respond to the barb. He poured himself another drink. "It used to replay in my mind. Corinth was worse for me than Shiloh. I couldn't drink enough to put it down and go on. Even now, it rises up like yesterday."

The day had grown dismal, with intermittent train lights filling the room, rain pattering on the railroad car. Fletch looked at raindrops coming on the windows, and Will could tell the old soldier was seeing sights that lived in his head. Fletch filled his glass again with another drink and went back to the window. He was silent for a long time.

"You think you want to know about Liela," Fletch finally asked.

CHAPTER 58

Corinth, Mississippi, 1862, Twenty-six years earlier

The day was hot for April. Up and down the line, the Missouri Regiment lifted shovel after shovelful of dirt building breastworks, they were told, around the Confederate works in Corinth.

"How much we gonna have to do?" Stoner's voice cracked. Everyone's throat was parched. Water was dear, and what they did get was filled with dust and crawlers. "I reckon, the idea is to keep building these trenches, to shield us as we dig our way plumb into Reb territory," Stoner said.

"And aim right into a Confederate's eyeball," the man on the other side of Fletch said. "Rebs got this dirty little hole sewed up. When I signed up in Joplin, it was to get outta farmin' and plowin' up dirt, and here I am, scoopin' more dirt than I do a farmin', and there in Joplin it was the mule doin' the work." He dug in a shovel full of dirt and packed it down into the long berm.

"They're guardin' them two railroads in the city," Stoner said between shovelfuls.

"You call this a city? Have you ever been to St. Louis? *There's* a city," Fletch said. "This is a mudhole with a name."

Someone down the line yelled, "I ain't never seen a worse place. Nothin' but swamp and dust. Nothin' much to fight for, I'm a thinkin'."

"That's why the ole man had a us corduroy the roads. General Halleck's no fool," Fletch said. "He knew dirt roads and swamps couldn't support an army."

"I'd a sight rather be here under him than Grant," the man from Joplin said.

"Grant. We shoulda been diggin' trenches like this at Shiloh." Fletch heaved another shovel load.

The soldier from Joplin said, "I's on picket duty south of town, and I seen the prize—it's them two railroads. They's them old slaves all around and they been sayin', the Rebs is bringin' in supplies and reinforcements all the time in the railroad cars. That's how they feed 'em. Bring in livestock and bring in fresh horses, new regiments, and even barrels of fresh water."

Conversation stopped. A drink of water!

"And we got to march where we're going with wagons carryin' in our water.," a soldier down the line said. "But they say if the Rebs was to lose the two railroads it'd be the end for 'em."

Fletcher looked at Stoner and knew he was thinking the same thing. They could make quick work of those railroad lines—both track and trains, if the colonel just knew it. Fletch thought maybe he'd say something—later. Now they just had to dig dirt, moving ditch and berm by ditch and berm closer to the Rebel camp and the railroad junction.

Both armies were licking their wounds after the massacre at Shiloh. Just twenty-two miles north, it was. When Fletcher and Stoner marched with what was left of their regiment from Shiloh to Corinth, the road had been one long, tented convalescence camp.

It was planting time and a farmer had been plowing in a muddy field. He stopped and watched the Yankee Army straggle down the road. Farmhouses and barns were burned out as the Rebs cut a swathe through the countryside after Shiloh, knowing the Union Army was behind them.

"They treat their own folks bad in my opinion," the man from Joplin said.

"Them Rebs are mad as snakes in a deluge after Shiloh," Stoner said. "We're gonna be in for real fight one of these days."

The day grew hotter, a storm coming, and Fletch wondered if somebody was going to pass out from the heat with no water to drink. By late afternoon, the rain began. Fletch and Stoner backtracked to tents behind the breast works. It was a cold rain and a cooling relief. Water filled the trenches and overflowed into some of the tents. The men without a place to sleep moved to higher ground and slept under trees.

The rain lasted four days, and the camp was a quagmire. After three days of rain, they found a corpse that had been washed out of a swamp. They couldn't tell which army he was from. All remnants of clothing had been stripped from him.

But the rain filled the streams nearby. Fletch and Stoner were assigned to go down to one of the streams with a wagon and get barrels of fresh water. Three women were there, too, with wooden buckets.

They ignored the Union soldiers at first, then one of them said, "We were told by the Rebs that you Yankees were seven feet tall and you're gonna take everything we got off the plantation and then kill us. They said you'd do that. The Rebs already took everything, so you might just as well kill us now."

"I'm not going to kill you," Fletch said, but he could hardly promise her any better treatment than the Rebs; the army took freely of whatever they needed wherever they found it. The Union Army had taken out long stretches of rail fencing to put over muddy roads. And they hadn't stopped there. They cut down trees to corduroy roads.

After the rain stopped and trenches dried out somewhat, they began again digging trenches, making step-by-step advances on the Reb camp.

Beauregard's Confederates kept up little scrimmages, knowing the Yankees were crowding in on them along the Confederate lines. Fletch knew that a battle was brewing. The two army encampments were now just yards apart. Fletch heard trains arrive and leave, reinforcements and provisions coming in.

Finally, one morning in early May, the army began to move. The ground was wet, and the underbrush was thick. When they passed through the underbrush, the Reb line appeared, rifles drawn. He saw the Memphis and Charleston tracks and what they were fighting for. The deafening roar of artillery and pounding horses' hooves filled the air, and Fletch knew the battle was on.

A cannon ball hit a tobacco barn in the field where the farmer had been plowing. It exploded, setting the barn on fire. Fire leaped to the outside row of a peach tree orchard. The roof of another tobacco barn caught fire and burned most of it off. The Rebs were coming at them in full assault, an inferno blazing on their left—no place to turn, just the raw, terrifying onslaught of vicious fighting men killing to keep from being killed.

Then it happened. Fletch grabbed at his shoulder where a bullet hit. Someone dragged him back behind the underbrush and he passed out. When he came to, he was in a tent behind the trenches with other wounded men. A couple of men came with a stretcher and took him inside the house where men were screaming in pain.

One of the doctors told him he was lucky because he'd be all right if he didn't get the typhoid. He was later laid on a pallet outside on the grass because the men inside were the ones with typhoid fever.

When Fletch got his bearings, he saw the house—a big, fine one with a gallery, and a wide, front yard now filled with wounded men.

A young girl—maybe eighteen or nineteen—came around with the doctor. He'd seen her down by the stream getting water. She wasn't much use to the doctor because she was angry that the Union Army had taken over her plantation, house and grounds, and it was their tobacco barn that burned, along with part of their orchard.

"I hate you Yankees! You come in here and destroy everything," she said as she bent over him, changing his bandages.

"It was a Reb cannon that caused your tobacco barn to catch fire," Fletch said, but he knew she didn't care.

"But they wouldn't be firing at you if you weren't down here trying to change who we are."

He felt sorry for her. "What's your name?"

"That's none of your business." She tossed her head, but finally added, "It's Liela." Then tears began to run down her cheeks. "You

Yankees give my papa something. He's upstairs with my mama, and he's got a bad fever. I think he caught the typhoid. I don't know what's to become of us." She walked away, through the rows of men lying on her yard, like someone walking in a trance.

CHAPTER 59

Baltimore, Maryland, 1888

Will had been without sleep for 20 hours, but he had lost track of time. It was as if he were moving in a space out of time. He had never felt so awake. He had found his father. He had succeeded. He felt he was moving on some new, higher terrain, the quest over. Or was it?

Trains outside had come and gone; train whistles were constant, and the rain had come hard against the windows through the day. But Will hardly noticed any of it. He'd had clients who liked to talk about their time in the war, but this was different. He was living this with Fletch—his father, the wonder of it still unreal. He roused from the spell the afternoon had cast over him.

Fletch turned back to Will, came and filled his glass again. "After I took that bullet, Liela nursed me back to health, but for both of us . . ." He lifted his glass and swallowed the contents. "It was the beginning of hell."

"So Liela took care of you when you were wounded, and you felt sorry for her," Will finally said. "That's not hard to understand. But that doesn't explain a lot more that I know happened." Will turned fully to face Fletch, determined for this self-absorbed man to see a little outside himself. "Did you ever think of us? Of Violet?"

"I planned to get Liela to write a letter to Violet, but she didn't come around with the doctor for a long time." Fletch seemed unfazed by Will's pointed questions. "We should get some dinner," Fletch quickly changed the trend of the conversation. "There's a hotel a couple of blocks from here. They have a dining room. It's where I take my meals."

The rain had stopped, but the streets were wet, the air fresh and November crisp. They left the railroad tracks, walked past a park on the way to the hotel. When they entered the dining room, it was clear from the friendly reception and excellent table that seemed to be reserved for him, Fletch was more than a regular; he was a favorite.

When they were seated, Fletch began tentatively, avoiding eye contact with Will. "Tell me about this Amy."

"She looks like your mother," was Will's abrupt reply.

"My mother?" He turned quickly to Will. "You've seen my mother?"

"It's been my mission, Fletch, to track you down. It wasn't something I planned. It was something deep down in my bones I had to do. I knew I would find you. Don't ask me how, I just knew. It led me to Corinth, it led me to Quincy, it led me to Paducah, it led me to a visit with Stoner and, somewhat incidentally, to Baltimore. But yes, I've met your mother—my grandmother."

A waiter came and stood by the table. "The usual, Mr. Fletcher?"

Fletch nodded.

"Make it two," Will added with a glance at the waiter. He looked about at the wide dining room, round tables filling the room, covered with bright white cloths and burgundy napkins, sitting under gas-lit chandeliers. A fire blazed in a fireplace not far from them.

"I knew there would be a day like this, Fletch; a day when I could look you in the eye and say, 'Look at me, see the son you missed knowing.'"

But Fletch's eyes did not turn toward Will, nor did he shrink before Will's hostility.

"Your portrait hangs in my house, opposite my mother's," Will persisted, spitting out what he had waited years to say, "the one you had painted for your wedding picture. I look at it every day and wonder one thing: Why?"

"Maybe you wouldn't have done as well as you have if I'd stayed," Fletch countered,

Will's hands came down hard on the table. He leaned into Fletch's face, trembling, anger flaring.. "Don't you say that! Don't you *ever* say that to me! I won't hear that I would've been 'better off' without my father. Don't you ever say that to me again!" At a nearby table a couple of lovebirds looked up, startled.

The abruptness of finding his father had ripped back the layer of his practiced, cool judgment and now he felt genuine rawness, long hurtfulness surfacing, deep rancor that wouldn't be quieted.

A waiter put a plate of ham, grits and baked beans in front of him. Will steadied himself, remembering the judge who had counseled him to keep his emotions in check.

"About Amy," Will picked up the conversation again, trying still to rein in his temper. "When she became an adult, the good parson had done his job—raised your child. She had no place to go. She wanted to live with me, but I have my own family. Amy now works for my wife's mother in the Dining Car Café."

"You have a wife?" From time to time, a brief spark of interest flitted in Fletch's eyes.

"Addie Rose."

"And this Addie Rose . . . what's she like?"

"She's . . ." Will stopped, looking for the right words. "She's a solid rock, no nonsense gal. Determined to see women get the vote."

"Oh, one of those." Fletch pulled a sour face as he tackled a piece of ham.

"I'm in complete support of her. In fact, I was accused, when I was campaigning, of running for the purpose of introducing a bill to get women the vote."

"And would you have? If you'd won?"

"It's one thing I would have done. Addie's father died when she was a child. "

"So you were *both* fatherless?"

"But her father died in an accident . . . He didn't choose to leave her!"

The waiter appeared at their table.

"I recommend the peanut butter pie," Fletch answered.

Will nodded. "Fine. Two."

Fletch seemed relaxed into his chair, waiting for dessert. It was irritating to Will that no matter what he said, Fletch was unperturbed, imperious. Maybe he wished his lost son had not found him, had not interrupted his life.

The pie arrived, along with coffee.

Will stared at the white-haired man beside him, watching him as he cut into the pie, wondering what he thought. "I've heard a lot about you," Will finally said. "Hollister, Amy, Casper, Claude Raymond, Stoner, your parents, I'd be interested to hear it from you," Will ventured, not sure how risky it was getting involved with this stranger. "You asked me to stay with you in the parlor car. I'll stay for the night, anyway."

The next morning Fletch went to his office at the Baltimore and Ohio building and Will went to see what Grogan had done about the insurance claims.

Grogan had papers spread over his desk. He pulled out one of the sheets. "I have a list of names; the ones that have been paid and the others still pending. I'd like to see if this corresponds with your records."

"There is no question the payments are due," Will said as he opened his file. "That was determined in court." He perused the names, comparing them with his own record. When he had finished checking Grogan's findings, he said, "I don't find any discrepancies. The question is, when will the railroad pay out on these claims?"

"We will start the process soon."

"What do you mean by 'soon'? I want to know how long will it take for the claimants to receive their money."

"Maybe two weeks to a month."

"Not good enough, Mr. Grogan. We have already waited—in some cases, two years."

Grogan was becoming annoyed with Will's insistent pressure. "I'm doing what I can, Mr. Fletcher."

"I'll see you tomorrow."

Will left and went to the telegraph office in the depot and sent a telegram to Addie.

"I found my father."

CHAPTER 60

Baltimore, Maryland, 1888

That night in Fletch's railroad parlor car, Will told him about the situation with the claims and Grogan's efforts.

"You'll get your payment. Don't worry about that," Fletch said.

His father didn't realize— or perhaps, didn't feel—the press of time. It was November. The Bar Association would start its investigation in January.

The car was warm; they had had a good dinner at the hotel and Will leaned back in his chair. "So after the battle for Corinth, what happened?"

Fletch poured himself a drink. "Occupation. And I stayed on in Corinth during the occupation." Will remembered what Stoner had said about Fletch's drinking. When he talked of old days, he seemed to fortify himself.

"I was going to ask Liela to write to your mother, like I said," Fletch went on. "But when I saw her step out onto the front steps, I went to her and saw she was terribly upset. 'My papa just died,' she said. "I don't know what's going to happen to us.'"

Fletch took a sip of his drink and continued. "I held her while she sobbed. I know she hated all of us, but she was so distraught it wouldn't have mattered who gave her comfort. 'We have nothing to eat,' she said. She kept sobbing. 'The Confederates took everything and then the Yankees came and tore down our fences and burned everything.'

"Her mother came out and dragged her from my arms, called me some names, and told me to leave her daughter alone. I felt sorry for them, but what could I do? We were the enemy.

"When I recovered, I went back to the trenches. There had been a lull in the fighting, and everyone said we had won the battle with the Rebs. But I didn't see how that could be, since they were still entrenched in Corinth.

"We kept digging ditches, trench by trench, in a strange way advancing on Beauregard's army in Corinth. We heard cannon fire coming from the Confederates' position; word came down we were in for another, even bigger attack. We were kept at the ready. Trains came in and went out, bringing in reinforcements. We were all plenty scared, and my shoulder pained me severely.

"The men sat round and talked of Shiloh. Most of us thought these might be our last days. We could hear the drummer giving out signals. And still we waited.

"Some said they were not getting ready for an attack; they were leaving. But most everybody thought we were in for another Shiloh.

"I remember saying to Stoner that, if we could get to a track some-where, we could put our ears to it, and we'd know if the railroad cars were full when they came in or full when they went out. And we'd know, but we didn't say anything to our sergeant.

"We saw smoke rising in the west above the trees. Homeless freed slaves began to pour into our camp, jubilant, and said that the Rebs weren't gonna attack, they were all gone, and they didn't want any traitorous old slaves havin' their food.

"We came out of our entrenchment and marched right into Corinth, as free as if we were going for Militia Day on the village green—but the town was deserted and mostly burned or smoldering."

Will studied this man he did not know, a white-haired man glory-ing in this time of triumph in his life. Was he trying to impress him? Will didn't think so. Fletch seemed within himself, remembering something remarkable in an otherwise flawed life.

"We encountered wagons setting in the streets," Fletch leaned back and chuckled. "They were logs painted to look like cannon, and straw dummies in Reb uniforms propped behind the logs with grinning faces painted on them. 'Quaker guns' we called them.

"All of those little skirmishes and cannon blasts and drum rolls were just a feint. Beauregard had pulled a hoax on us. We had Corinth all to ourselves, but we knew they'd never leave us there in possession of those railroads—they'd be back.

"When we moved into Corinth, any building worth anything had been set ablaze and the railroad dynamited. They had disabled a locomotive, taking it apart and dumping the parts, big and small, in the swamp.

"I finally went to the sergeant and told him that Stoner and I were engineers, and we could rebuild the engine if we could get the parts out of the swamp. He smiled and said that would sure help the situation if we could do it. The next day, the colonel sent word for me to report to his tent. He told me to rebuild it if we could, and he'd get the men to try to retrieve the parts. So he put a crew to work on the tracks."

Will's interest perked up with this. His mother had said that when she met Fletch, he and Stoner were learning to build a locomotive.

"The sergeant," Fletch went on, "had us wading sometimes waist deep in the swamp digging out the pieces of the engine. Soon, we had enough for me to start rebuilding. That took some doing, and I had plenty of onlookers. It was held up for a time because of a missing piece. Finally, the men found it, and when I was finished, a great cheer went up. We gave her a head of steam; my hand was back on the throttle, and I began moving the engine along the newly rebuilt track. For all that, I got promoted to sergeant and, a few weeks later, so did Stoner. So now we had the beginnings of a railroad again. After a time, we had trains coming in with food and ammunition and fresh reinforcements

As Will listened to the old soldier, he realized he hadn't thought much about what would happen beyond finding him. He had never thought about looking into the life of the man himself. What his father had become. He'd never considered how any man would feel about a son coming into his life after 25 years.

But where would they go from here? Would they go back to two isolated lives?

"We thought the Rebs had come to Corinth to lick their wounds after Shiloh," Fletch continued, "and then tucked tail and run deeper into the south," Fletch said, growing more animated as he emptied each glass of whiskey. "But when ole Buck Van Dorn saw we had the trains up and running, he decided to have another go at us. This time, we were in the cage defending our ground. They were snarling at us from outside. They needed that railroad town, my locomotive, and any other one that came in. Then the second battle for Corinth began. But we whipped 'em that time."

Will wondered if Fletch was telling him all this to put a little humanity between them; not exactly sympathy, but to mitigate Will's animosity. Finally, Will interrupted. "There has to have been a lot more between the time you met Liela and felt sorry for her, and the time the two of you had a child together."

Fletch was silent for a long time. Finally he began. "One day, I saw Liela. She had moved to the Hotel Tishomingo in Corinth that had been taken over as a hospital. She told me her mother had died of the typhoid fever also; her place was devastated and the house still in use by the Union Army.

"I suggested to her that one day we ride the train out as far as her plantation and look it over. It was still used as a convalescing camp, with tents all over the wide lawn. Hanging around behind the house were four or five old slaves. One was Casper, the one you met. They were ragged and filthy, but they were getting food from the Union wagons that fed the men.

"We found a horse and rode across the farm and saw the desolation. There were bones and half-covered decaying bodies that had been washed out of swamps when the rains came. We came back to the house; sickness was rampant, but with no battles, there were few wounded in the house.

"Liela took my hand, and we walked up the stairs to the two rooms where the family had stayed when the Reb army first took over the place. The room was filled with furniture hastily taken from the rest of the house and dumped in there. It spoke to me of a life they had lived. She left me for a few minutes and came back in a beautiful rose-colored dress. She took my breath away. She was a sweet, girlish woman who would have had a magical life but for the war. It had been months since I'd seen a woman who wasn't dirty, hungry, begging, trying to sell herself, or covered with blood, caring for sick men."

Fletch got up, opened a new bottle, and poured both of them a drink. Will knew he could make this easier for him, and he knew what was to come, but he wasn't going to give him the least comfort.

"She began sobbing and I held her, then I felt her shoulders shake. It was heart-wrenching, her family gone, her way of life gone. No means of support. Then I kissed her tears and . . ."

Will could not sit quietly with this man. He got up and walked the length of the car, trying to sort through his feelings. He saw the rawness Fletch and Liela were living in, and on some level understood, but his father had just described the betrayal of his mother. Finally, Will came back and poured himself a drink. "So that was the beginning of the affair?"

"The Rebs moved into central Tennessee." Fletch matter-of-factly picked up the story. "Grant was intent on taking Vicksburg and taking control of the Mississippi River from the Confederacy, but I was kept in Corinth. Railroads were Grant's supply line for his campaign against Vicksburg. I saw Liela almost every day. I don't say I was in love with her; I pitied her and had tender feelings for her."

"What about my mother, the woman you married in Galena?" Will interrupted. "What about your vows with Violet?"

"No one ever took Violet's place." Fletch walked to one of the windows and watched a train come in on a distant track. "Life was hell. The civility, the priorities of life were lost to survival."

As Fletch talked, Will wondered about the comment that no one had "taken Violet's place" in his life. Hard to believe when he had more or less established two other families. He hadn't planned to tell Fletch all that had appeared in the Amsley newspaper. That was his own business.

He was here to get payment for the firm's clients, but now a larger question was begging to be answered: Where were Fletch's truest feelings? Did Fletch even know? How would he react if he knew the newspaper in Amsley had called his son the natural child of the judge? What would Fletch say if he knew Violet had been publicly humiliated in the newspaper for committing adultery while she was married to him?

Outside, a train screeched to a stop, but Will didn't notice. He was putting together a plan. It could answer many questions, especially the biggest one. Where was Fletch's loyalty—if he had any?

"I have something to tell you that you may find interesting," Will began, a bit uncertain. He recounted the gist of the articles during his campaign, including the one accusing him of embezzling funds from the railroad to run his campaign. He withheld mentioning the last one, the letter to the editor about his mother.

Will watched as Fletch straightened up out of his chair, leaned forward, his eyes growing bright, his jaw set, his face flushing. "You're not taking that, are you?"

"What could I say, except it was a lie? The claimants don't have the money in their pocket. What were they or anyone else to believe?"

"You'll get your money," Fletch was on his feet, the warrior ready to strike. "I'll see to that, son. We'll get this straightened out and you are to fight back with everything you've got."

Will kept back tears. Fletch walked about the car, sometimes stopping by a window. He didn't realize what he had said, had not noticed, what it meant. But only five words counted with Will. Only five little words!; "I'll see to that, son."

Fletch was still ranting, pouring himself a drink, stoking the fire, but Will didn't hear any of it. If the old rascal had looked him in the eyes and said he loved him, Will wouldn't have believed him. But inadvertently, Fletch had told Will he cared, and cared intensely. The words reached deep into Will's soul and for a time he couldn't speak.

"But there's more," Will finally continued, waiting for Fletch's reaction. "It was a nasty campaign. A letter was written stating that I was in fact Judge Austin's son, and that my mother had had her husband declared dead so she could marry the real father of her son; and again that the firm Judge Austin had founded was using the money from the railroad funds to send his natural son to Springfield."

Fletch's fist came down hard on the table. He got up, unable to contain himself. "That is a damnable lie!" He walked around, impotent and furious. "You were born in Galena," he yelled at Will as if he were lecturing him. "You were two years old when we moved to Amsley. Who in hell said this?"

Then he stopped, turned to face Will. "Violet!" It seemed to hit him all at once. "They're calling Violet a whore! Violet would never . . . somebody's gonna to pay for this!"

Will shook his head. "It's broken her. She never goes out," Will spoke solemnly but he was smiling inside. Fletch had tipped his hand and he didn't know it.

"I'll go to her," he said.

That was one thing Will did not want, at least not yet. "Let's get the money problem fixed, and then everything else will fall in place."

"She doesn't deserve this," Fletch explained to Will.

Will looked at him in disbelief, then shook his head. "It's not the first time her heart's been broken."

CHAPTER 61

Baltimore, Maryland, 1888

The next morning, Fletch went with Will to Grogan's office. As soon as they were in the door, Fletch asked, "What have you found, Grogan?"

Grogan looked up at Fletch. "We have the names together, Mr. Fletcher. Now we need to get authorization from accounting to send the funds to the law firm in Illinois. Then our bank will transfer the funds."

"How long will it take to get that money paid to the claimants?" Fletch wanted to know.

Grogan shrugged. "Two weeks, maybe." Grogan shifted his eyes between Fletch and Will, then back to Fletch.

"Expedite it," Fletch said. "I plan to go there. I can deliver the money to the bank in Amsley."

Will turned to Fletch, questions in his eyes. This was the first time he'd heard this!

Then a smile came into Fletch's eyes as he put his hand on Will's shoulder. "I'll have them hook my car onto a train headed in the direction of Amsley. It'll be a train ride like you've ever had."

I'll bet, was Will's only thought.

Fletch left him and went upstairs to his office, and Will went by the depot to see if a telegraph had come from Addie. The telegraph operator handed him a message. "Eureka! Found him. When will you come home?"

He stopped by a park and sat on the bench thinking. His father was what he expected and yet the man was not what he'd expected. His journey was over. But really wasn't it just beginning?

When they left the hotel dining room that evening after dinner, a wind had come up and grown stronger until they had to lean into it to walk. Store signs swung, and the men they met along the street held onto their hats.

Back in Fletch's parlor car, the fire had almost gone out in the stove. Fletch stoked the fire and added wood, while Will lit the lamps. They sat down, still in their coats, waiting for warmth to come.

"Casper told me about a floating store," Will said, noticing leaves swirling by the darkened windows.

"Yes, but that came about later. Would you like a drink while we wait?"

"I wouldn't say no."

Fletch came back with a bottle and two glasses. "I finally left Corinth. Went to Tennessee to fight the Rebs there—the battle of Franklin. And then the war ended." He filled both of their glasses. "We could go home. I decided before I started hitching a ride on a train, I'd go back to Corinth; see about Liela. Stoner and I parted ways then. He didn't approve of it. Said I needed to get back to my wife. I always thought Stoner was a little bit in love with Violet.

"Liela had moved back to her farm. The army was gone. Men everywhere were trudging home. What she had, what was left of her place, was in shambles. Her father had owned slaves—fourteen, I think I heard her say. Most left. Casper and the others wanted a place to stay and be fed. But she had nothing to give them. "

"And you and Liela? Were you living together, then?" Will asked.

Fletch was slow to answer, his eyes averted. "The parson came by to talk to us about that—Hollister, it was, the one you met. Said there was gossip in the neighborhood. Liela spoke right up and said that an Army chaplain had married us. It was a lie, but she needed to save face, and I didn't say otherwise. She never talked of getting married. She knew I wouldn't stay." Fletch stood, took off his coat and laid it aside.

"I was ten years old then; Mother was teaching school." Will interrupted. "The judge came to our house every evening. He was courting my mother and I hated that, but I hated it mostly because there wasn't anything wrong with him. It ate at me, but I had nothing to say. I remember other things, too: boys running home from school because they were going fishing with their pa, they said, or helping him build something, or going hunting with him."

"I can't put those memories in your life. There's nothing to do but move on."

"I figured that out for myself, Fletch," Will snapped.

Outside, a train screeched to a stop.

"You asked about the floating store." Fletch was quick to deflect Will's barbs. "I went up and down the Tennessee River for a couple of years—twice a week." Fletch lit up a cigar and leaned back in his chair. "Every weekend, when I came back to Liela, I had some money to put in her jewelry box.

"I had sent word to my father for a loan. Casper and I built the boat from lumber on the plantation, and I went into business. He helped me as we fitted out the boat—had a covered top." Fletch smiled, "I was right proud of that boat. People needed everything. Destitute. They bought what they had to have. Still, we made a good deal of money because I came to them, and they didn't have to go to town. Most didn't even have a horse. Sometimes carpetbaggers rode along. They had money.

"Brought back cotton seed and hired those freed slaves to clean up twenty acres and start the planting again. We had no tools; they'd all been taken. Then we started working on a little patch for tobacco.

"When I came back on Friday nights from my run on the river, I'd line up Casper and the others and pay them for their week's work. It was a new thing to them, having their own money. They worked the farm like they always had with tools I brought back, and they helped rebuild the tobacco barn, too. We had no livestock. What one army hadn't taken, the other had."

Will turned on Fletch. "And you paid the black folks on Friday, and then held church on Sundays, preached and took the money back in the collection plate,"

"They didn't have a church. I held preaching in the old, burned-out tobacco barn. The roof was completely gone." Fletch hung his head, took a drink and looked across to a window, watching a train depart on a track on the far side of the station. "They put in the plate what they wanted to," he finally said. "It's easy for you to be moral and condemning when life is safe and plentiful. When you're living in desolation and destruction, and you're hungry, you do what you have to." Fletch's jaw set. It was the first time Will saw him get defensive. "They'd been slaves, but they were a sad lot; freed, but freed to take care of themselves. They were fed at least as much as any of us and sheltered."

Fletch gave a little chuckle. "We said with no roof over us, nothing could stop our prayers from going to Heaven. Liela said they could cut down some trees to make a log cabin church, then we could hold preaching there. "

"Let me see if I understand this," Will cut in. "You, who were living in sin with Liela, betraying your own marriage vows, retrieving on Sunday the money those unfortunate old slaves had earned and collected on Friday and delivering the message of the good Lord's redemption, while promising them their own church sometime?"

Fletch shrugged. "I made mistakes."

"Some folks would agree with you," Will retorted. He heard the rancor in his voice, but he didn't care. "Another thing you said; you wanted to stop on your way home to see how Liela was getting along. But Fletch, you stayed two damn years. What a two-faced jackass you are. Maybe I can forgive you sometime. I hope I can, but not now."

"I never forgot I was married, that Violet was the finest woman I'd . . ."

"So you say."

Fletch went to the stove, opened the door, punched around at the wood in the leaping blaze, pretending not to hear. He came back and settled in with another drink.

"My shoulder pain never let up, and life was gruesome. The echoes of war still drummed in my head. I began to drink more often to get started in the day. One time, I went on a real bender, and it didn't end for days. I missed preaching and didn't stock my boat and take my usual trips. I told myself it was all right; I deserved it.

"We'd accomplished a lot. I gave Casper and the others 30 acres of cotton in the field and 20 acres of tobacco. Liela had a garden. I hunted and fished. We were all eating now. To me, the whole place was haunted by battles and death. It hovered over the grounds. I'd get up at night and walk over the yard, unable to sleep until a drink would soothe me and I could get some sleep."

Will found this whole revelation interesting but it kept drumming through him that Fletch was trying to win himself some bit of favor.

"When I came back," Fletch went on, "I apologized to Liela for my drinking, and she told me not to explain myself. She said that, although she had told people we were married, she would never marry me because she saw that one day when the train whistle blew, I would leave. That hurt quite a bit, but she saw it right."

Will listened, begrudgingly seeing that his own life would not have been the orderly steady one it had been, had his father been there.

Fletch quickly took up the story again. "We began rebuilding the tobacco barn from lumber on the plantation. We needed a good roof that would protect the drying tobacco when rains came. With the money I made from trips on the floating store, we finally got enough money to build the roof. I hired a carpenter to build it, and that cost about all we'd saved. We put on a wide overhang and a double layer of shingles.

"When it was all done, we had a picnic in the yard. We had picnics anytime we got something put back together. I think now there was a reason I wanted to have those picnics. We had them where the tents had been, where all the sickness and injured had lain during the war. I'd go into Corinth and bring back a gallon of whiskey and celebrate. It was an excuse for me to drink. My shoulder hurt and I drank to help the pain, then I drank just to drink.

Will half listened, sometimes engrossed in what his father's life had been; but at the same time, he wondered why Fletch would do all he did for these people who were strangers when he had a family of his own. Did it make Fletch feel benevolent, virtuous? Did it assuage a guilty conscience for a family he'd deserted? Apparently, he didn't plan to become, sometime in the future, a wealthy plantation owner. The fact was obvious and hard to admit; he loved a young girl named Liela.

"We had a good crop that year, the first since the war. When the cotton was picked, we hauled it by wagon to Corinth and loaded it on the Memphis-Charleston Railroad headed for Natchez."

"Casper told us about that trip."

"I imagine he did. It brought back a wealth of memories to me, riding up front with the engineer, as if I had not really ever been gone. It made me restless to get back on my own—my way of life up north working the trains."

The car was warming; Will took off his coat, and settled back with the glass of whiskey he nursed. Fletch was reliving within himself long-ago days Will knew but his own thoughts drifted to his memories of the same time. He had often felt his life was a variegated landscape with one central missing piece, his father. He wondered if knowing of Fletch's life while he was gone would fill that missing piece. Or would that missing piece always be there?

"In Natchez," Fletch went on, "I worked with a broker down on the waterfront where the warehouses were and got a good price for the cotton. This would get Liela back to a decent life—not the one she once knew, but better than it had become. I think I really knew I was doing all that so I could get away.

Will already knew what happened. He wondered if Fletch would tell the truth or twist it to his benefit.

"I went into a saloon," Fletch said, "and had a few to celebrate the good deal I got on Liela's cotton, the money packed in a money belt around my waist, under my jacket. I was feeling pretty good about what I'd done, so I kept drinking. The next two days are lost in a fog. I got into a poker game and, being thought of as an important man in the plantation business and having the money to keep up appearances, I stayed in the game. When all the money in the money belt was gone and there was nothing more to put up, I put up the new roof on the tobacco barn for collateral. The men snickered loud on that one. But I told them, people were rebuilding all over the south and they'd get a good price for those shingles. So one of the players said he'd come and take off the shingles and haul them away. I wanted to get the money back, so I stayed in the game. But I lost. Liela would have nothing after a year of work. "

"Casper told me about the lie that laid on his conscience." Will smiled. Fletch had told the truth about what he did.

"I knew I couldn't go back and told Casper what to say. Finally Casper asked,'Where you go?' I said I didn't know.

"But I did know. It was 1867, the war had been over for more than two years. I was going back—to you and Violet. I got on a riverboat and went up the river to St. Louis, then on the train to Amsley."

"You decided to come home!" Will leaned forward.

"Well, I always intended to," Fletch said, as though Will should understand that. "I got off the train in Amsley, walked through the depot—the old familiar depot—and I was so glad to be home. I needed to get cleaned up before I went to see your mother. I didn't know how she'd react when she saw me. I had not communicated with her for eight years. Would she welcome me? Or something else. But I wasn't ready for what I heard." Fletch's words became distant.

"When I walked up to the house—where we used to live—I saw a frail, little lady on the porch, with a pan in her lap and a bucket of string beans by her, snapping the beans. I remember it like it was yesterday. I told her I was looking for Violet Fletcher and she said that it was Violet Austin now. She was the judge's missus. She wanted to know if I was bringing news about her husband that was lost in the war. She said it wouldn't do no good to go over to the judge's house, because they'd left on their honeymoon. Her words fell like rocks on my heart.

"I remember standing there, Will, dumbfounded. I had always visualized everything the same as when I left. Finally, I found my voice and asked her about Violet's boy—about you, Will. I remember just what she said: 'They took that boy with 'em on they honeymoon. Ain't that a hoot?' I stood there, the most awkward, lost soul in the world. The two women I'd grown the closest to, both of 'em thought I was dead. And I couldn't say anything—couldn't interfere in the lives of either of them."

"I went back to the hotel and laid in on a three-day drunk. I finally got on a southbound train for Kentucky."

"To go home and make peace with your family," Will said.

CHAPTER 62

Paducah, Kentucky, 1867, twenty-one years earlier

When Vachel Fletcher stepped off the Illinois Central train onto the wooden platform in Paducah, Kentucky, his heart was heavy. He was known as a dead man, but he wasn't. He knew what he was; he was a drunk. He'd messed up everything he'd touched and was doubtful about the reception he'd get. He had mixed feelings about seeing his parents. He'd lived past the war; they knew that. He had not paid off the loan he'd made to start the floating store. He had no money, no future. What kind of a future do you have if you're legally a dead man?

He gathered up his coat and valise and began walking the eight blocks out of town to the house he had always known as home, where his parents still waited to see him after the war. Most veterans had come home—months before.

He passed storefronts with names that were part of his childhood. Soon the residences began to be set back off the street, wide lawns with ancient trees now brilliant in fall foliage. He felt miserable, coming home with nothing to give an account of himself. He had argued with his father when he left to work on a short-run railroad venture in Illinois. The venture had failed. Failed when he left, destroying his father's dream that he would follow him in the business as he had followed his own father. He had failed in his marriage to Violet, failed in helping Liela, and his only child wouldn't know him.

He stopped in front of the McClintock house and looked up at the tree in their front yard, remembering when he and his younger brother, Raymond, Stephen McClintock and the Wagner boys had climbed that tree to watch paddle wheelers glide past Livingston's Point on the Ohio River.

He walked slowly on. He wondered if Stephen and the Wagner boys had survived the war.

He stepped up onto the front portico, between two of the four pillars, and knocked on the door of his childhood home. No answer. Would they welcome him or berate him? He remembered when his father used to put his hand on Fletch's shoulder and say, "Son, you're all right. You're stock from my side of the family. Raymond's your mother's boy."

He remembered the bitter scene when he told them he was going to survey land and help build the Illinois Central Railroad. After a long minute of silence, his brother, Raymond, had said he would take over the business, and his father had bellowed that he couldn't manage such an undertaking; it was a man's job. Later, when he wrote he was planning to marry a northern girl, born in Pennsylvania, they had not responded.

He went around to the back of the house, an entrance also, but facing the Ohio River. A terraced lawn led eventually to the river's edge.

He saw her before she saw him, his mother sitting on the veranda. She looked up, and then stood, her head cocked to one side, still unsure of her vision. She reached for him, "Can it be?" she whispered. "Can it be my boy's come home?" He held her to him and felt a frailness he hadn't remembered."

"Papa?" he whispered.

"Upstairs. Napping."

"Not down at the warehouse?"

"Claude Raymond runs it now. Took some years for that to happen. But your father wasn't too well a couple of winters ago, so he had to let him have it. Let's go up." She stopped again and hugged him.

"Oh, my dear boy, you'll be better for him than three days' worth of medicine."

When Fletch entered the room, Ben Fletcher was in his bedroom, sitting at a tall desk. He stood slowly, facing Fletch. "Welcome home, my boy." Fletch reached to shake his hand, but his father pulled Fletch to him in a great warm hug.

His mother hastily planned a family dinner and sent word for Claude Raymond and his wife to join them. Claude Raymond—smiled and shook his hand when he and Alice arrived. He said he was glad to see Fletch back home and looking healthy, but it was nevertheless a cool, crisp greeting.

They all sat around the table, under an oil lamp, the familiar breakfront behind his mother, with the cut glass bowl filled with honeycomb. His mother served her special meal: ham, baked beans, cooked yams, fried apples, and topped off with hot biscuits, butter and honey. Fletch felt a peacefulness wash over him that he had not known for a long time. The years melted away; he was a boy again, his feet under the home table.

"I have to ask," Raymond began, and Fletch knew from his tone, it was going to be confrontational. "What were you doing running a floating store in Mississippi?"

At least he didn't ask about the unpaid loan—yet.

"I decided to go back to Corinth, Mississippi, on my way home. We destroyed so much. I went back to help—a family. Their plantation had been devastated. It was where I was after I was wounded. Where they took care of me," he decided to add.

"What was in that for you?" Raymond said.

"I felt sorry for them."

"I'm surprised they'd have you on the place—a Yankee."

He didn't say only a young girl was left of the family. He continued to edit the story. "They were willing to take any help they could get. They were starving. . ."

Claude Raymond anchored his coffee cup in its saucer, and then looked askance at Fletch. "There is a matter of an unpaid loan from the company."

"Son, this is not the time or place to bring that in the conversation,"

Fletch's father said to Claude Raymond. "Right now, tonight, we are just grateful he survived the war and is home with us again."

"Does your wound trouble you much?" His mother abruptly changed the subject.

"I wish I could say no, but truth is, I can't get free of it."

"You won't be working, then?" Raymond's wife, Alice, was quick to conclude.

"If there's something I can do . . . I do have a loan to pay off." There it was, admitting to them he had failed, failed at everything, and was back home begging for whatever scraps they could toss him.

"You wanted to chase some dream you had. When you didn't want to sell tobacco, we made other arrangements." Raymond said it like a pronouncement.

"We're overjoyed, my dear boy, to have you here, under our roof again," his mother said, "but Raymond took over the business when your father had his heart attack. Raymond has done well."

"Yes," Ben Fletcher said, "sales are up, added more growers—selling to more companies overseas. Some want to make cigars, some snuff, some pipe tobacco. Raymond has taken it far beyond what I envisioned; got quite a list of suppliers, too."

Raymond looked smug, basking in this moment of adulation from his parents in the presence of Fletch.

"I'm sure everything is running well. I don't plan to disrupt anyone's life . . ."

"The management of the company." Raymond promptly supplied the words Fletch was reaching for. Although he was trying to couch his thoughts in acceptable civility, Fletch could feel the anxiety coming from Raymond. He had spent his life playing catch up to his older brother, and now he seemed to have succeeded.

"I am thankful to God to have both my sons here at home, and that you were not more seriously wounded or . . . so many homes are grieving now," Ben Fletcher soothed.

Raymond made no comment.

"I think we should have a party," his mother said. "Invite all our friends, all Fletch's friends."

"No, Mother, I'd rather you didn't." Fletch knew there would be questions, forcing him to say more than he wanted to or dared to.

"If he doesn't want that, Mother . . ." Raymond said.

"Well, we'll just have a few—but we'll have a little party," his mother persisted. "It wouldn't be right to act as if we're hiding him."

The next day, Fletch went down to the riverfront to the old warehouse, which had proudly boasted FLETCHER AND SONS, TOBACCO BROKERS in curling black letters before rain and river fog had faded them to gray. At one end of the warehouse was the same drab office he remembered, and there he found Claude Raymond.

Raymond came forward, very much in charge, and shook his hand, "I suppose you'd like to be shown around."

"If you'd like. When you've got the time."

"I've got the time."

They walked along through the wide, barn-like building with wide compartments holding different types of tobacco available for buyers. Outside, along the waterfront, rows of hogsheads awaited shipment.

A wooden walkway led from the long warehouse to a floating pier, which held dozens of hogsheads of tobacco ready to be loaded onto designated stern-wheelers headed for the Mississippi River, shipments to the east coast and on to foreign markets.

They came back to the office and sat down. Claude Raymond poured them each a cup of coffee from a pot sitting atop a Franklin stove. "So the prodigal son has returned and tomorrow night they're going to kill the fatted calf. A glorious celebration."

Fletch felt his brother's disdain, but he kept his thoughts to himself.

Fletch looked at the rows of hogsheads along the pier and said, "If I were doing it, I'd load all that onto railroad cars and ship them faster. Months faster."

"But you're not doing it, are you?"

"No, I'm not."

"Father's favored one, the one he imagined would be doing this." He waved his hand toward the warehouse. "I want you to know something: You are not going to come back here and worm your way into something you threw away. Do you understand me?"

What started out as a dinner for a few old friends evolved into a party, which filled the old house—friends, old college buddies—most of whom were also veterans. Even though Fletch dreaded it, had even gone to his room, had a couple of shots of Bourbon, he found everyone to be as welcoming as his mother. Maybe, he thought, she just knew the ones to invite, but he was having a tolerable time in the library, while making fast work of a bottle of bourbon and swapping war stories, when his mother appeared in the doorway and asked to steal her son for a few minutes.

Very soon Fletch learned what she needed and the real purpose of this party. He knew his mother, knew her to be a kind, gentle soul, a southern lady, true to form, but capable of quite sophisticated machinations. Even though most guests were in the wide hallway that stretched from one entrance to the other, Fletch with his mother found Albert and Adele Ferris and their daughter Bonnie, in the parlor waiting for him.

Albert Ferris had been his father's most serious competitor on the riverfront. Alonzo Ferris and Son (son now meaning Albert) were competitors in the tobacco business since his grandfather Asa Fletcher's day, for more than 50 years. The families were not enemies, but they certainly weren't friends either—not the kind that meet over Sunday dinner or are invited to parties.

Before the evening was over, Fletch saw the tidy little plot floating around in his mother's bonnet. Graciousness itself, she continued to talk for a while, then contrived to collect Bonnie Ferris and Fletch outside on the grassy terrace to see the wide Ohio River with the moon shining on it. It was, of course, a beautiful sight, moonlight splintering off the mildly cascading current, but a common sight both Bonnie and Fletch had grown up with. Once the three were outside walking on the terrace leading to the river, his mother was seized with a shivering chill in the air, and needed to go inside, leaving Bonnie and Fletch alone.

Fletch turned to Bonnie, "I don't think I've met you. You must have been a small child when I left here." She was no beauty, that was for sure, but she had a nice smile.

"I'm twenty," she answered and then fell silent.

"Well, that explains it. I've been gone for over twelve years. Went to college in Lexington, then worked the railroads, then the war."

"Lexington is pretty," she ventured. "I've gone there with my father."

"Are you cold?" Fletch asked.

"Not at all. I was surprised your mother needed to go in."

"Yes, that was surprising." Bonnie seemed like a sweet girl, awkward and shy.

"Are you going to stay? My father said you worked on a railroads."

"Yes, I have."

"That must have been exciting."

"Nothing like it." Fletch was warming to the conversation. He told her of reassembling a locomotive in Corinth, Mississippi, growing expansive as he talked, describing the importance it played in turning the war in favor of the northern army, in that particular area.

She said nothing.

"Would you like to go back in with the others?"

"Yes," she hesitated, "but I want to ask you to do something."

He looked at her, wondering what she could possibly want of him, and a bit surprised she had the courage to make a request.

"Will you dance with me when we go back in? No one asks me to dance at parties. It's because, my father says, I'm shy as a mouse."

Fletch laughed and said, "Of course I'll dance with you, but I'm a little rusty. The war has knocked some of the niceties of life out of me."

She said they would get along fine because she never got any practice. He followed her into the wide hall where a little orchestra was playing and most of the people were congregated. When he took her into his arms, she seemed like a little wisp of a girl. She kept her head down and said not a word.

After the party was over, Fletch met his mother in the parlor, right under the portrait of his grandfather. "What do you mean, tossing that poor girl in my face. It was embarrassing for both of us, and nothing can come of it."

"Why can't something come of it? I want to see you settled—settled here—not running off chasing some wild dream or something. I want you spending your life here with us—be a whole family again."

"But why her? She's a child. She's 20 years old and I'm 35."

"I know how old you are. You couldn't help the war—and that took years away from your true life."

"I am certainly not attracted to her. A nice girl, but—" he could hardly say the word,

"—mousy."

"I'll tell you why her, Vachel. Your brother has taken over the family business. It is his, and frankly he doesn't want you here, but . . . "

"Well, that's not news."

"But," she continued, "do you want to be here?"

"Mother, it's my life you're playing with."

"If you could marry little Bonnie, you would take over Ferris Brokerage—warehouse, pier, boats and all."

"I am appalled at your scheming. I can't believe it."

"I am thinking about what would be good for you and for all of us. It would give you a business of your own, make your brother relieved and happy—and make me very happy."

"It would also eliminate Fletcher and Sons' long-time competition."

"Well, yes, that too."

"Yes, that, too."

Fletch was trying to decide whether he should tell her all about his life, tell her part of it or none at all. Finally it burst out. "Mother, I can't . . ."

"It's that Yankee woman! I knew that was at the bottom of all this."

"It's not like that. I had gone to war and, as you know, I didn't go directly home afterwards. She thought I wasn't coming back and had me declared legally dead." He edited out the fact he had deserted her before the war and thought it not necessary to discuss his life in Corinth, Mississippi, either. "She has remarried. I am legally dead,"

She stared at him, silent for a long time. "Well, there you have it. Marriage is 'till death do us part.' You are, shall we say, 'unhooked.' Have you told your father any of this?"

"No."

"Anybody?"

"No."

She studied the floor for what seemed an hour, and then raised her head. "You are not dead. You're as alive as I am, and I am not allowing you to consider your life over. Don't ever tell what you told me to a living soul as long as you live."

"I can't just . . ." Fletch began to protest.

"Listen, son. I love you, and I am grateful beyond words you are back under this roof, but let's face facts: You have nothing. You chased a dream, and it came to nothing. You went to war, and you came back with nothing—except a wound. You're in mid-life and you have nothing to show for it. "

"I can't just go on and ignore the fact I married and fathered a son, and now I am a dead man."

"You are not a dead man, and of course, you can go on—you will. That Yankee woman considers you dead. She could have kept up hope—kept waiting; lots of women do. Bonnie Ferris will make you a fine wife and after what you have told me, William Vachel Fletcher, you have very limited options on your horizons—you're a dead man."

CHAPTER 63

Paducah, Kentucky

Fletch called on Bonnie's father to ask permission to court his daughter, hoping, even assuming, the father would give an emphatic "no." Instead, Albert Ferris agreed.

Through the long, cold winter, Fletch carried on a half-hearted courtship with Bonnie. She was a gentle little thing, with a bit of humor sometimes, and he gradually came to appreciate her more. But he hated what he was doing, entering into a relationship that would lead to a marriage that would not be a marriage but a lie, and deceiving an unsuspecting young woman he didn't love.

All the while, another man was raising his son with the woman he did love. Dread overwhelmed him when he realized he would spend the rest of his years in an unwanted marriage, selling tobacco—something he loathed and wanted to leave behind as much as he ever did. Any time he heard the whistle of a train, it saddened him even more.

The marriage took place in the parlor of Bonnie's home, followed by a huge wedding party, celebrated on board a sternwheeler. He took Bonnie on a train trip to Baltimore, then New York. Later, after he had taken over running the Farris Tobacco business, he took her to New Orleans and Washington, D.C. She was a sweet girl and he enjoyed showing her new sights.

He was finally amicably working with his brother, but neither Claude Raymond nor Bonnie's father would adopt the new idea of using train transportation. River transportation, they said, was dependable; it needed no repair or upkeep. The fact that, in winter, large chunks of ice floe in the river caused damage to ships and piers didn't carry much weight with them.

When Bonnie's father passed away, she inherited an old, ready-made company, and with that, Fletch changed the name to Ferris/Fletcher; Claude Raymond, who was now a de facto partner, changed his company's name to Fletcher/Ferris. It became a company with two halves, both owned by the Fletcher family. It was, Fletch had to admit, far more lucrative than any railroad job he'd ever had—but it wasn't the place he wanted to be. Bonnie had a healthy baby boy they named James, and a couple of years later, Benjamin came along.

Fletch spent his days buying or rejecting and sorting tobacco that came in from the growers, and then assigning shipments into the various holding stations in the warehouse. From there, the makers of cigars, cigarettes, pouch tobacco for pipes, snuff and chewing tobacco came to purchase what they needed. Hogsheads of tobacco were lined ten rows deep at his brother's pier waiting for the appropriate sternwheeler to transport them down the waterways, to the Mississippi River, and throughout the country or to Europe. Fletch broke with tradition and shipped to markets all over the eastern part of the country on the Baltimore and Ohio Railroad, and through Baltimore to overseas destinations.

He drank to comfort the pain in his shoulder. He drank to tolerate his days at work. He drank to forget his loveless marriage. He insulted one of Ferris's long-time customers, and Bonnie insisted he get a manager to deal with the growers and just tend the books in the back office. This made him angrier than ever. She said she wished she'd never met him, much less married him.

Yet Bonnie wanted another child, a little girl, she said. Fletch hated the idea—another dependent tying him down. When she got pregnant, they decided to try to start over with their marriage. Fletch suggested that after the baby came, they would take the boys on a prolonged trip to Europe. Bonnie was overjoyed—a new baby coming, and later, a tour of Europe and the British Isles. For years The Ferris/ Fletcher Company had commercial connections with Amsterdam and Copenhagen. Fletch told her he wanted to teach the boys something about the business, like his father had. She liked that.

When he finally held his tiny daughter, Frances, he didn't know why he had so resisted having another child. Bonnie didn't want to leave her. But finally, after the baby was over a year old, she consented to let Claude Raymond and Alice care for her while they went on their long-awaited trip.

On a sultry day in August 1889, they boarded the *Augusta Victoria* in Baltimore, destined for Hamburg, Germany. They would tour France and Belgium, the British Isles, and finally Holland and Denmark, then sail home in early November.

On the way back, before they arrived in Baltimore, James became sick and cried constantly. A couple of days later, Benjy came down with the same malady. The ship doctor wasn't sure what to call their illness. In Baltimore, Fletch brought in a doctor to look at his children. He wanted to get his family home quickly and safely, so he bought tickets for one of the new sleeper cars on the Baltimore and Ohio Railroad.

"It's influenza," the doctor said. He put them in a Baltimore hospital and quarantined the whole family. Benjy seemed to be the worst, but two days after they had been admitted to the hospital, James died. Then Benjy, who had been suffering with chills and a cough, got worse. The doctor said it was the Russian flu, a pandemic sweeping Europe and taking lives by the dozens.

Benjy was very ill, and Bonnie—heartbroken over losing James and not feeling well herself—dragged herself to Benjy's bedside and held him in her arms. Then she collapsed. Benjy lived four more days. The hospital took all their belongings—even the special things they had brought in trunks for their home—and burned them. The day Fletch sent James's body back, to be held in their frozen icehouse until all contagious germs were gone, Bonnie died. Eventually, Fletch was allowed to leave the hospital. Numb and half drunk, he arranged to ship the bodies of his family home in an isolated freight car.

Back home, Fletch was heartsick, a man moving mechanically through a fog. In less than two weeks his family had been wiped out. Only he and baby Frances still lived.

In the weeks that followed, Fletch moved about like a man whose spirit was paralyzed. What was there to go on for? His business had never been better. Southern planters were coming back after the war, again working and harvesting the fields, bringing in good tobacco crops. It seemed he was making money without trying, but at night he sat alone drinking.

That barren Christmas Day, he held his little daughter close to his heart, then handed her to his sister-in-law, Alice, as he left their house to place wreaths on three graves.

When New Year's Day came, he went down to the office of Ferris, Fletcher and Sons, desolate. He climbed a ladder and painted over the words "and Sons." As he walked the riverfront that night, he cursed God for continually taking away what he loved and wanted most. For weeks, he wandered about in the confusion of loss.

Then one night he went to a tavern, one like he used to haunt, and began drinking until numbness came. As he made his way home, looking at moonlight sprinkling on the wide Ohio, he heard a distant echoing sound—the low, melancholy whistle of a train. He heard the click-clack of wheels on metal tracks coming closer. He was in his cups enough that night to glimpse the other side of the coin of grief. The train sounded again, closer now, and in it he heard the rhythmic sound of train wheels on rails speaking to him—freedom, freedom, freedom.

In the spring he turned Bonnie's business (it had always seemed to be her business) over to his brother. He left Frances with Claude Raymond and Alice for he said, "a couple of months" so he could get away and short things out.

On a bright April morning he got on the train in Paducah, bound for Baltimore, hoping to find a job with the B and O Railroad. When they learned he had twice assembled a locomotive, he garnered great respect and was immediately considered as position after position opened up.

CHAPTER 64

Baltimore, Maryland 1888

"Amy, Liela's daughter, looks very much like your other daughter, Frances. They both resemble your mother, Fletch." Will threw the remark out to watch his father's reaction. So far, Will knew Fletch had buried two children and left three behind for others to raise. Were there others? Did he have regrets?

Fletch didn't respond. He took a drink from a glass he seemed to always have at hand, and looked away. "I realize no one is going to understand any of that, least of all my children. I don't ask you to."

Fletch neither defended himself nor seemed remorseful. It came to Will that maybe Fletch had accepted that he was a man thought to be dead, and perhaps, in a way, his life was that of a man whose life was over—and he was dead in some sense. Will didn't understand Fletch's lack of contrition, and it annoyed him.

That night, after a fine dinner in the hotel dining room, they talked for a while about the delinquent claim payments. Fletch wanted to know more about the train wreck, and he talked again of the war and how both sides dynamited tracks. Finally they went to bed.

It had taken Will a couple of nights to get used to the trains on nearby tracks, with perpetual whistles; grinding wheels coming to a stop; voices of passengers; and intermittent blinding lights that filled the railroad car and then dimmed. Eventually, he ceased to notice all of that. In the middle of the night, coming out of the haze of sleep, came a different kind of noise. It was Fletch yelling. Will sat up in bed.

His father stood before a window, a silhouette against feeble light. "They're coming. Get down, Stoner! You there? Oh God, there goes the damn cannon. They blew Dan . . . my God, they blew Dan's head off! There's his arm, flying. Get down, Stoner. The fire's coming on to us. You there, Stoner? I can't see . . . the smoke! Keep shooting. Load! Keep shooting. Load! You there, Stoner. You dead? Ruben's down. They got Ruben. I'm hit! Stoner? Oh, my God! You there, Stoner? The fire's . . ."

"Fletch, wake up. Fletch," Will kept shaking him. "Fletch, it's me, Will. "

"What . . . who are you? I'm hit!"

"No, Fletch. You're right here in your car. You're in Baltimore. There's no battle."

"I'm hit. The bastard's got . . ."

Will shook him. "Fletch, over here. Sit down." He pulled his father's arm.

"Oh . . ." Fletch sat down on one of the settees. Finally, he looked up, a haggard old man. "Who are you?"

"I'm . . . your son, Will."

"Will? My little boy?"

"Yes, that's right." Will finally answered.

Fletch stared down at the floor, shaken. "Could you get me a drink?"

After Fletch had settled down, back in his bed, Will lit one of the gaslights in the middle of the parlor car, and sat by his father's bed until he calmed.

"Go to sleep. I'll be here," he told Fletch. "We're warm and dry, Fletch, and safe. There's no Rebs in Baltimore tonight."

Finally, Fletch dropped off to sleep and Will crawled into the bed across from him. He stared up at the ceiling as another train rattled into the terminal, its light flooding the car. He understood something now. Fletch didn't feel much of anything—not joy, not sorrow, not guilt. He was a dead man walking around in a living world, a callous on his soul.

The next morning, Fletch was up and properly turned out for work as Will woke up. A pot of coffee simmered on top of the stove. Will saw no indication from Fletch's demeanor that he remembered what had happened in the night. As they sat at the little table by Fletch's humongous desk, drinking coffee, Will wondered how often, alone in his railroad car, did the old warrior live this hell in his head. He even felt some sympathy for him.

"Today," Fletch said, "I will call a meeting. Get those claims processed. I plan to personally take banknotes from the Baltimore bank to the Amsley bank and see that each claim is honored."

Will leaned forward over his coffee, "That's what I want to hear, that the claims are paid out, but I've heard promises before. Are you really going to Amsley?"

"You'll ride home in style and comfort," Fletch was his old self-possessed self. "Sitting in the very seat where you are sitting in now, watching the scenery slip by."

True to his word, as soon as he got to work, Fletch called a meeting in his office with Grogan, Curry and Mayhew. He explained the situation, of which they were well aware. He said he planned to leave in three days and wanted the banknotes prepared, and all paperwork done on each of the claimants by then. He informed them he planned to personally deliver the money to the bank in Amsley for the law firm to distribute, and he would stay until all of Baltimore and Ohio railroad obligations were completed.

Each man took notes. Grogan spoke up that he was already working on it.

"Good," Fletch responded. "Three days. Give me your best efforts."

After the meeting, Fletch went up to his office and Will went to the depot and sent a telegraph to Addie. "Be home Sunday. Have a surprise."

CHAPTER 65

Amsley, Illinois 1888

The trip from Baltimore to Amsley was like no other train ride Will had ever experienced, sitting on a soft settee, relaxing and watching the changing landscapes; ponds and wooded acres, towns and pastures.

Fletch sometimes joined him but more often he was at his big desk working. Grogan, Curry and Mayhew had prepared letters for each of the claims in three days as Fletch had requested. The letters, along with bank notes from the Baltimore bank were locked in the lower drawer of Fletch's desk.

Will's reputation and that of the firm's would be saved.

In the night, Will woke up and wandered over to sit on one of the velvet chairs. He glanced at his father sleeping soundly. For a while, Will watched as little hamlets came into view and then faded as the train moved on, stopping sometimes at some little station. Will thought of the mammoth map stretched across the wall in Mayhew's office in Baltimore, showing each of these stops.

His trip to Baltimore accomplished more than he had imagined possible. Getting the payment from the railroad was what he expected, but the unbelievable prize was finding his father. Now, about introducing Amy to a father she never knew—that would require some serious planning. Since she had never known Fletch, she harbored no particular resentment. But what about his mother? What would happen when Fletch wanted to see her? Will dreaded that immensely.

Once in Amsley, there was much discussion about where to lock down Fletch's railroad car after it had been unbolted from the train. All of the train tracks in Amsley were in daily use. It was finally decided that the only place was inside the roundhouse. One locomotive was already there for repairs, and since it was four o'clock in the morning, only two men were working on it. Fletch's parlor car was an object of fascination to them, but the locomotive they were working on was a fascination to Fletch.

About 9:30 a.m., Will ushered his father into the law office and called Oscar Jamison, Clemet Sampson and Otis Tolbert for a meeting. "Gentlemen, I'd like to introduce my father, William Vachel Fletcher. He is one of the vice presidents of the Baltimore and Ohio Railroad. He has brought letters and banknotes for each of our clients to settle the problems of the delinquent claims."

Jamison looked astonished. Sampson grabbed Fletch's hand and shook it, his face brightening into a smile. "That's good news, indeed. Welcome to Amsley, Mr. Fletcher."

Otis Tolbert, too, came forward and shook Fletch's hand. "Will's father! It must have been an amazing surprise to find you."

"A very good story," Fletch said. "I'll have to tell you about it sometime. But for now, let's get down to work."

"I am going home to see my wife," Will said. "I'll leave it to my colleagues to work out the details."

Sampson came to Will and patted him on the back, "Thank you for what you've done, son."

As Will traveled up Cameron Hill, his home in view, he couldn't have been happier, and he couldn't wait to tell Addie Rose all that had happened in the ten days he had been gone. He could hardly believe it himself.

He found Addie at the kitchen table having morning coffee. She met him with a great bear hug and a long kiss. "Oh, how I've missed you," she whispered in his ear.

Will held her thick body close and felt contented, back in his own home after, he felt, seeing the great world beyond.

"Carrie?" he asked.

"Still asleep."

He released her and they walked into the kitchen. "I've got so much to tell you," Will began. "The B and O has made their payments . . ."

"Oh, not that, Will. I want to hear how you found your father." She handed him a cup of coffee. "What's he like?"

He told her everything. "And you will never believe this, Addie. He lives in a railroad car, a fancy one at that, a parlor car."

She cocked her head to one side, thought about it for a minute, then said, "It's unusual, but that's kind of like him."

"There's not much about him that's—usual. And Addie," he leaned close, eager to tell her his biggest news. "I brought him home with me. Well, more accurately he brought me in his personal car."

"He's in Amsley! Does he know about Amy? What about your mother!"

"He knows about Amy. Mother? I don't know yet about that." Will took a sip of coffee. "I recounted to him everything I'd heard and knew for myself."

"And how did he take all that?"

Will leaned back, sobered. "He's absolutely stoic, nothing contrite about him."

"He has had a lot of disappointments," Addie cut a slice from a loaf of bread she had made the day before. "And your mother? Did he talk of her?

"He wants to see her."

Addie looked down into her coffee cup for a moment. "Of course, you can't stop him, but . . . I doubt that's going to go very well. How can she tolerate the sight of him?"

"Did you tell her I'd found him?" Will ask.

"I thought that was for you to do."

Will looked around, basking in the comfort of home and realizing, not for the first time, he wasn't much like his father at all. Addie poured him a second cup of coffee and added another kiss.

His fingers caressed her cheek. "How are you feeling?"

She shrugged. "Pregnant."

The next morning Clemet Sampson called a meeting in his office, which included Fletch. "The best way to close these cases," he said, "is to schedule appointments with each of the claimants and present them with their compensation."

Fletch immediately made his presence known. "I realize it's appropriate that one of the members of the firm facilitate this, but as a representative of the Baltimore and Ohio Railroad, I'd like to be there also for each of these appointments; to offer sympathies for their suffering, to apologize for the delay in payment, and to try to retrieve a little good will for the railroad."

"Agreed," Sampson said. "We welcome your input."

"There will be some testy comments to be sure," Will said.

"Leave that to me. I'll smooth things over." Fletch waved his hand, a dismissive gesture, as if it were some little task he knew he could easily handle.

Will had no doubt about that. "I will contact the editor of the paper, Wendell Cross, and ask him to attend each of the meetings so we can get retractions in the paper from that rotten publicity. We'll demand that he run stories about the injured parties receiving their payments, and especially correcting that story about embezzlement going on."

Both lawyers agreed.

"On that note," Sampson said, "it would be valuable to contact claimants on a personal basis; in other words, to schedule appointments at their place of residence. Fourteen passengers boarded the train in Amsley, so they're local. Eighteen live some distance away. I will contact those in town, but the others I'm leaving to you, Will," Sampson said.

"Maybe Tolbert can help with some of them," Jamison put in.

"Yes, sure," Tolbert said in a barely audible voice from the corner where he sat.

"It will be a valuable day's work. Clear the name of the firm," Sampson said.

"And clear Mr. Will Fletcher's name, too. We can't forget that," Tolbert said.

Will found most people at home—including Frank Skinner, whose damaging interview had appeared in the paper.

The next morning, Sampson held another meeting to see how things were going. "I saw eight of the fourteen here in town," he said, as he sat down behind his desk. "Jamison will see the other five."

"I have contacted nine people," Will reported. "We'll finish tomorrow."

"And Tolbert, how did your day go."

"Five," Otis said. "But I don't think I'll be able to go tomorrow. I have a pressing case load. Some things can't be put off, you know." He turned to Will. "I'm sure you can manage."

"I understand," Will responded, but he didn't understand. Nothing was more urgent than repairing the damage to the firm. The next morning, however, Tolbert was not at his desk, and they soon received word that he was ill and couldn't come in.

After the regular morning meeting, Will left with Fletch. They went to his railroad car—before Will left for the day—to set up meetings with the last remaining claimants.

Once back in his car, Fletch poured himself a drink and turned to Will. "Tell me about this Tolbert."

"He's from Chicago, recently out of law school, as I am. Wants to make a name for himself and, I imagine, return to his hometown where there's more competition, a faster game, more money."

Fletch said nothing for a while, toyed with his glass. "Interesting little fellow."

Will didn't answer. He had not thought of Tolbert as particularly interesting.

CHAPTER 66

Amsley, Illinois

Addie put Carrie down for the night, returned to the parlor, and found a place to sit close to the fireplace. Will came out of his office and joined her. "Addie, I think we need to plan a way for Amy to meet Fletch. I am concerned he'll discover her at the Dining Car Café on his own."

"What a shock that would be—that shy little thing meeting Fletch."

"It could happen."

Addie was thoughtful for a moment. "I'll make a special dinner tomorrow night so you can invite them both. How does fried chicken and apple fritters for dessert sound? Believe me, I want to meet this man, myself."

After work the following day, Will suggested that Fletch come home with him.

"My wife is very anxious to meet you."

Fletch looked hesitant and clearly surprised. Finally he said, "I'm honored to be invited into your home, Will." For once, some emotion seemed to surface and touch him.

Will had stopped at the Dining Car Café in the morning and asked Amy to come to the house and help Addie prepare dinner, with the implication that his wife was in the last weeks of pregnancy and needed help.

Dusk was coming on early, the sky leaden, as they rode up Cameron Hill, a sharp wind whipping at the buggy. Fletch said nothing, but was thoroughly assessing the place Will had built. Was he impressed? He said nothing. Fletch walked through the front entrance, and stopped, looking around. Will led him from the foyer into the parlor. It was impossible for Fletch not to see his son's success, and Will watched him, drinking in this moment he had never imagined would happen. Fletch saw his portrait and stood beneath it for a while. He then walked beneath the portrait of Violet. Will held his breath. What would he say? What was he feeling?

Fletch smiled slightly. "Many lifetimes ago," he murmured.

It occurred to Will that Fletch was not comfortable with this, his life stretching out before him. But then Addie came into the room and broke into Fletch's reverie.

"This is my wife, Fletch; Addie Rose."

Addie held out her hand. "We are very pleased to have you with us, Mr. Fletcher."

Fletch instantly regained his charm, took her hand and held it. "My son is a very lucky man to have such a lovely wife."

"You may not realize this, but you have been part of our lives even before we were married," Addie said.

"I doubt that's a compliment." Fletch still held her hand.

"Nevertheless, it's a fact, and it is nice to now have you as a guest."

Amy followed Addie and stood by, saying nothing, apparently assuming this was one of Will's clients.

"Anyway," Addie continued, "I'm so pleased Will's search has come to an end."

"Fletch, I have invited you here to meet someone special."

When Will had everyone seated, he turned to Amy. "Fletch, I want you to meet your daughter. This is Amy."

Amy's expression changed from confusion to shock. Silently, she stared at him, a man she had been told was dead. Her eyes drifted up to the picture. "It is the same," she whispered.

It seemed she could think of nothing to say until, finally, she asked, "You're my papa? I thought you were . . . My mother . . ." Tears rimmed her eyes. "I had no family. Not until I learned about Will."

Fletch came to her and touched her cheek with his fingers. He looked at her for a long time. Addie reached for Will's hand.

"Liela's child," Fletch said softly.

Amy studied him, intently. "You are good to look at, but sad."

He shook his head. "I didn't know, Amy, about you."

"Why did you lie to my mother?" It burst out from her.

"I thought I had to. There were reasons—maybe not good ones. Things happened that made me think it was the thing to do."

"I know about that. Casper told me one time."

"Casper?"

"My mother used to sit in the yard sometimes . . . crying. I asked her why she was crying, and she said, 'He's never coming back. Your papa's gone.' I was sorry it made my mother cry."

"Amy, I . . ." Fletch seemed at loss for words. "I'm glad you have Will."

"But I'm yours, too." Tears rolled down her cheeks.

Fletch sighed, glanced at Will, apparently hoping for an escape.

Will saw this timid, innocent girl had touched Fletch more than his own pointed confrontations had.

"Let's have dinner," Will said. "Addie's a very good cook. Makes apple pies that are famous. Right after I ate a piece, I proposed to her."

Everyone laughed, the dark spell broken.

"It's true. I'm the apple pie bride," Addie said as she took Fletch's arm and walked him into the dining room. "Now, it's Amy who works in the Dining Car Café making pies." Fletch seemed surprised and pleased when she directed him to a seat at the head of the table. Amy was seated beside him, and Addie took the seat on his other side. Will found a place at the opposite end of the table.

"The café? The one by the depot?" Fletch asked.

"Yes, my mother runs it," Addie answered.

"And your father was a railroader, too, Will tells me."

"I was born in Baltimore, where you live, and moved with my family to Amsley when I was fourteen."

Immediately, Fletch's demeanor changed. His old charm sparkled; he seemed to have found common, friendlier ground with Addie Rose. Or so he thought.

"And how did you happen to get from Baltimore to Amsley?" Fletch turned his attention fully onto Addie as he passed the platter of fried chicken.

She continued. "Will must have told you," she continued, "about my father's decision and the accident."

"That was truly a tragedy," Fletch answered, absently passing one dish after another.

"Yes, but the problem came later. She had nothing in the decision that determined the rest of her life."

"Unfortunate," Fletch answered distantly.

"More than unfortunate; unnecessary and unfair. It's why I work to get women the vote, have more rights, more respect, and independent decisions over their lives. I imagine you would agree, Mr. Fletcher," Addie said.

Fletch drew back, glanced at Will at the opposite end of the table, his expression hardened. "I don't understand what women want," Fletch said. "I see them marching and singing about something or other. Women are by nature of a far higher quality than most men I know."

"The pedestal does not protect women. It does not provide rights," Addie was warming to this familiar argument.

"I assume you will someday succeed," Fletch said to Addie, "but it will be without my vote."

"We'll get the vote."

"Will warned me you were a firebrand on this."

"Warned?" Addie shot Will a questioning expression.

"He mentioned it," Fletch pacified, attempting to negotiate through the minefield that seemed to have developed at the dinner table.

"Men are not keen on giving up their bastions of power," Will stepped in.

"I suppose," Fletch answered half-heartedly, the subject apparently not to his liking. After the coffee and apple pie had been served, and conversation seemed to have dwindled to mechanical, superficial courtesy, Fletch said, "I should be going,"

Will got their coats from the closet, but when he opened the door, cold air blasted into the room, carrying with it the swirling snowflakes of a blizzard. "We can't go out in that." Will closed the door. "The hill down to the rail station will be treacherous—especially in the dark."

Addie turned to Fletch, as they stood in the entrance hall. "You must stay. There could be ice already on the road."

Fletch looked about. Was there no escape? He looked as if he had been trapped. Snowed in with two children he had abandoned, plus one exceedingly insufferable suffragette, as he often called them. He looked back at Will, Addie, Amy all standing by the front door, all watching him. He looked resigned for the worst.

"Yes," he took off his coat and handed it back to Will, "It looks as though I'll have to impose on your hospitality for a little longer."

"Of course," Addie said, "A very wise decision. We have plenty of bedrooms."

Fletch simply nodded and followed Will back into the parlor. He sat on the settee by the fire, just under his portrait.

"Please excuse me. I'll see you for breakfast tomorrow morning. I need to make sure my little girl is asleep," Addie said.

Amy came in and sat by Fletch. Timidly, she took Fletch's hand. "I thought the day I learned that Will was my brother and I had a family was the grandest day of my life, but this day has given me the greatest surprise I have ever known—to meet my own father. To find you were not dead, as I'd been told. Maybe," she began cautiously, "we could talk sometime, if that would be all right?"

Fletch was visibly moved by this gentle girl. Maybe, Will reasoned, it was because she asked for no apology from him.

"Of course, my dear. Of course. We can talk—many times. As many as you want."

"Thank you," she whispered. "I'll wish you good night. It doesn't feel right to call you 'Papa.' Maybe someday it will."

Fletch stood and took her hand again. "I would be pleased, when that time comes."

The room was quiet. Outside the house atop Cameron Hill, snow-flakes swirled against the windows. Light from the hearth drew them together in something of a spell. In the semi-darkness, Fletch sat just under his bigger-than-life painting and it struck Will that everything about his father was bigger than life.

"Addie and I have talked," Will began. "We want you to know you have a family to come to—Addie and I, little Carrie, the new baby when it comes—and Amy. You are a welcome guest here. You'll be given the respect of a father when you're in my home,"

"You've decided I deserve that, Will?"

"I wouldn't think that you deserve anything. You have lived large and left a littered path behind you, but it's like this: I have chased a phantom, a phantom I hated. In the pursuit, I never thought of him as a person, or that when I found him, he would necessarily become a presence in my life. Never thought how I would live with that. How I could reconcile with that."

"And now?"

"Not sure, yet. I see that you were fated to live in a time when sensitivity didn't count, only survival counted. I see the mark it has left."

"I am pleased you can forgive me."

"Forgive? I didn't say that," Will came back sharply. "I said I'd give you the respect accorded a father."

Fletched stared into the fire and slightly nodded his head.

Will wondered if Fletch even cared that he was offering him a place in the family. Maybe he was laughing inside at Will's attempt to give him something he never wanted. Thinking of it frivolous, irrelevant to his life.

"Something else you need to know. You left a wound that doesn't heal. I wish that was not so, but it is. It will always be between us."

"No doubt," Fletch acknowledged. "When you offered me a place in your family, you didn't mention your mother."

Will watched the dancing flames of the fireplace, the ticking of the clock behind them. "I can't speak for her," he finally said.

CHAPTER 67

Amsley, Illinois

The first of the claimants was scheduled at 9:30 a.m. on Wednesday morning in Will's office. He had requested the editor of the *Amsley Record*, Wendell Cross, to attend, and in spite of himself, he was secretly overjoyed that Fletch wanted to see this through and help him save his law practice. Will brought in Frank Skinner, whose story had appeared first in the paper.

"Vachel Fletcher is a representative of the Baltimore and Ohio Railroad and, of course, you know Mr. Cross," Will explained as Mr. Skinner took his seat.

"Sure, we've crossed paths before." Skinner laughed at his own little play on words.

"I hope, Mr. Skinner, the payment you are receiving puts to rest any impressions you had that there was embezzlement involved. The railroad had its own reasons for the delayed payment." Will glanced at Wendell Cross, making sure he was getting this on record.

"And, Mr. Skinner," Fletch said, "I offer my most profound sympathies for the pain and inconvenience you've experienced because of this late payment. It is our greatest concern that our passengers trust us to keep them safe and facilitate their traveling experience."

Will watched his father in action, a master of charm and persua-
siveness, with just a dash of conman.

"And," Fletch was saying, "we want to continue serving you, so
I am giving you two free passes, good for six months, anywhere on
the B and O line." Fletch handed Skinner the passes, shook his hand
and patted him on the back.

Skinner looked at Fletch, overwhelmed. "That's mighty kind of
you."

"Now you've got a little money in your pocket, and free passes;
take the wife on a nice trip, compliments of the B and O." Fletch
patted him on the back again.

Skinner looked a little sheepish. "I wouldn't a-spoken up like I
did for the paper if that young man hadn't a come around to see me
and asked if I thought my money was being used for Mr. Fletcher's
campaign."

"What young man?' Will and Fletch jumped on that at the same time.

"Works right here." Skinner waved his hand as though taking in
the whole office space. "Got me to thinkin' . . ."

Will turned on Wendell Cross, who had been writing furiously.
"Is Otis Tolbert the source for your information?"

"Well, he works here," Cross was instantly defensive. "I considered
him a reliable source."

"I mighta said too much," Skinner drew back, clutching his check
and passes.

"No, you didn't, Mr. Skinner," Fletch put in. "You've been extra-
ordinarily helpful. You just enjoy those passes, and if there's anything
else we can do for you, let us know."

Will stared down at Cross who held his notebook on his lap.
"Wendell, you have to retract those articles and that damaging letter.
I know that's awkward for you, but I lost the election because of it;
I'm sure of it. And it's a certainty it brought on Judge Austin's death.
And that story about my mother . . . all lies, Wendell. Everything he
told you was a lie. The railroad is now paying their debts, as you can
see, and I demand that you sit in on every meeting. This firm had
nothing to do with the delayed payments."

Wendell Cross nodded his head, "I see. I see. But Tolbert seemed a proper source," still trying to square himself.

Throughout the day, Will and the other lawyers met with claimants; Cross taking notes and Fletch exercising his considerable talent for soothing ruffled feathers.

When the last meeting concluded, Fletch turned to Will. "I think it would be a very fitting thing to pay a call on the sick—your partner, Otis Tolbert."

When they arrived at Otis's door in Mrs. Smith's Boarding House, no one answered their persistent knocks. After several knocks, they tried the door and found it was open. Otis was not there, and neither were his clothes.

"Looks like he's skipped out," Fletch said.

"The sheriff needs to know about this."

They got into Will's buggy and rode to the sheriff's office. Fletch then left Will and began the three-block walk to the roundhouse and his railroad car. As he passed the depot, he went in. Only a few passengers were scattered in groups here and there, waiting for the next train.

Fletch walked up to the ticket window, pulled out his billfold, and found a little paper in its folds. He held it up to the ticket agent. "I am Vachel Fletcher, a vice president of the Baltimore and Ohio Railroad."

"Yes sir, I know who you are—that fancy car in the roundhouse."

"Yes, well, I have a request. If an Otis Tolbert wants to buy a ticket, sell it to him, but send a porter for me. I need to talk to Mr. Tolbert before he leaves."

"The thing is, Mr. Fletcher, he already bought his ticket. This morning it was. Train to Chicago. That train don't leave for an hour and half."

"Did you happen to see where he was going in the meantime?"

"No, sir, I had people waiting . . ."

"Yes, of course. Thanks."

The sun was setting and the air carried a sharp, winter chill as he walked toward his parlor car. Fletch had started to pull his collar up close when he noticed a huddled form sitting by the side of the roundhouse. He walked over. "Tolbert? What are you doing out here, in the cold. Come on in with me. It'll be warmer in my car. I'm surprised to see you out here. I suppose you didn't have too much luck on that errand Jameson sent you on."

"No; besides, I got sick and couldn't come into work."

"It's not going to help your health much staying out here. Follow me." Fletch was surprised that Otis actually picked up his suitcase and followed him.

Once inside, Fletch offered him a drink. "I'll see if I can find something around here for you to eat. I imagine you're hungry." In the little icebox he found a couple of ham slices and part of a pie. "Better than starving," Fletch said, as he put a plate before him on the little table and got Otis a fork.

Otis quickly tackled the food, not looking up.

Fletch went to his desk, and then swung his chair around to face Otis. "You're from Chicago?"

"Born and raised there." Otis cut into one of the ham slices.

"They said you were sick. The way you've polished off that food, I'd say you're feeling better."

Otis nodded. "Maybe some."

"I imagine it would make any man feel sick to think he was facing a libel suit."

"A libel suit?"

"Yes, of course. A libel suit. You know, the embezzlement story— and that one about Will Fletcher being the natural son of John Austin. I'm impressed with you. You have a creative mind, Otis. You know that?"

"What makes you think I had anything to do with that?"

Fletch ignored him. "You, being a lawyer, probably know that a lot people with creative minds are doing time in prison."

Otis glared at Fletch in defiance. "The newspaper editor says you were the source for all those words he is now going to have to retract. Otis, I don't think he's your friend anymore."

"I hear my train." Otis got up. "That's the Illinois Central."

Fletch stood up, took Tolbert's shoulder and looked into his face. "You're going to miss that train, Otis."

"No, I'm not. I've got my things outside." Tolbert started for the door. "I'll just go get my . . ."

Fletch swung around in his chair, opened a desk drawer and held a gun on Tolbert. "Sit down, Tolbert, you're not going anywhere."

"You can't hold me against my will. I've had enough of this backwoods place . . . hayseeds."

"If you try to walk out that door, I'll shoot your leg, and I'm a pretty good shot."

Otis slowly sat down, a scowl on his face.

The train came to a grinding stop outside the round house.

Otis started to get up and Fletch lunged at him, grasped Otis's collar with one hand, and sent a hard punch in his face with the other. Tolbert went sprawling against the game table and slid down to the floor. Fletch picked him up and glared into his face, "That was for my son, Otis. And he *is* my son." Before Otis got his bearings, Fletch landed another punch. "And *that's* for what you said about my wife."

Otis crawled a few feet to Fletch's desk and tried reaching for the gun, but Fletch got it. The train whistle sounded outside and then with an "All aboard!" the train started slowly pulling out.

"That train's going to pull into the Chicago station in a few hours, Otis, but Otis Tolbert won't be on it," Fletch stood up, towering over him. "It was your last chance."

Otis, now sitting up on the floor, glared up at him.

"You and my son fight in three-piece suits, high, stiff collars and ties, Otis," Fletch pulled him up and slung him back in the chair. "But you see, I learned to fight in the mud."

Fletch, gun in his pocket, marched Tolbert to the depot and asked a porter to find William Fletcher and the sheriff, and bring them to the depot. And the newspaper editor, he added as an afterthought.

The porter looked at Tolbert but apparently decided it was best not to ask questions.

It was more than an hour before both Will and the sheriff arrived. The porter said the newspaper editor couldn't leave; the press was running.

Will looked at the swelling coming on Otis's face and turned away smiling, partly because Otis got what was coming, but mostly—and of much more importance—because he saw that something had finally disrupted Fletch's complacency. And that made Will happy.

"Just as well," Will said at last. "Let's just take my cunning little partner over to the newspaper office where he started his schemes."

The sheriff looked at Otis and surveyed his bloated face. "What happened to you?"

"He slipped on the ice." Fletch said.

CHAPTER 68

Will stood in front of the big, oval mirror in his bedroom. Addie was still asleep. He was fully dressed in his best suit. Addie opened her eyes, looked at him—still drowsy—and rose up on her elbow. "What are you doing all dressed up? You look like you're going to court to try a murder case."

"That would be easier than this day's going to be."

"And what might that be?

"I am going to take Fletch to see Mother."

"Oh," Addie dropped back onto her pillow, pushed her long hair behind her ears. "When did you decide that?"

"In the night. I couldn't sleep." He sat down on the bed. "It has to come. Fletch has mentioned it a couple of times." He leaned forward and kissed her. "I put him off. I made a point to say my mother was worried for me until all of the claims were settled."

"And did he accept that?"

"He didn't argue, anyway."

"Do you need my help?"

Will looked down at her, thinking. "You might go see Mother; take Carrie. I have no idea how this will turn out."

Addie pushed her clumsy body up and sat on the edge of the bed.

"This is something I definitely wouldn't want to miss! But why are you so dressed up?"

"I thought it might help."

She laughed. "Like wearing armor into battle?"

"Something like that.."

The morning was cold and gray. The town was just awakening; here and there, yellow light glowed from windows in the dawn. Stores, not yet open, had Christmas wreaths at their entrances. Christmas was now only two weeks away. Will had never been this nervous, even when he walked into court for his first murder trial, defending Delmar Eckert and believing from the start he was bound to lose. In fact, it felt a lot the same, like he would be a major player in a disaster he couldn't stop.

When he arrived at the parlor car, still in the roundhouse, Fletch was just getting up.

"So early, Will?" he said, as he opened the door. "And dressed for preaching?"

"I'd like us to take morning breakfast together at the Dining Car Café, if you have nothing better to do."

"Certainly." Fletch gave him a wry look. "Big plans for today?"

"Maybe. We'll see."

The old warrior fixed him with shrewd eyes. "Could it be that today we're going to meet Violet?"

Will dropped his eyes for a moment then met Fletch's. "We have some things to talk about."

The Dining Car Café was warm, wreaths hanging in every other window facing the tracks. A middle-aged woman was there with her two grandchildren, waiting for the next train. One of the porters from the depot was having his morning coffee.

Amy met them, coffeepot in hand, as Will and Fletch found a table near the stove.

"Thank you, my dear." Fletch nodded familiarly to Amy. Will concluded Fletch had become a frequent customer in the café since he came to Amsley.

Fletch leaned back. "Why are you so reluctant to have me see your mother? Does she even know I'm in Amsley?"

"Listen, Fletch," Will leaned forward. "She's not the girlish young woman you left. She is still beautiful, yes, but a woman with white hair and, in this town, an object of deference by everyone. You understand what I'm saying, what that means—respected. " His eyes held Fletch's. "She was left with a child to raise alone, deserted by her husband. She learned later of a woman in Mississippi, then a wife in Kentucky. She was injured when her husband had a stroke and fell on her, making it difficult for her to walk, and then the paper came out with a poisonous letter calling her an adulteress. She is a recluse now. I don't know whether you realize what's been in her life. I don't know if she'll see you. Really, I doubt it."

Fletch swallowed his coffee as he listened to his son, from time to time glancing out at the pale December morning. Finally his eyes met Will's. "But I must try. I have to try."

"In answer to your question. No, she doesn't know you're here. She only knows my trip to Baltimore was a success."

"I need to see her."

"You know, Fletch, I'm not interested in what you need. My concern is that Mother is never hurt again."

Fletch merely nodded.

Will knew his father would try to court her back; he'd seen his gift of persuasion. Will knew he couldn't really stop Fletch if he decided to take things into his own hands and go to Violet.

"Well, then," Will put two coins down on the table for the meal, stood up and put on his great coat. "I'll pick you up in my buggy and we'll go there this afternoon."

As Will, with Fletch by his side, started toward the judge's house, the sun was still struggling to shine through the grayness of the day.

Fletch touched his arm. "I'd like to see the little house we lived in when you were small."

Will turned down a side street, lined with winter-barren trees, and drove slowly past it. "Stop here," Fletch said. He looked at the tiny house with a porch across the front, a cordon of wood stacked under the front window, and two red, paper bells hanging on the door. "The last time I stood on that porch, I learned my wife had just married someone else." Finally, he said, "Let's go on."

As they approached the judge's house, Fletch beside him, thoughts pounded through Will's mind, his hands clutching at the reins. What was this going to be, bringing his parents together?

As they walked up the steps to the entrance, Will turned to Fletch. "I'd like a couple of minutes with Mother. I haven't seen her since I returned." Fletch nodded in agreement. Both Addie and Sarah met them at the door. Inside, the stair railing was draped with garland and a tall Christmas tree stood in the foyer where it always had, next to the bust of Abraham Lincoln. The whole house smelled of cedar.

Will turned to his father. "Excuse me for a minute."

Will found her sitting by the fire in her favorite chair. He went to her, kissed her cheek. "I have much to tell you." He sat in the chair opposite her by the fireplace.

"I know you saved the firm's reputation and salvaged your own. I'm proud of you, my son."

"A retraction will be coming out soon about all that was in the newspaper."

"Retraction?" She looked up, apparently surprised.

"Addie may have told you; the poisonous words were Otis Tolbert's."

"What about that letter?" she asked.

"He wrote that, too. I'm suing him for libel."

"Libel?" Violet's eyes flashed. "I'd like to strangle him!"

Will smiled. "Someone has already done something of that nature."

"The people of this town now judge me a whore because of his venom."

"That will be corrected, Mother."

"To some extent probably, but people prefer to believe salacious lies rather than the uninteresting truth." She looked into the leaping flames of the fire, having lost interest now that she knew it was Otis Tolbert behind her grief and that he would pay for it.

"I am not alone in the libel suit," he told her.

"The entire firm, I would suppose. They were damaged, too."

"Not exactly." Will looked up at the ceiling. This was going to be harder than he thought. "Something else . . . a discovery. In Baltimore."

"You're going to tell me you have found another lead about your father!"

"I've always wanted to know . . ."

"It's an obsession, William." She looked away and he saw her slightly shake her head.

"I found him, Mother. I found—Fletch."

She turned back instantly, caught her breath. "I don't believe you."

"I found his name on a plaque in the headquarters of the Baltimore and Ohio Railroad home office."

She said nothing, but everything in her demeanor changed, alive, on guard, eyes bright, sharp, questioning.

"Mother, do you want to hear about him?"

"I think we already know."

Will stopped. "I suppose you're right; we already know."

Will decided to throw out a trial question first. "Mother," Will began with hesitancy, "what would you do if you saw Fletch?"

She did not hesitate. "I would get up out of this chair and I would go to him."

Will was startled by the immediacy of her response. For a moment he stared at her, not knowing exactly what to say. He went to the foyer where Fletch waited by the Christmas tree.

Fletch came and stood, framed in the doorway.

Violet gasped; her hand went to her mouth. "Fletch!" Tears filled her eyes. "I don't believe . . . it can be you." Then she lifted herself up from the chair, unsteady for a moment, and then, in full possession of herself, she walked toward him. Will caught a glimpse in his mother's face of a girl she once was, a glowing joy that made her seem young and strong again.

"Fletch," she breathed. She came to him and raised her hand to his face tracing a line on his worn face. For a long time they said nothing as she gently touched every line.

He covered her hand with his. "I never left you, Violet," he whispered. "My heart never left you."

"I know, Fletch." She smiled. "I always knew that."

ACKNOWLEDGMENTS

A lthough the story is fictional with created characters to live out their personal challenges, historical events related in this book happened; the birth of the railroad industry, the Civil War, and the Suffrage movement. For this, I owe much gratitude to the resources that made the era come alive.

Newspapers, such as *The Flora Daily News and Record* and *The Missouri Republican,* illuminated for me the times, images and activities. Many other publications shed light on those early days: *Suffragette Sally* by Gertrude Colmore; *Paducah Gateway, A History of the Railroads in Western Kentucky* by Donald E. Lessey; *Corinth, 1862, the Siege, Battle and Occupation* by Timothy B. Smith.

A very special thanks goes to History Professor Leigh Morris, History Department, University of Illinois, for the wealth of knowledge he shared with me about early railroads in Illinois.

Two organization in which I have long time membership, National League of American Pen Women and The Palm Springs Writers Guild have given me support and instruction as well as inspiration from fellow authors.

Thanks goes to Kerri Robertson for her book cover design and to photographer Kathy Rappaport for the author photo.

Endless appreciation goes to my critique group, Roccie Hill, Dr. Sid Sharzer, Jenny Gumpertz, Eileen Cinque, Sherry Joyce, and Carol Hazelwood, who told me the truth.

For wise council and editing, my thanks to Alaina Bixon, Kathy Bjork and Lynn Green. For generosity of time and inspiration, my appreciation goes to Mary Anne Ayers, and for courtroom proceeding advice, thanks go Kevin and Ashley Shok. Gratitude always to Mark Anderson publisher of AquaZebra Publishing

And finally, my gratitude always, to my family who keeps me diligent.

Printed in the USA
CPSIA information can be obtained
at www.ICGtesting.com
LVHW041337260224
772825LV00003B/431